D1580357

THE REVOLVER, 1865–1888

THE REVOLVER
1865—1888

By

A. W. F. TAYLERSON
M.A., F.Inst.D

BONANZA BOOKS
NEW YORK

*Published in the
United States of America
by Crown Publishers, Inc.
First Publication* MCMLXVI

© A. W. F. TAYLERSON, MCMLXVI

ALL RIGHTS RESERVED

Manufactured in the United States of America

**This edition published by Bonanza Books,
a division of Crown Publishers, Inc.**

(B)

CONTENTS

Reasons for selecting period—scope of book—political background—technology—War—Acknowledgements

Percussion revolvers—Adams, Tranter, Colt and Birmingham "trade" revolvers—Deane's Patent revolver and optional percussion metallic cartridge designs—dissatisfaction with the muzzle-loader—Paris Exhbition of 1867—Carbine stocks.

The cartridge—Casimir & Eugene Lefaucheux—single-action and double-action locks—Scandinavian adoption—Paris Exhibition of 1867—British revolvers—Guerriero's patent—Continental developments—"fist pistols".

The cartridge—H. Smith & D. B. Wesson—Rollin White's patent—British copies of Smith & Wesson revolvers—rim-fire calibres—W. Tranter's revolvers—U.S. infringements of White's patent—J. Rupertus—"Suicide Specials"—Colt and Remington arms—British patents—front-loading cartridges—Continental weapons—Smith & Wesson exports.

The cartridge.

John Adams's revolver—"Adams's Patent Small Arms Company, Ltd."—John Adams's Patents—"Adams's Patent Small Arms Manufacturing Co.; W. Watts Locke & Co., Proprietors"—Adams's Army revolvers—Police revolvers—Colt revolvers—Remington revolvers—Webley "Constabulary" or "Bulldog" revolvers—Webley's "New Army Express" (No. 5) revolver—Webley and Adams link-up suggested—Tranter revolvers—Tranter's patents—European service revolvers—Chamelot Delvigne and Nagant locks—Swiss revolvers—German service revolvers.

CONTENTS

LIST OF PLATES

LIST OF PLATES

LIST OF FIGURES

ACKNOWLEDGEMENTS

IN thanking those who made this book possible, my first debt is to the authors (whether living or dead) whose names are listed in the Annotated Bibliography at the end of this book.

For help in practical matters, I am principally indebted to Clifford Lawson, John Bell, and Douglas Fryer; it is no exaggeration to say that the book would have foundered without them.

The pictures were a combined operation, and it is a privilege to acknowledge the sources from which they came. Messrs. Wallis & Wallis, of Lewes, donated the plates which bear their name, and this was but one of the many kindnesses that I have received from these famous arms auctioneers. A. N. Kennard, Esq., of The Armouries, H.M. Tower of London, arranged for me to have access to the magnificent collection in the Students' Room, and personally assisted in taking every one of the plates from that collection. Malcolm Pendrill of Reigate took all the pictures at the Tower, and also photographed all the weapons from my own collection in the plates that acknowledge no source for the arms shown. Messrs. Phelps & Marchant, also of Reigate, photographed the pistol in Plate 16, when it was in my collection.

On a number of individual problems, I received unstinted assistance from P. A. Bedford, De Witt Bailey III, F. Wilkinson, Ray Riling, J. R. Lee (of New Zealand), H. Taylor, E. M. Perry, J. Darwent, E. Buchanan, S. B. Haw, P. S. McCarthy, D. Cooper, and Rolf H. Müller. In the task of actually writing and collating the material, I was helped by T. W. Eagle, H. L. Blackmore, C. Blair, and W. Reid; anyone who has ever tried to write a book will appreciate how invaluable professional assistance can be. However, in some places, I went my own way, and any defects in this book are my own doing!

Most grateful thanks are due, also, to Mrs. E. M. Beazley (of Reigate), who wrestled with my miserable handwriting, and typed most of the manuscript.

Finally, I have to thank the staff of the Patents Office Library for their unfailing courtesy, and for their skill in running down books and papers for which I could sometimes provide only the most slender of leads. They have a hard row to hoe in the ordinary course of commercial inquiry from people working in the twentieth century, without facing demands from the nineteenth.

INTRODUCTION

"revolver, n. Pistol with revolving mechanism enabling user to fire
several shots without reloading."

*The Concise Oxford Dictionary
of Current English* (4th Edn.)

"NEVER complain, never explain" is good advice to any author, but
a brief explanatory Foreword must be offered on the intended
scope of this book. Sufficient knowledge is assumed in the reader to
make unnecessary the usual potted history of firearms, and I hope that
these brief introductory remarks will be enough to guide him over the
field to be explored.

The choice of the year 1865 as a starting point is not arbitrary. This
was the year in which British arms manufacturers were freed (by its
expiry) from the yoke of an early firearms patent held by Robert Adams
and his associates, which had protected the most satisfactory method for
constructing revolving pistols, and these are the arms with which this
book is primarily concerned. From this commencement the concluding
year follows naturally, as that in which the Webley revolver thrust aside
its last native competitor, to replace in private hands the honour of
arming pistol-carrying personnel in the British Armed Forces.

In an effort to simplify the story, two substantial Appendices have
been used. The first lists all relevant British patents, giving their dates,
periods of continuance, and a note of their subject matter; the second
is a "Who's Who" of patentees for revolving firearms, and it sketches
some principal features of the patents. By stripping this biographical
material, it has been possible to tell a more coherent story, and the
reader can refer to the Appendices when a name is mentioned in the
course of the narrative. Where other books are mentioned, the same
system has been adopted, the name of the author, and title of the book,
being listed (by Chapters) in a Bibliography.

In a word, the book seeks primarily to show what was the latest and
best in revolving arms, during a period prolific in invention of every

kind. A separate Chapter records some of the ideas genuinely in competition with the arm of principal interest, but elsewhere in this book the intention is to deal only with arms covered by my chosen terms of reference.

Some mental strait-jackets must be shed at the outset, for although the cinema, the television set, and the paper-back have dispelled the need for any preliminary description of "a revolver", a moment's consideration will show that the "Peacemaker" or Colt revolver pistol shown in Plate 21 is not the only means of achieving rapid small-arms fire by the use of a revolving or rotating carrier for ammunition feed to the actual point of discharge of the cartridge.

Continuous experiment showed that the principle was at its best when

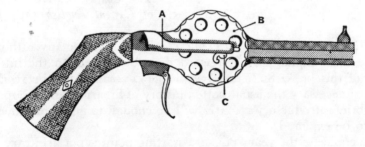

FIG. 1. *Pistol "System à Noel", Noel & Gueury's Patent.*
(Br. Pat. 659/1865.)

Pulling the trigger operates the "mule-ear" (i.e. side-swinging) hammer "A" to fire the fulminate charges in the radially bored chambers. These are contained in are movable turret chamber within the casing "B". The turret may be removed by opening a retaining gate on the left of the pistol. A pivoted safety-catch "C" may be turned up under the hammer nose to hold it off the loaded chamber, and will fall clear automatically as soon as the trigger is pulled and the retaining pressure of the hammer removed from it.

applied to a pistol discharging cartridges in a revolving carrier, and by rotating this carrier in a particular plane, but no great effort of imagination is required to see that the carrier can as readily revolve in two other planes set for convenience at 90° to that normally accepted (as, for example, in Fig. 1), nor to concede that ballistic advantage may be secured by withdrawing the cartridge from the carrier for discharge in a seperate chamber integral with the barrel. Crudely sketched, we thus have the ideas of BATE and KRNKA (see Figs. 2 and 3), and casual examination of Appendices I and II will reveal other such variant mechanisms. To set the frame in which the story unfolded, it is enough to glance at the political and economic background of these years.

Queen Victoria reigned throughout the period, which spanned

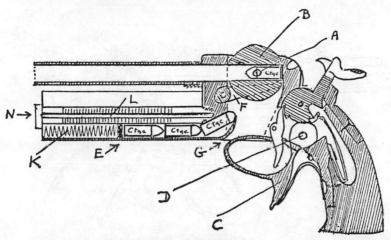

FIG. 2. *Bate's Pistol.*
(Br. Pat. 10944/1884.)

Note rotating breech-piece "B" and rotary magazine "E".

Breech actions, revolving-chamber; magazines—Relates to firearms of the self-loading or repeating type. The Figure shows in section the improvements applied to a pistol. A rotating breech-piece "B", which is carried on trunnion arms "A", at right-angles to the axis of the bore, is actuated by the movements of the trigger-guard "C", about its pivot "D", and transfers cartridges from the magazine "E", to the firing position shown in the Figure. After firing, which is effected in the ordinary manner, and as the breech-piece "B" is rotating, the claw-like ends of a pair of pivoted levers "F" remove the empty shell, which escapes through the opening "G". The rear-part "H" of the breech-piece then comes opposite the cartridge and the latter is forced into the chamber by the spring "K". The return movement of the trigger guard brings the breech-piece back into place. The magazine consists of a series of chambers arranged around a central axis "L", each containing a spring-actuated piston, which forces out the cartridges contained therein. A spiral spring "N" produces rotation of the magazine and, as each chamber is emptied, a pawl is automatically released, allowing the spring "N" to assert itself and carry round the magazine, until the next chamber, containing three or more cartridges, is opposite the loading opening.

broadly, on the political front (following Palmerston's death in 1865), the Whig and Liberal caretaker Ministry of Earl Russell; the short-lived Derby–Disraeli Conservative administration (1866–8); and the longer terms of the alternate Disraeli or Gladstone governments under Liberal (1868–74; 1880–85) or Conservative (1874–80; 1885–6) banners. Lord Salisbury presided over a Conservative Cabinet, when the story closed.

Commercially, it was a period when demand see-sawed from slump to boom and back again, whilst for agriculture the upswing never came at all.

Difficult readjustments were necessary in wage rates, in the use of

B

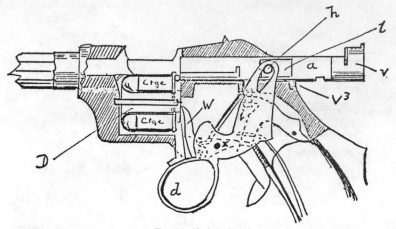

FIG. 3. *Krnka's Pistol.*
(Br. Pat. 14088/1888.)
Note rotating magazine "D".

The invention is shown applied to a pistol. The longitudinally-sliding breech-bolt "a" is operated by the lever "i" which is pivoted at "x". When the breech-bolt has been pushed forward, the continued pressure on the loop "d" causes the upper end of the lever "i" to produce through the pin "h" a turning motion on the breech-bolt "a", and so to bring the projection "l" in front of a support on the standing breech, thus locking the breech-bolt during discharge. The magazine "D" is rotated by the pawl "w" carried by the lever "i". When the gun is closed a knob screw "v" can be turned to lock with a recess "v³", and thus to prevent the arm from being accidentally opened. The magazine is removed from the gun for reloading. The firing-bolt is carried in the breech-bolt, and is cocked during the closing movement in the usual manner.

craftsmen, in operating factories and workshops, in dealing with emergent Trade Unions and in replacing cheap child-labour, as a result of certain welfare legislation like the Factories Acts Extension Act, The Workshops Act and the Education Act. The authorities found these measures hard of practical enforcement at first, but they persevered in this task to the inevitable discomfiture of any manufacturer who had previously depended upon cheap handwork and contractor-supplied labour to keep down his manufacturing costs and maintain a competitive position against Continental and American opponents.

Technically, in all undecaying fields of industrial production, there was real development under the lash of need to replace increasingly expensive human hands with machines and appliances that produced more goods for a smaller outlay.

The gas-engine had been introduced by Lenoir, a Frenchman, during 1860, and improved by Rochas two years later; by 1888 efficient engines of 100 h.p. were available, and even small producers could mechanize their works, where formerly only the largest of units could economically employ the power output of a steam engine. In metallurgy, the iron-masters of the British Midlands faced Steel, at last, not merely as a competing metal but as a material for which, in many fields, there simply was no substitute.

As to small-arms, the period saw the successful development of many ideas and devices already either existing in the minds of certain inventors, or struggling for acceptance in crude embodiments. Breech-loading magazine rifles were widely accepted by civilians, whilst the breech-loading revolver (with a metallic cartridge for it) had been in service for nearly a decade, in the French Navy, and was already a serious competitor to the conventional muzzle-loading cap-lock revolver for travelling or home-defence.

Whilst not remembered as a period of general conflict, the years concerning us were far from wholly peaceful.

1861–5	The American Civil War
1864	The Schleswig-Holstein campaign
1866	Austrian campaigns in Italy
1866	Prussia against Austria
1864–8	The Hau Hau Wars in New Zealand
1870–71	The Franco–German War
1868–72	The Te Kooti Wars in New Zealand
1876–8	War of Independence to free Serbia from Turkey
1878	War of Independence to free Rumania from Turkey
1878–80	England and Afghanistan
	English field operations against the Kaffirs and Zulus or in the Transvaal
1879–81	Chilean War against Bolivia and Peru
1881–4	English field operations in Egypt and the Sudan
1883–5	French field operation in Tonkin and China
1885	War between Serbia and Bulgaria.

Although much of this activity would now be classed as little more than "brush-fire" in extent (except, as always, by those miserably and personally involved), it served to keep the attention of designers, manufacturers and buyers focused upon the need for magazine firearms to replace the classic single-shot weapons. The revolving cartridge-feed principle found general approval as the multi-shot system for personal side-arms, at least.

It is against this background that the events in this book must be considered.

CHAPTER I

PERCUSSION REVOLVERS

AT the opening of the period, and with admittedly important exceptions, the cap-lock or percussion revolver, loaded by skin or paper cartridge from the front of the cylinder and fired by a separate cap, still led the field as the choice for most major consumers of heavy calibre arms, but it was rapidly becoming obsolete in the face of American and French breech-loading designs.

As a weapon for the buyer of ordinary means, the percussion revolver dated only from 1847, when SAMUEL COLT (q.v.) (of Hartford, America) had first introduced his heavy, thumb-cocked cavalry revolvers to the U.S. Mounted Rifles. The weapons were not solid-framed, for their barrels were secured to the end of the cylinder-pin by a cross-key, but this defect was remedied, in 1851, by the Englishman, ROBERT ADAMS (q.v.). In that year, he patented and introduced a self-cocking revolver in which the barrel and frame were forged as one piece, and thereafter this type of construction remained a monopoly, until the expiry of his patent, in 1865.

By that year, in the United Kingdom those pistols outnumbering the products of all other makers were the Beaumont-Adams, the Colt, the Tranter, and the "Birmingham" weapons produced (by firms like Pryse & Redman, Tipping & Lawden or Cooper & Goodman) for retail by others. All of these designs dated effectively from the mid-1850's.

Table I shows that care was taken to maintain certain early patents on this type of weapon for considerable periods of time, of which the designs of ROBERT ADAMS, W. HARDING, W. TRANTER, J. KERR, and J. ADAMS (q.v.), were the most important. However, reference to Table II (demonstrating the scarcity of muzzle-loading revolver patents after 1865) suggests that this particular type of revolver had reached its apogee before the period opened, for only the patents of C. M. H. DOWNING and A. M. CLARK (for LINBERG & PHILLIPS) are relevant.

As examples of the reigning types mentioned above, four specimens are shown in Plate 1.

The Beaumont-Adams revolver and the "Navy" Colt Belt pistol are obvious choices for inclusion, the former being an improved version of ROBERT ADAMS's self-cocking pistol of 1851, with the lock modified to cock by thumb or trigger.

The Beaumont-Adams was principally retailed in the 54-bore calibre, but was also available in 38 or 120 bore. It was a five-chambered, double-action weapon with a 6-in. barrel, promoted by the London Armoury Company Ltd., of Bermondsey and Bow, and embodied the solid frame of Robert Adams, the improved double-action lock-mechanism of F. B. E. Beaumont, and the lever ram-rod of James Kerr. It shared with the Colt pistol the distinction of purchase and issue (from 1854) to selected personnel in the British armed forces.

The "Navy" Colt was probably the most popular of all the cap-lock revolvers sold by that famous Company. In the United States its fame was matched by the equally remarkable Model 1860 Army revolver, but comparatively few specimens of the latter weapon reached this country by reason of the need to supply it for the Union Army during the American Civil War. Thus C. B. Norton (writing in 1872) confirmed sales of Colt weapons, from January 1st, 1856, to December 30th, 1865, at the following totals to show the popularity of these arms:

Pistols	554,283
Rifles	6,693
Muskets	103,970

The "Navy" revolver was a six-chambered weapon in ·36-in. calibre, and with a 7-in. barrel. The single-action mechanism was that originally designed by Samuel Colt himself, and used by the Company in all their percussion revolvers from the models of 1847 until that of 1863. As a measure of the success enjoyed by this "Navy" pistol, John E. Parsons has traced serious Turkish inquiries for quantity delivery at late as 1879.

The muzzle-loading revolvers of William Tranter (the third maker covered by Plate 1) were also based upon the solid frame construction of Robert Adams, but embodied lock mechanisms patented by the former in 1853 and 1856 respectively. Sold in competition with metallic-cartridge revolvers produced by their inventor, as well as with the muzzle-loading weapons of other makers, these arms secured an excellent reputation for their finish and reliability. Both types of Tranter percussion revolver were produced in various calibres, but the 54-bore weapons illustrated are representative of their general appearance.

To illustrate the Birmingham "trade" revolver of muzzle-loading type, the weapon shown as (ii) on Plate 2 will serve. To modern collectors these are known as the "wedge-frame Webleys", but their manufacturing background was so obscure that their true source remains in doubt. Lock mechanisms might vary, but were normally based upon designs patented by Joseph Bentley (of Birmingham and Liverpool) in 1857. Although the house of P. WEBLEY & SON (q.v.) may have made some of them, it would be unwise to associate these arms solely with that firm. Lacking the finish of the other weapons illustrated, they still enjoyed popularity in a price-bracket that permitted emigrants and householders to buy a reasonably reliable revolver for which no serious or prolonged service was ever considered.

One further "trade" revolver has been selected for illustration, and appears in Plate 51. The Deane-Harding percussion revolver shown in Plate 51 was made slightly before our period, but typified the arm made for Messrs. DEANE & SON, of London Bridge under the patents of WILLIAM HARDING; (q.v.), by the Birmingham firms of Tipping & Lawden, Pryse & Redman or Calisher & Terry. Although comparatively rare, this revolver has been selected for inclusion here as also representative of the pistols which were produced during a brief period when makers attempted to supply arms that could be used either as muzzle-loaders or with metallic cartridges.

This type of arm must be carefully distinguished from the fully converted weapons discussed later in these pages, and one distinguishing feature lay in the fact that a user could select the cartridge to be used in his revolver by reference to the accessories sold to him with it.

The distinction lay between this option to use a particular type of cartridge (which is of concern here), and the final and irrevocable gunsmith's conversion of a muzzle-loading revolver to use metallic cartridges and no others.

Weapons representative of the two types appear as Plate 3.

The cased Harding revolver (retailed by DEANE & SON; (q.v.), but made by Pryse & Redman) is an optional ·32 rim-fire or 120-bore percussion weapon protected by JOHN DEANE's Br. Pat. No. 626 of March 8th, 1862. Although the patent was allowed to lapse in 1865, the firm was still actively promoting this arm in 1869, against the Colt "Thuer" conversion, patented in the U.K. by F.A.K.W. von OPPEN (q.v.) and illustrated in Plate 64.

On removing the cartridge cylinder and cartridge retaining plate from Deane's revolver (see Plate 65), the owner could substitute a conventional percussion cylinder and either load with caps and paper cartridges, or use the powder flask and bullet-mould contained in the case. The lever-rammer was retained in the pistol for such loading, and a simple rod-ejector was screwed into the butt-cap for removing metallic cartridge cases. The hammer-nose had a rim-fire blade permanently pinned to it.

The other revolver illustrated in Plate 3 is a true (and irrevocable) gunsmith's conversion from cap-lock, and now chambers a ·450-in. centre-fire Boxer metallic cartridge.

The weapon began its life as a muzzle-loading revolver embodying WILLIAM HARDING's patented lock-work and frame construction (see Table I), but had a new centre-fire cylinder made for it. The lever-rammer was removed (the resulting apertures in the frame being filled with brazed inserts) and a simple rod-ejector mounted in its place. The hammer nose was then sharpened to strike the primer of the metallic cartridges, a loading gate fitted and the weapon re-proofed.

Other revolvers permanently converted from percussion to centre-fire appear in Plates 19 and 47, and a 54-bore ·450-in. rim-fire specimen of John Deane's revolver is shown in Plate 65, but such arms are quite rare now, and had only a brief active life.

It is plain that dissatisfaction with muzzle-loading revolvers began to appear during the American Civil War, although difficulty in securing metallic cartridges stifled the serious use of breech-loading revolvers during that war. French, Italian and Scandinavian service adoptions of such arms are noticed in the next Chapter, and C. B. Brackenbury reported some interest in the new systems, at the Paris Exhibition of 1867. "Revolvers [he wrote] are chiefly made to load from behind; indeed those issued for use in the French and Italian navies have long been arranged on this principle, Colt still adheres to the old plan; but it is said that a knowing American patented the 'notion' of piercing the chamber through from end to end, even before any use was made of the invention."

Such a palpable reference to the SMITH & WESSON/ROLLIN WHITE (q.v.) dominance over other American makers for conventional metallic-cartridge revolvers, confirmed that echoes of their infringement squabbles with would-be native competitors were certainly heard in Europe, but that the White U.S. master-patent carried no weight on the Continent.

Lefaucheux, of France, had anticipated Rollin White on the Continent with his breech-loading pin-fire revolver of 1853, and despite the encouraging consumption of muzzle-loading revolvers in the American Civil War, many Continental manufacturers were well under way in pushing pin-, rim-, and centre-fire metallic cartridge revolvers, from the start of our period.

The muzzle-loading revolver was, however, well entrenched as a design, and Captain Majendie, R.A., who was one of Britain's official observers at that same Paris Universal Exhibition of 1867, reported in 1868 upon the "Portable Arms" in Class 37, but could find little British enterprise in this field. Tables I & II show that the British could have contributed handsomely to it, yet he found nothing of note there to suggest that either U.K. manufacturers or their customers had learned anything much from such U.S. weapons as had been proved under actual field service, or their French counterparts. He commented, pointedly, that "the English display of arms is, on the whole, meagre . . . Messrs. Reilly have . . . some revolving pistols, the majority of which are adapted for very small rim-fire copper cartridges . . .", and could say no more for the British Government display of small arms (prepared at the R.S.A.F., Enfield) than that it was "very complete and well arranged". This must have been about as close to damning with faint praise as any ambitious officer would care to range.

It appeared from Majendie's notes that the Colt Navy revolver and Deane & Adams's revolvers (i.e. the Beaumont-Adams) actually appeared at the Exhibition, still in their percussion forms, as the patterns issued to the British services. However, he was able to report prior to actual publication date that "a general disposition towards breech-loading revolvers has sprung up in this country. Several papers have advocated the supercession of the capping or nipple revolver by a revolver adapted to a cartridge containing its own ignition; and the Government have recently adopted a breech-loading revolver submitted by Messrs. Adams with a metallic, centre-fire cartridge, designed by Colonel Boxer, R.A." This pistol is later discussed.

Curiously, Captain Majendie admitted in print that he too had heard about SMITH & WESSON's enterprise in the U.S., over the patent of ROLLIN WHITE (q.v.) on the bored-through cylinder, but he took an opportunity to berate their principal balked competitor. If his report was studied at the Colt factory at Hartford, another blow must have been struck at Anglo–U.S. relations for the year. "Messrs. Colt [he wrote] exhibit a case of revolving pistols and rifles. These arms possess no special novelty and, indeed, are behind the age, in so far as they are none of them adapted for cartridges containing their own ignition; while on the Continent capping revolvers are as much out of date as muzzle-loading guns. Messrs. Colt have, in some instances, fitted movable stocks to their pistols. If they would go a step further and adapt their pistols for self-igniting cartridges these stocked revolvers might serve as useful arms for yeomanry regiments and various mounted corps."

Whilst Captain Majendie's attendance at Paris, as Assistant Super-intendent, Royal Laboratory, Woolwich, presumably required that he concentrate his real attention and professional skill for the study of cannon, the comment quoted above was either intentionally misleading or betrayed a bad memory on the second count. The Royal Small Arms Factory at Enfield had already provided such stocks for some of the "Deane and Adams's" service revolvers and 10-in. single-shot Cavalry Rifle Pistols to convert them into "Pistol Carbines" for Special Service. Further, the Royal Laboratory itself had assisted in producing an approved, sealed-pattern, cartridge for use in 18 carbine-stocked revolvers for the Australian police. This ·500 in. (38-bore) skin cartridge was for use in the heavier of the two Deane & Adams's issue percussion weapons to which he had earlier referred, and the pattern had only been sealed about three years prior to his report from Paris.

In general, then, it appeared that this curtain-raising Exhibition showed considerable awareness of the disadvantages in the muzzle-loading design, and of the advantages in the breech-loading competitors. The history and progress of these latter arms is traced in the Chapters that follow, but Plate 59 should be born in mind whilst studying them. The muzzle-loading revolver took many years to become obsolete.

CHAPTER II

IN a pin-fire cartridge, the igniting cap is buried in the base of the case and fired by a pin protruding at a right-angle, when struck by the falling hammer. For weapons of quality, the system never achieved a popularity in Britain to match that which it enjoyed on the Continent, either for use in shotguns or as ball ammunition.

The cartridge was conceived by a Frenchman, Casimir Lefaucheux, about 1828, and began to appear as an effective round for breech-loading shotguns, after 1836. In this period, a short brass base was wedded to a cardboard tube, and improvements by Loron, of Versailles, and Bernimolin of Liège, found some favour.

In 1841, William Bush (of London) produced an improved cartridge with a really well-formed metallic base, embodying a separate cap chamber, and the Continental designers Houiller (1846), Chaudin (1847), Leroy & Mathieu (1848) and Bourchier (1849) further improved the ignition. As a result, the pin-fire ball cartridge became a practicable proposition for use in other types of firearm.

At the Great Exhibition of London, in 1851, Casimir Lefaucheux exhibited one of the first revolving arms in this field, using a pin-fire cartridge with an entirely metallic case. It was a self-cocking pepperbox (i.e. multi-barrelled) pistol, embodying an elderly self-cocking lock mechanism known as the Mariette system, and Lefaucheux had patented the application of his cartridge to this pistol in February, 1846.

In 1854, his son Eugene patented the use of his cartridge in a conventional revolver, having taken the precaution of securing British patent protection through J. H. JOHNSON (q.v.) in the same year. This was a single-action (i.e. thumb-cocked) pistol, with a simple push-rod cartridge ejector. The cased weapon featured as Plate 4 serves to illustrate the type (apart from its unusual length of barrel and the presence of a detachable stock), and the cartridge was considered of sufficient merit for the Father to be awarded a Medal of Honour at the Universal Exhibition of 1855.

Despite their crude appearance, these revolvers were no playthings. His Excellency, the Minister of the Imperial Navy of France, held comparative trials of various revolvers, from which the Beaumont-Adams and Navy Colt percussion revolvers were selected for test against the Lefaucheux arm. As a result, on September 16th, 1856, the council of naval armaments adopted the Lefaucheux pin-fire revolver for the use of the French fleets. The Italian Navy followed suit in 1858, and the Scandinavian countries took up the weapon in 1864, During the American Civil War, Union purchases alone totalled some 12,000 revolvers, and a smaller quantity found their way into Confederate hands.

A peculiarity of these early pin-fire arms was the boring of their chambers with a light opening taper towards the mouth. This permitted the use of an iron muzzle-loading insert when the conventional ammunition was wanting. These "iron breeches and chimneys", as they were then known, had a percussion nipple inserted where the pin would have been on an ordinary round, and could be loaded, fired, reloaded, and removed without damage to themselves, or to the pistol.

Prior to 1865, a double-action mechanism was introduced for the pin-fire revolver, permitting the weapon to be either thumb-cocked or to be cocked and fired by trigger pressure alone, but neither the source nor the true dating for this improvement are easy to trace. Two double-action mechanisms were commonly found in pin-fire revolvers of Continental manufacturers (both *prima facie* acknowledging Lefaucheux parentage), whilst such weapons of British proof adhered to one mechanism but did not normally acknowledge any source of inspiration at all.

The researches of Skaar and Nielsen (at the Haermuseet, Oslo) demonstrate that both single and double-action weapons were available in 1864 for the Scandinavian purchases already noticed. The Norwegian Army weapons bought in that year included both locks, for the 11 mm. calibre selected, and all were stamped "INV<u>on</u>E. LEFAUCHEUX BREVETE. S.G.D.G. (PARIS)", although this legend may, in fact, have acknowledged the parentage of the cartridge, rather than that of the lock-work.

For historical reasons, which cannot be pursued here, the armies of Sweden and Norway adopted a standard practice over the purchases of 1864, and differed from the Danish Army in one respect.

In Norway, the Model 1864 Lefaucheux pin-fire revolver was issued to officers, N.C.O.s and trumpeters of cavalry and field artillery from an initial purchase of 1,500 weapons in Paris. A small batch of 200 were also made at the Kongsberg Arms Factory between 1867 and 1868. These two batches of revolvers served through the entire period, and some single-action survivors were remodelled in 1898!

Although generically described as the Model 1864, two varieties of revolver were actually purchased in that year. The bulk consisted of 1,100 single-action weapons of coarse construction for issue to troopers; the remaining 400 comprised 200 single-action revolvers (of slightly better quality) and 200 double-action weapons, for issue to officers according to the mechanism of their choice. It appears that this practice of issuing to officers double- or single-action revolvers at their choice was maintained in 1883 when the 9-mm. Nagant centre-fire revolver was adopted to top-up available supplies, and the 800 revolvers purchased were thus a mixture of types.

Whatever the date of origin for the double-action lock in this type of revolver (and some authorities date it as early as 1858), the mechanism was well established by 1867.

Thus, Captain Majendie, R.A., when reporting upon the small-arms shown at the Paris Exhibition of 1867, stated flatly that "the principle of arranging the hammer for trigger-cocking has been adopted by M. Lefaucheux in common with the majority of French makers". This statement hardly supports the view that Lefaucheux developed a unique double-action lock for these revolvers, and it seems best, therefore, to leave it that double-action pin-fire revolvers were available from all the principal producers prior to 1864. A specimen offered as typical, for an arm of fair quality, appears at the foot of Plate 47. This is a six-chambered, 9-mm. weapon, marked "E. Lefaucheux In^{vr}. Brevete" and is principally remarkable for the ingenuity with which the frame is constructed. This component is not a single forging, but consists of three separate pieces and a loading gate. The pistol is rather improbably numbered "1133289", and bears the proof marks of Liège.

Considering the enormous quantities of pin-fire cartridges made (and possibly yet to be made) it is amusing to note that opinion regarding their use in revolvers was divided, even in 1867. Thus C. J. Brackenbury (writing in that year) remarked that ". . . Another point worthy of remark is that pin-fire seems to be dying out, and that central-fire cartridges are more approved generally than those called rim-fire", in regard to the exhibits at the Paris Exhibition.

Captain Majendie, R.A., was one of Britain's official observers at the Exhibition, and found little of note to mention regarding the pin-fire revolvers in the French court. His professional eye fell with little comment upon the French revolving arms of Perrin (centre-fire revolvers);

Lefaucheux (pin-fire revolvers improved from the original thumb-cocked mechanism to double-action trigger cocking as well. A double-barrelled, 20-chambered, pin-fire revolving rifle. A sword revolver. A detachable skeleton stock for revolvers); Devisme (*coups de poing*, i.e. pepperbox revolvers for metallic cartridges); Le Page-Montier et Faure (revolver using a cartridge "novel and ingenious, but expensive in its arrangement . . . easily and often recharged"); but he appears to have met a true salesman at the exhibit of M. Jarre, whose curious pin-fire "harmonica" pistols (see Chapter V) were touted as capable of firing fifty shots in a minute!

As to the Belgian Court or exhibit, dominance appears to have lain with the Liège houses of H. Dresse-Ancion, Laloux et Cie, M. Lambin and Lepage & Chauvot, but Captain Majendie offered no verdict upon the technical merits of their revolvers. His comment was reserved for the prices at which these could be obtained, viz.:

> Pin-fire, 6-shot revolver rifles 55 fr.
> Pin-fire, 10-shot revolver rifles 75 fr.
> Revolver pistols (French Service pattern) 21½ fr.
> Sword revolvers 50 fr. complete or 72 fr. for the "large".
> Couteaux de chasse with revolvers 45 fr. to 50 fr.

The lock-mechanism embodied in weapons of the type shown in Plate 47 is illustrated in Cuttat's 1877 translation of *Les Armes a Feu Portatives*, etc., by the noted Swiss authority Rudolph Schmidt, and it differed markedly from that normally found in the pin-fire revolvers of British retail.

Major Dowell has dealt fairly comprehensively with these double-action arms in the varieties catalogued by the Birmingham house of P. Webley & Son (q.v.), and the present writer has found little to suggest that Webley's range of such revolvers was not fully representative for this country.

In his *Modern Breech-Loaders* (published about 1871), W. W. Greener featured very similar pin-fire revolvers to those shown by Dowell, and dismissed them contemptuously. "These revolvers [he wrote] are all made of a cheap kind. The best English makers prefer constructing them on the central-fire plan. The great defect in these pin revolvers is that ten to fifteen per cent misfire. With well-made central-fire, misfires are of rare occurrence."

One pin-fire revolver of a type illustrated by both Dowell and Greener appears as Plate 6. This specimen (a twelve-chambered 9-mm. weapon) bears Birmingham proof marks. It is otherwise unmarked, except for the legend "No. 1000" which is minutely and carefully engraved on the spring safety-catch, and also *underneath* that member on the action-body. This latter component (unlike that in the "Lefaucheux" pistol) is a solid forging.

These curious weapons (which Greener illustrated as ten-, not twelve-chambered) had their cylinders machined out internally and externally to cut their weight, and rare Continental variants existed chambered for as many as twenty cartridges. The peculiarity of these revolvers is further shown in their use of the bar safety-catch to be seen in Plate 6.

This component (a flat spring) has two studs on the underside which penetrate into the lock mechanism through suitable holes in the wall of the action body. The tension of the spring urges these pins inwards, but the side of the trigger should normally foul the forward pin to prevent full penetration of the larger safety-pin on the rear of the bar.

However, when the hammer is eased back clear of the chambers, an incline on the trigger is presented and the rear safety-pin becomes free to snap in under the hammer toe. This holds the hammer nose clear of the cartridge firing-pins and the weapon may be loaded or carried in safety.

Continued retraction of the hammer drags the trigger rearwards and (at full cock) the side of the trigger again bears on the forward pin and holds the safety-bar clear of the hammer-toe when the pistol is fired. A similar sequence of events obviously occurs in double-action firing, i.e. when merely pulling the trigger to cock and discharge the pistol.

This safety-bar is duplicated in the original Austro–Hungarian Gasser service revolver, with which we deal later, and it is a matter of concern to us as helping both to date revolvers embodying it, and to identify the possible source from which the design originally came.

Bornecque stated that the original French "system Lefaucheux" pinfire revolver adopted in 1856, was replaced by a double-action centrefire weapon in 1870, and it is a matter of record that the Austrian trooper's Gasser was adopted in that year.

Against this background it seems reasonable to suggest that Major Dowell's provisional dating of his catalogued Webley pin-fire revolvers in the years between 1860 and 1865 may be too early, unless his catalogue is clearly dated in those years. In the writer's submission, it may be possible to date pistols of the type shown in Plates 47 and 48 during the period of his choice, but those embodying the Gasser-type lock, bar safety, and one-piece frame would appear to date around 1870.

Having regard to the immense popularity of the pin-fire round (surviving even today) it is disappointing that so little was apparently done to improve the revolving weapons in which it was used.

If eccentric arms of the type patented by O. FRANKENAU (q.v.), P. POLAIN (q.v.) or F. DREVENSTEDT (q.v.) are ignored, only one British patent stands out to demonstrate a serious effort to improve the basic Lefaucheux design.

The patent of A. GUERRIERO (q.v.) contained eight claims of improvement, and these spotlight the weaknesses of the parent weapon with merciless clarity. It was dated as of March, 1863.

Claim One proposed the recessing of the cartridge heads, to permit them to bulge on firing without jamming the rotation of the cylinder.

Claim Two proposed a narrow hammer-nose, so that the pin of the cartridge would only be struck if the chamber was accurately aligned with the barrel.

Claim Three proposed to protect all cartridge-pins by a removable breech-plate or cap secured to the rear of the cylinder. This had narrow slots in it which only admitted the hammer-nose if the chamber was truly aligned with the barrel.

Claim Four proposed to cover the front of the cylinder with a plate to prevent bullets jarred out of the cartridges from fouling cylinder rotation.

Claim Five discarded the Lefaucheux system of screwing the barrel on to a thread cut on the end of the cylinder-pin, in favour of a lever-operated eccentric cam which pulled the barrel tightly to the frame and automatically took up any slack.

Claim Six provided for a one-piece butt, in place of the screwed or pinned Lefaucheux assembly.

Claim Seven related to the ease of cleaning permitted by the above improvements. The weapon broke down into four parts, without need for any tools, and could be readily brushed out.

Claim Eight protected a spring safety engaging the hammer-breast.

Some of the more simple improvements suggested by Guerriero were adopted in later pin-fire revolvers, but the existence of a pistol exactly as he patented it is unlikely. However, shortly after the Patent Agent had secured his patent and assigned it over to him, another lease or assignment of Guerriero's patent was registered at the British Patent Office, in the names of "Cauvin, Pavese, Williamson & Weiland". So far, no clue has emerged from the past to identify these men, or to explain their interest in the design, but their act suggests that Guerriero's improvements were accepted as such.

Another pin-fire revolver made by A. FAGNUS & CO. (q.v.) is shown in Plate 8, and showed some appreciation of the defects inherent in the standard Lefaucheux method of construction. The specimen shown was retailed by Charles Kerr, of Stranraer, but was retailed by a number of other British gunmakers also. The solid frame was a genuine step forward in design, and the cartridge ejection system was ingenious, if rather impractical. As can be seen from the Plate, if the cylinder axis pin was withdrawn, the cylinder could be removed and the cartridge cases punched out against a vertical arm on the end of the axis pin. Under conditions of active service, the use of a chain to attach cylinder to pistol was endearingly realistic.

The self-cocking ·44 revolver by Chamelot & Delvigne offered no mechanical features of improvement over the standard pin-fire weapon by other makers of the day, but it was one of the few arms examined that handled well and is included for that reason only (see Plate 7).

The two double-barrelled revolvers shown in Plate 7, on the other hand, both demonstrated the worst features of the pin-fire arm; they were fragile, bulky, and handled with the easy grace of a bag of marbles. The Lefaucheux specimen is probably identical in mechanism to the rifle mentioned by Majendie, and fired twenty ·32 cartridges alternately from its two barrels by means of a vertically sliding member beneath the hammer. This was struck each time the hammer fell, but only reached the inner circle of cartridges in the cylinder every second shot. The other revolver bears no maker's name, and also had the cylinder chambers disposed in two circles of ten; in this arm, there was no sliding member for the inner circle, merely two beaks on the hammer to accomplish the same purpose.

The "J. Chaineux" 20-shot revolver on Plate 8 disdained two rows of chambers, and used the same internally machined cylinder as the twelve-shot arm shown in Plate 6 to carry its 7-mm. cartridges.

Plate 8 shows two anonymous pin-fire "fist pistols", and these are the last type of revolving arm considered here. As earlier mentioned, the pin-fire revolver started as a pepperbox pistol, and the popularity of this arm continued long after 1888. However, shortly after 1865, the original Lefaucheux design was superseded by more compact pistols of the type shown. These were gate-loaded, solid-framed weapons of mediocre quality, and were normally offered in the smaller calibres of seven or nine millimetres. A rod-ejector was often screwed into the butt of these arms, but even this simple refinement was sometimes omitted.

CHAPTER III

RIM-FIRE REVOLVERS

THE rim-fire cartridge had a metallic rimmed case, in which the primer (or firing compound) was sandwiched into the fold of metal that formed the rim at its base. When the hammer struck this rim, the primer was crushed and detonated between these two thin walls, backed by the unmoving metal of the cartridge chamber in the actual weapon. The idea was twenty years old by 1865, having originated as a small-calibre non-lethal round for target pistols, and even today these particular cartridges are often called "Flobert" rounds, in honour of the man who first offered them. A variant of the idea was included in the 1847 Houiller patent, earlier noticed in regard to pin-fire cartridges, but it is not known today whether this improvement was actually used in revolving arms.

The honour of first applying this type of cartridge to revolvers is now accorded to the Americans, Horace Smith and DANIEL BAIRD WESSON (q.v.), and brief mention must be made of the background to their invention.

Until 1857, SAMUEL COLT (q.v.) held an American master-patent which the U.S. courts had upheld to give him a monopoly right to manufacture revolvers in which the cylinder was mechanically rotated by cocking the hammer. As a result of this patent, no other American arms manufacturers could produce anything but manually rotated revolvers or self-cocking pepperboxes, although the patent did not run outside America.

In 1856, Horace Smith and D. B. Wesson (who both had sound experience as gunmakers) came together to design and produce a revolver with a mechanically rotated cylinder that would be marketed as soon as the Colt master-patent expired. As an improvement, they proposed to make this arm as a breech-loader, chambering small rim-fire cartridges of a type which they had patented in August 1854. This was an expensive, almost hand-made round, and by 1857 the partners were still experiencing difficulty with it. The primer spread across the whole cartridge base, and tended to bulge out the weak metal (jamming the revolver) when it was fired. Several years of experiment were needed to perfect a technique for spinning the case, as it was being primed, to lodge the primer only in the rim.

Prior to commencing production of their revolver (in 1857), the two men learned of a patent (U.S. Pat. No. 12648 of Apr. 3, 1855) held by ROLLIN WHITE (q.v.), which included protection for the principle of ". . . extending the chambers through the rear of the cylinder for the purpose of loading them at the breech from behind . . ." and the two partners secured a sole assignment to themselves of this feature in White's patent.

It is no purpose of this book to retrace the story of this American monopoly in breech-loading revolvers as thereafter enjoyed by the two partners. John E. Parsons and Messrs. McHenry & Roper have written it superbly, and the notes (in Appendix II) upon ROLLIN WHITE are sufficient for this purpose. Sufficient to say that from 1857 to the expiry of White's patent in 1869, the Smith & Wesson partnership enjoyed a monopoly as profitable and as well enforced as that formerly held by Samuel Colt.

Their rights were contested in the U.S. courts, but it is true to say that from 1859 to 1869 no American revolver manufacturers made any breech-loading revolvers without either paying royalties to the Springfield partnership or making their weapons for Smith & Wesson.

Overseas, however, it was quite otherwise. In England, an 1854 patent of J. H. JOHNSON (q.v.) barred Rollin White from securing a British equivalent to this U.S. master-patent, and elsewhere his idea was widely infringed. For years it has been a popular taunt with many American writers, that the British makers stole the basic Smith & Wesson revolver design with the connivance of the British Patent Office. If this be so then the margin of profit on such British-made revolvers must have been gigantic, for the numbers surviving today are few and argue a limited production (see Plate 9).

The more sober and painstaking researches of J. E. Parsons or McHenry & Roper tend to the dismissal of this story, at least by inference. Thus the former has demonstrated that the American demand for the Smith & Wesson No. 1 (·22-in.) revolver was so enormous that orders stood two years behind by July, 1864, and that (despite access to stocks of infringing revolvers handed over by would-be U.S. competitors) the Smith & Wesson partnership were forced to eke out supplies with blemished, second-quality arms. No better case is revealed for the ·32-in. (No. 2) weapon shown in Plate 13. This was introduced in 1861 and was lagging the demand by March 1864, although running in the 22,000 serial range by that date; these facts can only support the idea that nothing was stolen from Smith & Wesson, who were far too busy with their own markets to care if the design was copied outside America.

As can be seen from Plate 9, these early Smith & Wesson revolvers were single-action (i.e. thumb-cocked) arms, hinged at the top of the frame. On release, the barrel was tipped upwards on this hinge, the cylinder removed, for the cartridge-cases to be punched from the chambers against a rod protruding beneath the barrel.

Again, apart from the curious British Patent of T. J. VAIL (q.v.), no designs even of "Smith & Wesson type" appeared in British patent records until that of W. R. LAKE (q.v.) in 1869. This omission does not make sense if Smith & Wesson were experiencing any serious loss in demand to pirate competitors. Certainly, the authority of another American, C. B. Norton, appears to support the contrary view expressed above. Written in 1872 (and revised in 1880), his book on American Breech-Loading Small Arms stated that Smith & Wesson made no effort to sell their top-break revolver abroad until 1867, when they exhibited the arm at the "Paris Exposition". Great interest was aroused, and large shipments to Japan, China, England, Russia, France, Spain, Peru, Chile, Brazil, Cuba "and elsewhere", then resulted.

It must be admitted that Dowell confirmed production, during 1865–6, of a Webley copy of the tip-up Smith & Wesson revolver "under licence", but the present writer can trace no suitable patent requiring such permission to be sought by that firm. Whatever unique features the original U.S. patents of Smith & Wesson may have protected, the weapons actually produced in Birmingham acknowledged nothing to them. If this be regarded as proof of "pirate" production, the protagonist must be asked to account for Smith & Wesson's failure to take appropriate legal action to enforce any claim to monopoly. Their record as shrewd and effective litigants in the U.S. courts argues that they would have contested bitterly any Birmingham infringements that seriously damaged their market for the tip-up revolvers.

The case was, of course, quite otherwise in regard to their heavy-calibre Army rim-fire revolver. This was hinged on the lower end of the frame and embodied the automatic cartridge extractor patented for them by W. R. LAKE (q.v.) in Great Britain, and C. A. King in the U.S. By the date of quantity production for this revolver, the rim-fire ignition had been discarded in favour of a centre-fire round, but the original design was made to chamber either the ·44 Henry Rim Fire, or the ·46–26–230 Short Rim Fire cartridges and merited recognition here (see Plate 66). It was closely copied in Belgium and Germany.

Popularity of the rim-fire cartridge in the United Kingdom was attested by the range of calibres in which it was manufactured by (or for) Eley Bros. Limited, of London. Even in 1886, their ammunition lists still offered the round in nine pistol calibres, namely, the ·230, ·297, ·320, ·340, ·380, ·410, ·440, ·440 Henry and ·442.

In America, on the other hand, the cartridge was available in even greater variety, and A. C. Gould (in the 1888 edition of his book) reported the following pistol calibres as then in current manufacture.

·22 C B						
·22	Powder	3	grains	Lead	30	grains
·22 (long)	,,	5	,,	,,	30	,,
·25	,,	5	,,	,,	38	,,
·30	,,	9	,,	,,	55	,,
·32 (short)	,,	9	·,	,,	82	,,
·32 (long)	,,	13	,,	,,	90	,,
·38 (short)	,,	18	,,	,,	150	,,
·38 (long)	,,	21	,,	,,	148	,,
·41	,,	13	,,	,,	130	,,
·41 (long)	,,	13	,,	,,	130	,,
·41 (short)	,,	21	,,	,,	200	,,
·44	,,	26	,,	,,	200	,,
·44	,,	23	,,	,,	200	,,
·46	,,	26	,,	,,	230	,,

The principal British manufacturer of rim-fire arms was WILLIAM TRANTER (q.v.), whose sturdy uncomplicated percussion revolvers have already been noticed here. The revolving mechanisms and inventions of this maker are specifically covered in relation to his centre-fire arms, and only one single-action model of his revolvers was definitely confined to use with rim-fire cartridges. Thus two weapons shown on Plate 68 demonstrate that his double-action revolvers were supplied in both rim and centre-fire embodiments, for although the illustrated weapons are of the rim-fire type, collectors will be familiar with them in the latter variation also.

The weapon illustrated at the left on Plate 68, however, was typical of the true Tranter rim-fire revolver and was retailed by J. H. Crane of London. The specimen shown was in ·320 calibre, had a 3½-in. barrel (rifled with five grooves in a slow right twist) screwed into the solid, gate-loaded frame, and had a single-action mechanism. The ·230 version was almost identical in appearance, but commonly had a bronze or brass frame and was understandably smaller. On both weapons, the revolving ratchet for the cylinder was cut into the actual metal, not formed and mounted as a separate component in the style of some other revolver makers. The lock mechanism (to which access could be had through an irregularly shaped inspection plate, on the left side) was almost identical to that later used in the Colt Company's "Clover-Leaf" or "House" revolver of the early 1870's, which is shown in Plate 14. Tranter patented the butt-assembly and cylinder bolt features of his pistol in 1863, but the Colt protection in the U.S. dated in 1871.

On most of these rim-fire Tranter revolvers, cartridge ejection was achieved by removing the cylinder and punching out each case with the cylinder-pin; a press-in rocker latch secured this latter component in use. However, some of these weapons had broad notches cut at the rear of the cylinder, and the cases could be prised out by their rims when this refinement was present, without removing the cylinder (see Plate 68).

British rim-fire revolvers signed by other makers, or made up anonymously from percussion parts (see Plate 16), still exist in fair numbers. The optional rim-fire/percussion arms of J. DEANE & SON (q.v.) have already been noticed, and quite similar solid-framed, double-action weapons by G. H. Daw of London, or Charles Reeves and P. WEBLEY & SON (q.v.) of Birmingham were also made. For the purposes of this book, however, such arms can be regarded as variants of centre-fire designs, and it is to the revolvers of WILLIAM TRANTER (q.v.) that the reader must look for British developments of this type of revolver. The single-action Army revolver shown in Plate 10 shows that other English makers toyed with the rim-fire cartridge (a similar weapon was made by the Birmingham firm of Tipping & Lawden), but for volume of output, Tranter had no equal amongst native manufacturers.

Due to their rarity, few other rim-fire revolvers of the period 1865–8 have aroused any serious interest amongst collectors, although recent years have seen a change in this attitude. During the years of the Smith & Wesson monopoly in America, a number of makers attempted to market infringing arms, but were brought to heel in savagely contested legal actions or by the threat of them. Plates 10 and 11 show three of these infringing arms, two by Allen & Wheelock of Worcester, Mass., and the third by James Warner of Springfield, Mass., but all are rare today.

The less-publicized fate of Jacob Rupertus was typical of the frustration that gripped American revolver manufacturers, until the expiry of White's patent in 1869. Rupertus was a skilful designer of cheap breech-loading firearms whose patents were, for some years, developed by the important Tryon company of Philadelphia; from 1863 to 1866, the company traded as "Tryon & Brother", at various addresses in the city.

Their rather cramped premises at Second Street were converted into a factory making revolvers, shotguns and gun components for the partners (G. W. Tryon, Jun., and E. K. Tryon, Jun.), and for the gun-trade generally, Under the Rupertus patents some ingenious breech-loading pistols (single- or double-barrelled) were made at this factory, and sold from retail shops at 120–122 North Sixth Street, or from the warehouse at 625 Market Street.

Amongst his designs (the firm later alleged) Rupertus produced a small, single-action, rim-fire revolver of genuine promise, and it was proposed to sell this weapon alongside the conventional pistols. The retail style proposed for this operation was to be the "Rupertus Patent Pistol Company, Tryon & Brother, Sole Agents", and an initial contract for 7,000 assorted pistols and revolvers was put in hand. Eventually, however, the revolver was recognized as an infringement of the Rollin White patent, and discarded. With typical ingenuity, Rupertus converted his design into an eight-shot pepperbox, which he actually patented in July 1864, but although the Tryon company reorganized as "Tryon Bros. & Co." in 1866 and continued in business long after 1888, the revolver was never revived.

After the expiry of White's patent, an extraordinary range of cheap, solid-framed, single-action revolvers (in calibres from ·22 to ·41) were manufactured in America. These "Suicide Specials" (as American collectors term them now) were almost all of miserable quality and finish, but interest is now becoming aroused in them on the score of wonderment that any firearm could be made to sell at so small a price.

The researches of Donald B. Webster, Jun., have established over twenty American firms (a few of distinction) as concerned in the manufacture of "Suicide Specials", but, as in the case of many British revolvers, the names appearing on the arms were mainly those of re-tailers and dealers.

The Colt company produced a number of single-action weapons similar to the "Suicide Specials" (but of incomparably better quality) under their famous name and trade-mark; two of these rim-fire "House" or "New Line" revolvers appear as Plates 11 and 14, whilst a centre-fire specimen is also shown, for comparison, on Plate 11. This latter arm is known to collectors as the "Cop & Thug" model, from the scene embossed on the butt cheeks.

The Remington factory, at Ilion, N.Y., made their own "New Line" revolvers, under a frame construction patent of W. S. Smoot (U.S. Pat. 143855/1873), which were labelled by model numbers, as No. 1 (·30); No. 2 (·32); No. 3 (·38); and No. 4 (·38 and ·41). Specimens of the last two are shown in Plate 10. All were single-action revolvers with five chambers, until the last of the series, the "Iroquois", which was a seven-chambered ·22 pistol.

Both Companies also produced rim-fire versions of the percussion revolvers of the Civil War period; some were conversions, and others were made at the factories in their rim-fire forms. The Colt weapons more strictly belong in the appropriate Section of Chapter IV, since the centre-fire cartridge was generally preferred. However, a rim-fire conversion is shown in Plate 18 to illustrate the type.

Remington came to terms with SMITH & WESSON (q.v.) during the life of the Rollin White master patent for the bored-through cylinder, and some of their famous New Model ·44 percussion revolvers were adapted to the ·46 rim-fire cartridge. John E. Parsons recorded that over 4,500 of these pistols were fitted with a new five-shot cylinder (in place of the original six-shot), which was marked with the date of White's patent. Following the expiry of that patent, Remington began to offer a variety of converted arms and these are represented by the revolver shown in Plate 10. This particular conversion was generally confined to the smaller arms, and involved the use of a cylinder with a backing plate to hold the cartridges in the chambers (and to support the bases on firing); reloading required that the cylinder be removed completely, and it was quite practicable to substitute a percussion cylinder at need. The larger Remington revolvers were better modified, and had loading gates and ejector rods that allowed loading and unloading without dismantling the weapon.

Although little can now be traced to show an English echo to the great American interest in rim-fire revolvers, the British Patent Office records show that many U.S. designers and manufacturers had sufficient

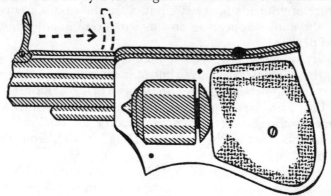

FIG. 4. *E. Boardman's "Little All Right" Revolver.*
Arrow indicates direction of travel for "squeezer" trigger *on top* of barrel.

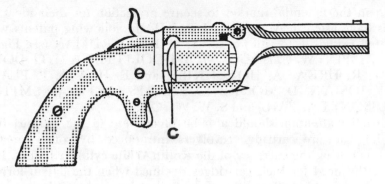

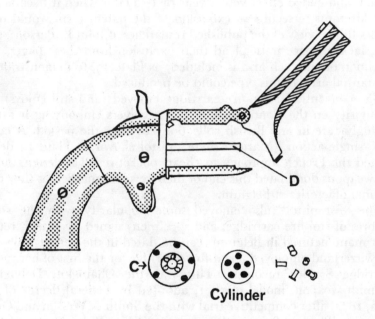

Cylinder

FIG. 5. *C. Sharps's Br. Pat. 1844/1863.*
Suggested embodiment.

Above: Suggested type of revolver for use with Sharps's first type of cylinder plate. The plate "C" is screwed home on the threads cut on the rear cylinder circumference.

Below: Revolver dismantled for loading. Note that plate "C" is pierced to admit the hammer nose, and that it carried the cylinder rotation teeth. Cartridges were expelled against "D", after removal of "C".

faith in the potential market to secure protection for their ideas. We thus have listed in Appendices I and II, the following patents which related primarily to rim-fire arms: E. P. BOARDMAN (see Fig. 4): S. CRISPIN: W. C. DODGE: J. B. DOOLITTLE & G. O. DOWN-ING: R. DREW: A. HOTCHKISS, and E. H. & A. P. PLANT: B. F. JOSLYN: D. MOORE: C. SHARPS (see Fig. 5): SMITH & WESSON: T. J. VAIL, and S. W. WOOD.

Strictly, attention should also be given here to the curious front-loading rim-fire cartridge revolvers introduced by some American makers during the currency of the Rollin White cylinder patent. How-ever, the need for such cartridges declined when the patent formally lapsed, and ended effectively a year or two later when it became clear that attempts to secure an extension of the patent term would not be successful. In view of the published researches of John E. Parsons, there-fore, lack of space must plead their exclusion from these pages, but a specimen of one such arm is included, as Plate 15, to demonstrate that substantial arms of this type could be produced.

The conventional rim-fire cartridge enjoyed (and still enjoys) great popularity on the Continent but true revolvers embodying it are sur-prisingly rare in any British collection covering the period. A curious little single-action "Mariette Bvte" pistol shown as Plate 12 demon-strated the French approach to cheap pocket revolver design, but pin-fire weapons dominated this end of their revolver market, as they did in the manufactories of Belgium.

The "fist pistol" also enjoyed some popularity with the smaller calibres of rim-fire cartridge, and specimens signed by British retailers (but manufactured in Belgium) can be dated in the period 1867–77.

Switzerland employed a rim-fire cartridge for the first of her metallic cartridge Service revolvers. This was the Chamelot, Delvigne & Schmidt weapon, model of 1871, adopted by Federal decree of April 24th, 1872, after competitive trial with the Smith & Wesson and Galand revolvers. The first 800 pistols were supplied by Pirlot Freres, of Liège, who owned the Chamelot-Delvigne patent and supplied an almost identical (but centre-fire) arm to the Italian Army. Surviving stocks of this Swiss rim-fire weapon, Model 1872, were finally converted to accept an equivalent 10·4 mm. centre-fire round, on the adoption of a new revolver in 1878.

The original Model 1869 Smith & Wesson self-extracting revolver (see Plate 66) continued to be developed as a rim-fire weapon for the overseas market. Both Mexico and Turkey bought a "No. 3" improve-ment, chambered for the ·44 Henry round, and the latter government (in 1877) purchased a special consignment of the centre-fire "Russian

Model" revolvers adapted for the same rim-fire Henry cartridge. As can be seen from Plate 31, this rim-fire "Russian-type" revolver was copied by the Belgians with the same devotion as that which they lavished upon the centre-fire weapon shown in the same Plate. Smith & Wesson also secured an order for 5,000 "New Model No. 3" pistols (more particularly described in Chapter IV), in 1879, which were adapted for the rim-fire round and provided further evidence of Ottoman satisfaction with this form of ignition.

CHAPTER IV

CENTRE-FIRE REVOLVERS

REVOLVERS made between 1865 and 1888 by the Colt and Remington Companies of America receive little attention here. Apart from the excellent specialist books already published upon them, they present little of interest in terms of technical advance. The quality of Colt or Remington pistols (within their price-range) was unrivalled, but design merely stagnated in these years.

Some attention is paid, however, to the arms made by Smith & Wesson, despite the comprehensive works upon them already published by John E. Parsons and McHenry & Roper. The Smith & Wesson design team worked with tremendous effect from 1869 to 1881, and the results cannot be ignored here, even at the risk of repeating much that has already been said.

Basically, however, concentration is directed to revolvers of lesser renown, and the principal division adopted lies between rod-ejecting weapons, and those pistols with hinged or movably linked barrel/frame assemblies giving automatic cartridge extraction.

The centre-fire cartridge was old in design by 1865, older even than the pin and rim-fire rounds. As early as 1812, the Swiss, Pauly, had developed a breech-loading pistol which used a central-fire metallic rimmed cartridge, and the revolving arms of Michallon (1844) and Genhart (1856) used curious front-loading centrally primed metallic cases. Genhart's pistols and rifles were of a "turret-type" personified in the period of this book by the designs of F. DREVENSTEDT (q.v.), but they were not quite obsolete by 1865. The inventor carried on a gunmaker's business at rue aux Chevaux, 42, Liège, into the period, and sold his "revolver horizontal", "revolver vertical", and "revolver de Salon" from that address.

In England, however, interest in the centre-fire cartridge was not aroused until 1858, when Pottet introduced a satisfactory "gas-tight" centre-fire shotgun case. He improved the round, after 1858, and it was taken up in England by Francis Schneider and G. H. Daw, of London. After 1862, the cartridge proved satisfactory for sporting arms, and attention began to be directed to its use in rifles, pistols and revolvers. Despite American use of solid drawn (i.e. one-piece) metallic cartridge-cases during the Civil War, British opinion clung to the coiled brass case, with separate iron base. It was not until 1868 that a suitable revolver cartridge was approved for the British service revolver, and this Boxer cartridge (named after its inventor) was little more than a brass ferrule, to which was riveted an iron base. In later years, Britain accepted the solid-drawn brass cartridge-case, but the enterprise shown in this respect by Continental cartridge manufacturers at the Paris Exhibition of 1867 was not matched here.

Section I: Part 1—Solid-frame revolvers

Alphabetically, as in merit, "Adams's Patent Central-Fire Breech-Loading Revolver" must head any study of British weapons in this category.

Plate 24 shows the version normally encountered, which was a gate-loaded, double-action, six-chambered pistol with a permanently aligned rod-ejector mounted on the right of the frame.

Adams's revolver was adopted by the British Army in 1868, and was not made in either of the Government small-arms factories. The actual source of manufacture is still obscure.

"Adams's Patent Small Arms Company, Limited" was incorporated on August 15th, 1864, specifically to purchase and develop Br. Pats. 2824/1857 and 1758/1861, along with the rights to equivalent patents in other countries. The patentee was JOHN ADAMS (q.v.), of 14 St. Paul's Road, Camden Square, London, who had been associated with ROBERT ADAMS (q.v.) in producing the famous Beaumont-Adams percussion revolver during the late 1850's.

The Company had a capital of only £10,000 for division between the promoters, and John Adams was appointed the Managing Director for seven years. His fellow shareholders were F. Mortimore (Chairman), J. W. and J. S. Rooth. P. Browne, E. M. Ricketts, and J. F. Shattock.

Adams secured ten paid-up £10 shares as a contribution to his patent costs, and three hundred paid-up shares as the purchase price for his patents.

During its entire history the Company never called up this modest nominal capital in full, and we can assume that it really constituted a syndicate. The members would have split the royalties paid on each revolver made under Adams's patents, in proportion to their shareholdings.

The registered offices were at 391 Strand, London (after December, 1865), and the Company ceased to operate in July, 1881, shortly before the last expiry of John Adams's revolver patents. The Enfield pistol that superseded his design for service purchase had been approved in the previous August.

Some confusion attended the dissolution of the Company, for it transferred its business to Messrs. William Watts Locke & Co. in July, 1881, but did not achieve formal dissolution until April 1894.

Five British patents of John Adams's existed during the life of the limited liability company, and records now destroyed have confirmed that the first two (2824/1857 and 1758/1861) were duly assigned to it in 1866.

The first of these patents related principally to a percussion revolver, but contained general claims on frame construction and for designing a lock mechanism permitting the action body to be machined out internally by circular cutters, The revolver is rare today and we can assume from this that these cited claims were the probable focus of interest.

U.S. Patent 30602 of November 6th, 1860, had also been secured by John Adams, to protect so much of this design as the American Examiners would accept as novel, but the patent was assigned to T. POULTNEY (q.v.) before sealing, and may not have been available to the Company.

The second British Patent also sought to avoid the master-patent of ROBERT ADAMS for the one-piece revolver barrel/frame forging. It accomplished this by making barrel and cylinder frame in one piece, for attachment to a separate butt component holding the lock mechanism.

The revolver was an optional percussion/metallic cartridge arm and specimens are rare, but the frame design was basically that used in the Marks II & III Service revolvers of later concern.

On July 28th, 1866, John Adams secured Br. Pat. No. 1959 to improve the methods for producing his 1861 frame, and also sought protection for a revolver loaded at the front of the cylinder with special centre-fire metallic cartridges. Inevitably the latter idea invites comparison with Colt's "Thuer" conversion cylinder, patented two years later by F.A.K.W. von OPPEN (q.v.). No detailed similarity existed, however, and the well-known Crystal Palace and Woolwich Arsenal trials of 1869 matched the Colt against a conventional (if converted) Adams pistol of the type shown on Plates 19 and 20.

In October, 1867, he secured Br. Pat. No. 2961 as a patent of improvement upon his 1959/1866. This protected the loading-gate and rod-ejector used on these original John Adams's service revolvers of

1868, which were weapons converted from the old Beaumont-Adams muzzle-loading arms purchased in 1856 or 1857. This gate and ejector were also used in the later revolvers, Marks II and III.

On December 28th, 1868, he obtained U.S. Pat. No. 85350, which was a mosaic of the practicable features from his British patents of 1866 and 1867.

Finally, as Br. Pat. 2258/1872, John Adams protected an alternative type of cartridge ejector-rod, mounted upon a swivel on the front face of the pistol frame and pressed home into a recess in the cylinder-pin, as shown in Plate 28, when not in use.

If, as earlier suggested, the purpose of the limited liability company was to develop John Adams's two original patents, it should also have had title to those above-mentioned, and to any protection overseas. However, the actual manufacture and sale of Adams's revolvers may have rested out of these hands, for it is difficult to see how operations could be effectively financed from a capital so modest. Inevitably, the services of "ADAMS & CO." (q.v.) suggest themselves in this service, as established rifle manufacturers and wholesale gunmakers in near-by Finsbury. Against this view, it must be admitted that Directory listings for the limited Company usually showed a "Manufactory & Show-rooms" at 391 Strand, and that surviving correspondence from W. Watts Locke, in 1883, referred to "our Factory here", as using special steam machinery.

After 1881 the old company name disappeared in favour of a new trading style as "Adams's Patent Small Arms Manufacturing Co.; W. Watts Locke & Co., Proprietors", which saw out the remainder of the period. The British Services passed over Adams's revolver in favour of an Enfield weapon of 1880, and some further products were taken up by the Company. Torpedo fuze pistols were manufactured for the Admiralty after 1883, along with yacht equipment and light armaments. It is also worth noting that the address of "Adams & Co." changed in 1881, although no connection between the two firms has yet been demonstrated.

John Adams's revolvers are now recognized in only three models using a metallic cartridge.

The ·450 centre-fire weapon shown as Plates 19 and 20 is representative of the original service revolver approved in 1868, and bears the reissue or conversion date of June, 1869. Originally a "London Armoury Company (Limited)" muzzle-loading revolver of Beaumont-Adams's model 1856–7, it has been converted in accordance with John Adams's Br. Pat. 2961/1867.

The Minute Books of the Director-General, Ordnance, for 1869, record that 7,000 of these revolvers were available for conversion (at a cost of £1 1s. each), and a suitably engraved bullet mould in the R.S.A.F. Pattern Room, at Enfield, records the last approved bullet for the muzzle-loader as sealed in April, 1867.

To follow this converted pistol came the true John Adams's revolvers of the type shown in Plate 24, which are found bearing service Marks II and III.

For purposes of rough dating, a Mark II pistol (Serial No. 3863) has been observed as dated December, 1871, whilst a Mark III weapon (Serial No. 12103) was dated November, 1878.

The principal points of note on these ·450 Army revolvers, were that they bore commercial London proof marks, and that the lock mechanism was still basically the old Beaumont-Adams's design of 1856 (see Plate 1) but with the sear switched down to the rear of the trigger guard. Their debt of design to John Adams lay in the frame construction, ejector-rods and loading-gates, under his patents of 1861 and 1866.

True John Adams's revolvers embodying the refined rod-ejector patented in 1872 are not encountered as frequently as the preceding model. Both versions were available commercially (weapons with 4-in. barrels have been observed), but the later pistol does suggest manufacture exclusively for private purchase.

In a random selection of fifteen revolvers, only two had the swivelling ejector and both were Birmingham proved. In addition, both cylinders were stamped "C. 455", suggesting that the weapons chambered the original Enfield revolver cartridge as an alternative to the ·450 Adams round.

Whether under the management of John Adams or the later rule of Watts Locke, the revolvers never lacked promotion.

A Medal of Merit was secured at the Vienna Universal Exhibition of 1873, another was won at Dublin, and a Gold Medal resulted from the New Zealand Exhibition of 1882.

The size of any resultant orders may have been modest, but in the heyday of this weapon exclusive adoption was claimed for H.M. War Department; the Metropolitan Police; Indian and Colonial Governments; the New Zealand Government; City of London Police and City Prisons; and for the Governments of Portugal, Chile, Mexico, China, Turkey, and Brazil.

By October, 1883, Watts Locke & Co. were offering a "new Model Revolver No. 5" to the Receiver of the Metropolitan Police District. So far this weapon remains unidentified, for their covering quotation can be read as offering five different revolvers to the police.

The letter suggested that one pistol (a pocket-sized revolver, in ·450 c.f. calibre) was the most suitable, but offered cheaper weapons with actions ". . . other than Adams's patent and using rods similar to (pistol) No. 2".

It seems significant, since Adams's revolvers are virtually unknown in any but the Army size, that contemporary pistols from P. WEBLEY & SON (q.v.) should present a similar model numbering in regard to their improved pattern 1883 civilian and police weapons.

This latter firm offered quite a range of solid-framed Pocket or Constabulary revolvers under such well known titles as the "R.I.C. No. 1", the "R.I.C./83 Model", the "Webley No. 2 Pattern", and so forth, and were one of the largest suppliers of firearms to the gun-trade.

The possibility that these "trade" revolvers were included in the range sold by Watts Locke & Co. is raised again in remarks upon Webley arms.

Before turning to another British revolver manufacturer whose arms were predominantly of this solid-frame type, formal acknowledgement must be made to the famous weapons of Colt, Remington and Webley.

In the centre-fire field, the Colt Company produced one weapon known to every reader, whether collector or layman. Their single-action revolver (known as the "Peacemaker", the "Army" or the "Frontier" weapon) was not a particularly well-designed arm. The lock remained basically as used in their old muzzle-loading revolvers, whilst the trigger guard and back-strap were (as before) attached to the frame by screws. The rod-ejector was weak, and easily disabled by rough handling, and the cylinder-pin sometimes jarred out, in firing, to the embarrassment of the user. However, with all these defects, the arm became a fighter's side-arm, and it is little exaggeration to say that whatever parts broke, or failed, the pistol could still be fired (see Plate 21).

The revolver was introduced about 1873, and was in continuous production throughout the period, latterly in competition with two rather frail double-action revolvers from the same factory. To summarize the details of these Colt weapons, the remarks of A. C. Gould (in the 1888 edition of his book) served well.

"New Model Army, single-action; overall $12\frac{1}{2}$ in.; barrel $7\frac{1}{2}$ in.; calibre ·45; weight 2 lb. 5 oz. Rifling 6 grooves, one revolution in 16 in. Groove depth ·005 in. 6 shot.

Cartridge. Powder 30 grains; Lead 250 grains. Centre fire, externally primed."

"New Model Army, double-action; overall $12\frac{1}{2}$ in.; barrel $7\frac{1}{2}$ in.; weight with $7\frac{1}{2}$ in. barrel 2 lb. 7 oz. Calibre ·45. 6 shot. Any length of

D

barrel, and for the U.S. regulation cartridge, or the ·44 magazine rifle cartridge. Revolvers taking the latter are known as the 'Frontier' model."

(This rather frail Model 1878 double-action revolver appears in Plate 21, and the fragile lock is seen in Plate 22. It had the advantage, over the single-action pistol, of a butt integral with the frame, but it was a miserable arm.)

"New Model ·41, double-action, centre-fire. Calibre ·41 in. 6 shot. Barrels 4½ in.; 5 in. and 6 in."

"New Model ·38, double-action, centre-fire. Calibre ·38. 6 shot; barrels 2½ in., 3½ in., 6 in. and 7 in."

(These Colt "Lightning" revolvers are represented in Plate 21, where it can be noted that the old system of a separate trigger guard and butt-strap was maintained in the series. A specimen lock appears in Plate 22, and explains why a serviceable "Lightning" revolver can so seldom be found.)

"New Police ·38, single-action, centre-fire. Calibre ·38. 6 shot. Barrels 4½ in., 5 in., and 6 in." (see Plate 11).

"New target revolver, in ·38 and ·32 calibre, made in the Army model frame."

(These revolvers were single- and double-action arms of the types already mentioned, with extra care taken in their sighting and lock adjustment.)

"Pocket revolvers in calibres ·22, ·30, ·32, ·38 and ·41, with 2-in. barrels."

(These were single-action, stud trigger arms, of the "New Line" type shown in Plate 11. An exception, virtually obsolete by 1888, to the solid frames of this series was the ·22 revolver shown on Plate 41.)

Colt revolvers sold well in the United Kingdom, but professional opinions were not always favourable. With crushing brevity Greener stated that the Lightning revolver ". . . is known as the 'Bulldog' and takes the ·380 long cartridge; other sizes, as ·410, ·442 and ·450 are made . . . all these revolvers are expensive".

The provisional British patents secured for the Colt Company by H. E. NEWTON (q.v.) present something of a puzzle here. The Provisional Specifications are not illustrated and make positive identification difficult for the arms protected. Presumably they would have duplicated William Mason's U.S. Patents 247374 and 248190 (both of 1881) if the applications had been pressed. The British specifications related to double-action revolver locks (4579/1881; 4689/1881), and to an auxiliary cylinder-bolt on the side of the loading-gate (4602/1881). The equivalent U.S. Patent strongly suggested that double-action Army pistols, model of 1878, would embody the improvements, but no Colt revolvers of that model are known to embody these lock mechanisms.

Before leaving this maker, it is in point to mention the sales achieved by Colt arms in this country. In 1871, Norton gave pistol sales at 300,000 on an available production capacity of 500 per day. This would presumably be the swan-song of machinery for making those older types of Colt revolver (with key-fastened barrels and open frames) personified in Plate 18. Production of their solid-frame single-action Army weapon started in 1873, and by the close of 1889 over 130,000 of this model alone had been turned out. It is a measure of their surprisingly substantial market in this country, that the latter year alone saw 2,120 Colt revolvers pass through the Birmingham Proof House to compete with other pistols.

Conversely, the Remington Company appears to have been indifferent to this market for revolving arms, if the scarcity of their pistols in British collections be any guide. Real interest was aroused in the U.K., by their rolling block rifle designs, and assignments or leases under these patents were taken by Geiger, Norris, Westley Richards and others from the mid-1860's and onwards. However, with the exceptions noted in Appendix II, no traceable patent protection was sought here for Remington revolvers. Possibly the novelties in their principal U.S. patents had already been anticipated by British patentees, but a more logical explanation would be in agreement with competitors to split up overseas markets. Whatever the reason, the Model 1875 Remington revolver shown in Plate 67 achieved excellent sales to Egypt, and their "New Line" No. 3 centre-fire revolver (already noticed in Plate 10) showed an excellent grasp of manufacturing technique.

In England, two major names were associated with this type of centre-fire revolver to the exclusion, almost, of all others.

The solid-frame arms of P. WEBLEY & SON have been so ably covered by Major Dowell that little new matter can be offered here, but it must be accepted that the manufacturing resources of this company (from 1865–88) have never been seriously described, and that it is difficult for any collector to be sure that a revolver signed by the firm was made by it. The "Webley" revolvers shown in Plates 10 and 23 must be viewed, therefore, with this reservation in mind.

The first, and most important, of the Webley solid-frame, double-action centre-fire revolvers is shown in Plate 23, and appeared in 1867. Prior to that year, the firm had made a few optional percussion/metallic cartridge pistols, but the arm illustrated (which was adopted by the Royal Irish Constabulary in January, 1868) was new in appearance, if not in mechanical design. It was very popular, selling in a variety of calibres, but was superseded in 1883 by the weapon shown also on Plate 23; this continued until the First World War and was available in a variety of models, which were catalogued by calibre. The Model 1883 served as the vehicle for Silver & Fletcher's patented extractor and hammer (see Plate 55), and it also sired a special Metropolitan Police model, and another line of pistols with "parrot-beak" butts, which sold under the trade name of "The British Bulldog".

At some time after 1878, Webley were inspired to produce a weapon similar to the Colt double-action Army revolver shown in Plate 21; this they called the "New Model Army Express", or "Webley's No. 5". As can be seen from the specimen in Plate 23, this was a sturdy pistol, and the Government of the South African Republic were sufficiently impressed to issue it; a rare single-action variant was also made (in 1881) for the Cape Mounted Rifles (Colonial). At about the same period, the first Webley revolver shown on Plate 23 went into production, but its rarity today suggests that it aroused very little interest. In general, it was very similar to the "No. 5" pistol, but it embodied the safety loading-gate protected by M. KAUFFMAN'S Br. Pat. 3913/1881 (q.v.).

The contemporary opinion of J. H. Walsh does not support the view that all revolvers marked "Webley" were necessarily made by them. In the 1884 edition of his book, he stated flatly that "the modern, solid-frame, non-extracting revolvers which are being made by the leading manufacturers may be classified as follows: Webley's No. 5, Webley's R.I.C., Webley's Metropolitan Police, Webley's British Bulldog", and he later mentioned that the Metropolitan Police revolver was adopted in November, 1883, as a ·450 calibre arm with a 2½-in. barrel.

It is in point now to recall the Watts Locke & Co. letter to the Receiver of the Metropolitan District, earlier mentioned in relation to Adams's revolvers. It has been shown that they offered a ·450 pocket revolver to the Receiver in October, 1883, and Walsh confirmed adoption of such an arm in the November. Recalling that the offer included a "revolver No. 5", there can be little doubt of a connection between the Webley and Adams's companies, but it would be interesting to discover which Company was actually making the revolvers offered.

Any study of this type of revolver inevitably throws up a variety of solid-frame revolvers signed by British gunmakers but obviously never made by them, together with converted arms of the type noticed in this (and the preceding) Chapter. Specimens of such "trade" revolvers appear in Plates 51 and 58, where the names of their retailers are also given.

Dowell assigned the credit for making many of these revolvers to

P. WEBLEY & SON (q.v.), but the opinion of the present writer is that it would be premature to accord Webley's such dominance at this time. Thus, apart from possible output at the factories of Cashmore, Reeves and Westley Richards (which have received but scant attention from writers to date), a study of Appendices I and II throws up one man as the manufacturer principally interested in patents for solid-frame metallic cartridge revolvers.

The background of WILLIAM TRANTER (q.v.) is outlined in Appendix II, and only the scope of his relevant British patents will be explored here. Revolvers actually stamped "W. Tranter's Patent" are shown in Plate 68, and those rim-fire arms with trigger guards were also produced in centre-fire models.

On the basis of present research, the view cannot be urged that Tranter monopolized the manufacture of revolvers under his various patents, for although the recent destruction of Patent Office records makes tracing of any patent licences genuinely difficult, the Tranter weapons themselves do not suggest centralized manufacture for every model.

Some Tranter revolvers (notably those illustrated at centre and right, in Plate 68) do appear to have been standardized and made to a rigid pattern. However, the smaller models of the double-action arm varied so widely in appearance and finish that licensed manufacture by other makers seems to be indicated. Tranter's patented novelties were present in such arms, they were marked "W. Tranter's Patent", but uniformity of detail and dimension were absent.

On the matter of his various designs, William Tranter's Br. Pat. 212/1853 requires mention here, although it protected the famous double-trigger percussion revolver shown in Plate 1. A few of these weapons were converted to use metallic cartridges on the system claimed in the inventor's Br. Pat. 1889/1865, and some others were made in the 1880's (allegedly by Kynoch) as true centre-fire arms. His Br. Pat. 1913/1856 also related to cap-lock revolvers (see Plate 1). It is important here not only as protecting the lock mechanism used in those single-trigger muzzle-loading arms, but as the basis for the locks of the double-action cartridge weapons shown in Plate 68. The machining of revolver frame lock-cavities on a lathe face-plate was also claimed in this Patent.

Br. Pat. 2067/1862 (so far as it related to revolvers) appeared to protect the cylinder-bolt used in the stud-trigger rim-fire pistol shown in Plate 68, but it had an unillustrated Specification and positive identification is difficult. Also described were a circular inspection plate over the lock mechanism, and a spring-loaded cylinder-pin, both being strongly prophetic of types later used in some American "Suicide Specials", noticed in Chapter III.

Br. Pat. 1862/1863 related to the lever ejector shown at centre in Plate 68; to a rearward swinging loading-gate; and to butt-caps and cylinder-bolts. The arms shown in the Specification were the stud-trigger, single-action pocket pistol and a larger holster-sized revolver with a frame almost identical to that shown on the Plate.

Br. Pat. 1889/1865 was not primarily concerned with revolvers, but included a claim for combining a breech-piece with the revolving cylinder. Almost certainly this system was intended for converting per-cussion revolvers to use centre-fire cartridges of a type also claimed in the patent. A revolver converted in an almost identical manner is shown in Plate 48. However, the Specification suggested using a central stem and one indexing pin for the breech-piece, instead of the three-pin system shown in the Plate. On September 9th, 1873, the Birmingham Small-Arms and Metal Company Ltd, filed a Disclaimer and Memor-andum of Alteration on this Patent which Tranter (a substantial share-holder in the Company) had assigned to them, under two deeds dated in April and June of that year. The effect of the alterations was to limit protection to the cartridge and the revolver system, and some guide to the reason for alteration appeared in the fiat of the Attorney-General giving leave for it. The *quid pro quo* for permission to alter the Specifica-tion was that the Company should take no infringement proceedings (under the amended patent) against Mr. Westley Richards and the National Arms & Ammunition Company, of Birmingham, in respect of the manufacture, use or sale of cartridges.

Br. Pat. 2113/1866 included a claim for a revolver lock mechanism, amongst matters of no concern here. The lock claimed was virtually a restatement of the old Beaumont-Adams's mechanism of 1855, with the hook connection between hammer and trigger now switched from former to latter. In practice, however, Tranter does not appear to have used a top sear in his revolvers, and the weapons shown at centre, right and bottom, in Plate 68, have their sears in the bottom of the frame for operation by the horn at the rear of the trigger. In other respects their locks conform to this Patent.

The Complete Specification to Br. Pat 2228/1867 did not refer to revolvers at all. However, the Provisional Specification did claim for such arms a lever interposed between hammer and cartridge-head to prevent the latter bulging on firing.

Br. Pat. 285/1868 clearly illustrated the revolver shown at right on Plate 68 and related to the hammer and rod-ejector used in that arm. A centre-fire cartridge with an "M"-shaped anvil was also claimed.

The hammer had no firing-nose, but struck a separate sliding-pin in the frame, and it was shaped to act as a safety-cover to that pin. The ejector-rod (swivelling out for use on a screw at the front of the frame) was later adapted to seat in a cavity in the cylinder-pin, when not in use. It will be recalled that JOHN ADAMS (q.v.) secured protection on such a refinement.

Br. Pat. 3622/1868 claimed two types of cartridge extractors for revolvers, amongst a number of other devices, and a lubricating bullet presumably suitable for hand-gun cartridges. The first type of extractor was for use in revolvers with frames jointed at the top rear angle in the style shown by Martin on Plate 48. With the barrel tipped up clear of the action body, a rack and pinion (manually operated) worked a centre-pin extractor to clear all the cartridges from the cylinder. The other extractor was of a type familiar to collectors and appears in Plate 24. Here the conventional rod could be swivelled sideways to lie along the frame of the revolver, below the cylinder. A flush-fitted variant was claimed. Although not mentioned or claimed, the loading-gate on the arms illustrated was of a side-swinging type normally used by Tranter on such revolvers as centre and right on Plate 68.

Br. Pat. 3557/1869 included a refinement to the hinged-frame extractor claimed in 3622/1868. Here (instead of using a short, thumb-operated rack) a really substantial lever was hinged beneath the barrel to operate the extractor when the barrel and cylinder were tilted up. Both systems were really developments to the extractor of A. SPIRLET (q.v.)

Finally, Tranter's Br. Pat. 2509/1871 refined the second type of ejector claimed in his Br. Pat. 3622/1868. A spring acted upon the mounting swivel for this ejector and flicked the rod into alignment with the chambers, or beneath the barrel, at will.

In Europe solid-frame revolvers enjoyed great popularity, but the organization of the arms industry encouraged survival of rod-ejecting revolvers with complex and obsolete barrel/frame assemblies. Large pools of skilled, but cheap, hand-labour existed in Belgium, France and Austria, which slowed introduction of the forging or milling machinery that had early encouraged major American and British manufacturers to adopt a solid frame, even for their inexpensive arms. In due course even the workshops of Liège adapted themselves to produce such arms, and the cheap "Bulldog" or "Constabulary" weapons poured out, but service revolvers were the outstanding embodiment for this frame construction in Europe.

Unfortunately, it proved difficult to locate some of the European service revolvers for illustration in this book, and the arms shown must be accepted as examples only. The earliest of them is probably that by "Pirlot Freres à Liège" (see Plate 24), the original manufacturers of the Chamelot Delvigne lock used in the Swiss Army revolvers of 1872, and a glance at the adoption table in Chapter 5 will show how widely that lock was distributed in its refined form. (A specimen lock, from a French M/74 revolver, is shown in Plate 22.)

A so-far unidentified revolver is shown in Plate 24, and is marked "Thornton's Patent", although no patentee of that name appears in Appendices I or II. The lock, the use of centres for mounting components, and the removable sideplate all suggest that the patent in point was actually Br. Pat. 5504/1881 by BLED, RICHOUX and WARNANT (q.v.), Version Two of the lock mechanisms shown in Fig. 6 being the one embodied in the pistol. The weapon was made in England, and the small thumb-piece shown behind the hammer springs off the sideplate when it is drawn back. The practice of claiming a "Patent" on weapons was quite widespread, even where the maker himself held no patent. Provided that a patent existed (or had existed), such a usage of the word was not illegal.

The French Chamelot Delvigne revolver shown on Plate 26, and the Italian weapon with it, were representative of the revolvers that embodied that famous lock (see Chapter V), but the competing Nagant mechanism was almost as popular. A specimen lock is shown in Plate 25, and the Dutch M/1873 service pistol from which it came appears in Plate 28. This particular arm had no ejector-rod attached to it (a separate rod was carried in the holster), but later revolvers remedied this defect. Thus the Belgian's officer's revolver, M/78, had the ejector-rod mounted on a sleeve turning round the barrel, which was latched in the manner taught by E. NAGANT's Br. Pat. 4310/1879 (q.v.). Other frame and lock refinements from the patent were later embodied in Belgian and Scandinavian pistols of the early 1880's.

Curiously enough, the most enterprising adoptions for the solid-framed service revolver occurred in the small Swiss forces.

Initially, Switzerland adopted a rim-fire revolver in two calibres; a 12-mm. weapon was issued to Army guides, and a 9-mm. pistol served for mounted N.C.O.s of artillery. Both revolvers had the Chamelot Delvigne lock, as originally developed by Pirlot Freres of Liège, but neither cartridge proved ballistically efficient in test. Accordingly, an improved 10·4-mm. round was adopted to replace both, and lock modifications by H. Stabsmajor Rudolph Schmidt were embodied in a new revolver. The resultant arm was known as the "Chamelot Delvigne et Schmidt" revolver, M/72, and it was approved for appropriate issue, under Bundesrath Ordinances of April 24th, and July 10th in that year.

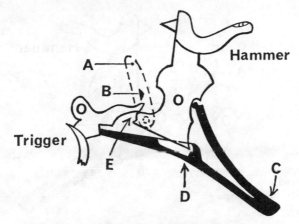

FIG. 6(a). *Bled, Richoux & Warnant's Revolver Locks.*
(*Version One.*)
(Br. Pat. 5504/1881.)

The mainspring "C" (shown partly cut away at "D") also acts as a trigger spring. A shoulder at "D" bears on the back of the hammer and rebounds it to half-cock after firing.

"A" is the cylinder pawl, which carries a stud "B" on its inner surface. When thumb-cocking, this stud plays no active part, the trigger-nose and hammer-toe engaging conventionally at point "E". When trigger-cocking, however, the trigger-nose catches stud "B" as it rises and pulls the hammer to full-cock through the linking of "A" to the latter component.

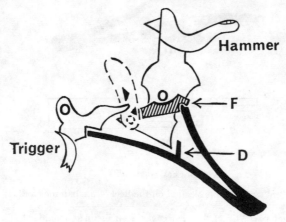

FIG. 6(b). *Bled, Richoux & Warnant's Revolver Locks.*
(*Version Two.*)
(Br. Pat. 5504/1881)

In this variant, the mainspring acts upon a pivoted arm, "F" mounted on the side of the hammer, and the rebound shoulder at "D" is modified in form. The sequence of operation is similar to Version One. The "Thornton's Patent" revolver in Plate 11 embodies this lock.

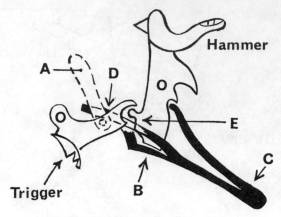

FIG. 6(c). *Bled, Richoux & Warnant's Revolver Locks.*
(*Version Three.*)
(Br. Pat. 5520/1881.)

In this variant, the mainspring "C" again serves as a trigger-spring and also acts to rebound the hammer at "B" after firing.

However, the thrust of the mainspring "C" is here divided by slitting the lower arm into two parts, thus:

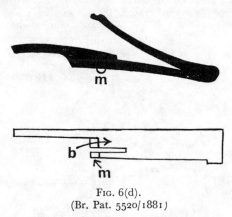

FIG. 6(d).
(Br. Pat. 5520/1881)

The lump "m" engages a projection on the heel of the hammer and effects the rebound.

The larger part "b" of the arm engages an inclined shoulder "D" on the inner side of the pawl "A". It thus acts as a trigger-spring, since "A" is linked by its pivot to the trigger.

Engagement of the hammer-toe "E" in the recess shown in the trigger-nose thrusts the hammer back in trigger cocking. If thumb-cocked, the hammer is held at full-cock by the conventional bents cut in "E", which engage the trigger-nose as in lock, Version One and Two.

A centre-fire version was adopted by the Italians, in the same year, and a specimen marked "Glisenti, Brescia" can be seen in Plate 26. Like all these European service revolvers, this was a six-chambered pistol.

In 1878, the Swiss moved into line with most of the major powers, and substituted a centre-fire round for their rim-fire cartridge. It was a simple task to adapt their existing stocks of revolvers to the new ignition, and these arms became the Model 1872/1878, in 10·4-mm. centre-fire calibre.

In the same year, a new centre-fire revolver was approved for issue to cavalry and artillery officers, N.C.O.s of dragoon and guide units and for mounted N.C.O.s and trumpeters of heavy, mountain, and field artillery.

This M/78 Schmidt revolver embodied a lock mechanism similar to that taught by C. F. GALAND's Br. Pat. 2308/1872, but its inventor acknowledged his debt only to a rod-ejector by J. WARNANT (q.v.). The sideplate on the left of the frame swung open on a forward hinge to give access to the lock, and the latter could be dismounted without using any tools.

In 1882, another Schmidt solid-frame rod-ejecting revolver was adopted by the Swiss, this time for issue to unmounted officers. It was a smaller weapon than the M/78 and used a 7·5 mm. centre-fire cartridge. From 1887 onwards a copper-jacketed Rubin bullet replaced the original paper-covered ball.

The revolver had a lock of improved Nagant type (see Plate 25), ingeniously modified, *d'après Abadie*, to permit faster loading and unloading. Opening the loading-gate disconnected the hammer from the lock, and the cylinder could then be rapidly revolved by simply pulling the trigger. In this manner, each chamber was automatically aligned with the ejector-rod and loading-port, by a single movement, and it was unnecessary even to glance at the weapon to achieve this.

The Abadie modification was simplicity itself, for it merely involved the formation of a suitable cam on the inner end of the loading-gate pivot. When this gate was swung to the rear, the pivot turned and the cam on it forced back the hammer catch (seen on the breast of the hammer in Plate 25) to disconnect hammer and trigger.

After 1887, a further safety feature was introduced. If the loading-gate was open the weapon could not be cocked; conversely, if already cocked the hammer could not fall. This type of safety device was a hardy annual in revolver design; a similar idea by M. KAUFMANN (q.v.) has already been mentioned, and the British "Enfield" self-extracting revolver, later mentioned, also embodied a gate safety.

In turning to the service revolvers of Germany, few words are needed to conclude this part of the Chapter. Both the cavalry trooper's Model

1880 and the officer's Model 1884 were designed by a Commission and really differed only in their dimensions. As can be seen from the M/80 pistol shown in Plate 26, these were single-action, solid-frame revolvers without exterior rod-ejectors; instead of the usual external tubed rod, the cartridge-cases were punched from the chambers by using the cylinder-pin, and this component could be readily withdrawn for the purpose. A specimen lock-mechanism from a Model 1884 is shown in Plate 22, but an interesting variant is shown beneath the trooper's pistol in Plate 26. Both weapons are marked "F. Dreyse. Sommerda", but the officer's weapon has undergone an ingenious modification at other hands. In the version shown, the hammer is cocked by pulling the forward trigger, and fired by that at the rear.

Some of these revolvers (in the conventional form) were made at the Arsenal in Erfurt, and were so marked; another interesting series of markings can sometimes be found engraved upon the butt-strap, where the history of the weapon's passage through various service units was recorded.

Section I: Part 2—Rod-ejecting revolvers without solid frames

Good-quality, centre-fire revolvers of this type were largely transitional, being often constructed with materials and equipment left over from the muzzle-loading era. Such arms by Colt were well-known, and other cheap English or Continental arms of the type shown in Plate 16 were also common.

However, this type of revolver also existed as the earliest of true centre-fire pistols, and the remarks upon PERRIN & DELMAS (q.v.) are in point. The Perrin revolver was also patented in France, during 1859, and a Certificate of Addition to the patent was secured during 1865. The resultant self-cocking revolver, with a rod-ejector beneath the barrel, had the curious distinction of having barrel and frame forged in one without any top strap to connect them.

After the passing of such early arms, however, these revolvers still merited separate attention as a result of the Austro–Hungarian adoption of a *système* Gasser side-arm, which replaced a single-shot Werndl cavalry pistol in 1870. The house of Leopold Gasser made these arms and had two factories for their manufacture, at Vienna and at Saint Pölten. If Colard is to be believed, these factories had a production potential of 100,000 revolvers and 45,000 long-arms annually, but he failed to make clear whether Gasser also made the Austrian naval revolver as part of this output. The latter arm differed from a *revolver du troupe*, M/70, only in its method for uniting barrel to frame, and in its loading-gate.

The cavalry revolver (seen in Plate 28) was a six-shot, double-action pistol, chambering a long 11-mm. centre-fire cartridge, *système* Roth, of the same dimensions as that used in the Werndl carbine. This round was fairly authoritative and had a penetration (at 150 paces) of three 26-mm. deal planks spaced 15 cm. apart. The lock mechanism of this arm was not complicated, but is rather more simple to illustrate than to describe, and the explanatory drawings from Colard appear as Plate 27. The bar-safety earlier described in relation to the pin-fire revolver can be clearly seen in Plate 28.

Although fragile in appearance, the Gasser proved surprisingly robust in service. Eight hundred test rounds were fired in one pistol, in which the powder charges had been increased from the standard 1 gr. 48 to 2 gr. 2, but no damage resulted. In other experiments, cavalry and artillery units carried their weapons loaded through three months of field manœuvres without shaking loose one bullet from a cartridge to jam a revolver. The personnel eventually armed with this pistol are mentioned in Chapter V.

The big *revolver du troupe* was admitted to be unwieldy at an overall length of nearly 13 in. (and a weight of almost 3 lb.), but it had one major virtue in using a standard carbine cartridge-case: Colard's book (in 1874) made no mention of the cartridge used in the naval Gasser revolver, but his manner of description suggested that it was the same 11-mm. round. It was obviously impossible to issue the cavalry arm to men on foot, and a smaller weapon was introduced for infantry officers. Colard called this the "Gasser-Kropatschek" revolver, and dismissed it as merely a smaller version of the cavalry arm, and in a 9-mm. calibre. The arm was about 9 in. long and weighed only 1½ lb., but the special Roth cartridge gave flatter trajectories and higher muzzle velocities than the cavalry round.

The service life of any of these three Gasser revolvers (naval, infantry and cavalry) is now obscured by the subsequent appearance of the Model 1882 solid-frame arm, and of later pistols stamped "Roth-Gasser" or "Rast-Gasser", which used an 8-mm. Roth cartridge. Modern collectors frequently describe these later arms as "gendarmerie" revolvers, and many embodied take-down design features similar to those taught by E. NAGANT's Br. Pat. 4310/1879 (q.v.). Since Born-ecque (another Continental author) recognized a Model 1898 Austrian service revolver in the 8-mm. calibre as in limited issue to infantry at the turn of the century, it can be assumed that the original Gasser M.1870 and M.1882 arms remained with the personnel mentioned in Chapter V, until at least 1898.

The Model 1870 Gasser was widely copied in smaller calibres, both in

England and upon the Continent. P. WEBLEY & SON (q.v.) catalogued a similar arm in no less than four centre-fire calibres, and modest sales were apparently achieved. The specimen arm shown in Plate 29 cannot be labelled as the work of any particular maker, but was retailed by J. H. Crane of the Royal Exchange, London. Although conforming in almost every way to the Gasser arm, this revolver is actually in a rim-fire calibre of about ·44, and it may be relevant (as to the source of its manufacture) to note that J. H. Crane was a substantial retailer of Tranter revolvers, some of which (see Plate 68) used rim-fire cart-ridges of this calibre.

The curious "Pidault & Cordier" revolver shown in Plate 29 is in-cluded here for lack of another classification into which it may be placed. Chambered for a centre-fire cartridge of about ·44 calibre, the presence of the hinged lever on the right of the barrel suggests that it may once have been a percussion revolver; however, it can only be loaded by re-removing the cylinder and back-plate, and it may possibly have been an optional percussion/metallic cartridge pistol similar to the Deane arms shown in Plates 3 and 65.

In America, only the Colt company produced quality arms in this category, retaining their old keyed barrel/frame assembly until 1872. It is no part of this book to retrace the history so painstakingly estab-lished by Parsons, Serven or Shumaker for these arms, and a bare notice of them must suffice.

The "Thuer" conversion patented by F. A. K. W. VON OPPEN (q.v.) is noticed in Appendix II (see Plates 17 & 64), and more con-ventional arms were produced from percussion forgings once the master patent of ROLLIN WHITE (q.v.) had lapsed in 1869.

It is not always easy for the collector to decide whether a Colt re-volver of the type shown on Plate 18 has been converted from per-cussion or if it was originally made as a centre-fire arm. However, Serven teaches that low serial numbers bespoke a weapon produced at the factory, whilst high serials indicated arms manufactured and sold as muzzle-loaders but later returned for conversion. Systems patented by C. B. Richards (U.S. Pat. 117461 of July 25th, 1871) and W. Mason (U.S. Pat. 128644 of July 2nd, 1872) were both used to con-vert and to manufacture a number of ·44 centre-fire Colt Army revolvers. The conversion breech-plate on the small-frame ·38 calibre pistol in Plate 18 differed somewhat from that used on the larger pistols, but the revolver shown was reasonably representative of this type.

Although verging on the "lunatic fringe" of revolving pistol design, the double-barrelled centre-fire revolvers of F. A. LEMAT (q.v.)

merit notice here in addition to the remarks made on their inventor in Appendix II.

Shown in Plate 61 is the pistol basically protected by his Br. Pat. 3131/1868, but it also embodied the improved hammer shown in his Br. Pat. 588/1877. The lock was single-action, and the cylinder turned upon a central shot-barrel instead of the conventional cylinder-pin. The revolving chambers were loaded through a gate on the right of the frame and unloaded by using the familiar rod-ejector. A side swinging breech-block (visible between its supporting shoulders, in Plate 61) gave access to the shot-barrel and also operated a horned cartridge extractor. The firing-pin on this breech-block could be struck by flicking down the hinged arm visible beneath the hammer. The weapon illustrated measured 9½ in. overall, and had barrels 3½ in. in length. Nine 9-mm. centre-fire cartridges could be loaded into the cylinder, and the shot barrel accommodated a similar 14 mm. cartridge. The top barrel was stamped "Col. Le Mat Bte. Paris" and a serial or assembly number "3" appeared on most of the principal parts.

Although strictly misplaced here, a 9-mm. pin-fire Le Mat revolver is also shown in Plate 60, for purposes of comparison. This weapon (No. 65) had a muzzle-loading 15-mm. shot barrel fired by the usual hinged striker nose, and was marked "J. F. Govern Canat & Cie, à Paris, Système Le Mat Bte. SGDG". In appearance it conformed more closely to the original percussion designs than the centre-fire pistol.

Le Mat promoted his revolver for so many years that dating the various models is extremely difficult. However, the arms were certainly produced with all the refinements covered by his British patents and it is therefore suggested that these be used as a guide for dating. On this basis, the pin-fire weapon probably dated around 1865 whilst the centre-fire pistol dated after the patent of 1877 relating to its hammer.

A story has been current for many years that Le Mat revolvers were adopted by the French marines, but no evidence appears for the claim. Certainly Figuier (writing in 1870) does not support it, for his book illustrated a rim or centre-fire version of the Le Mat which he proposed for adoption by the cavalry. It seems certain that he would have mentioned marine adoption, if it had occurred, and it is more probable that the French marines were issued with the Lefaucheux M/1870 centre-fire revolver (a revamped version of the double-action pin-fire, but not a weapon within the category here considered).

Section II—Self-extracting revolvers

In tandem with the rod-ejecting revolvers already described came other designs from which all the cartridge-cases were simultaneously (or automatically) extracted. The methods proposed for thus unloading were varied, but can be considered as broadly divided in the manner demonstrated in Plates 47 and 49, that is between weapons in which barrel and cylinder were hinged to the frame (i.e. "Break-open" revolvers), and those arms otherwise constructed.

Two early break-open revolvers can be conveniently considered here, although the opening of their frames did not accomplish any extraction of cartridges. These pistols are shown in Plate 30, and were made by Devisme of Paris, whose early appearance in centre-fire design has already been mentioned in Chapter I.

The small self-cocking pepperbox (or "*Pistolet de Poche*" as its maker termed it) was the first of the centre-fire *coups de poing* or fist pistols to achieve popularity. As shown at the Paris Exhibition of 1867, the weapon was in 7-mm. calibre, and corresponded very closely to the specimen shown in Plate 30. Lifting a hinged cross-bolt on top of the breech permitted the barrels to be tipped down on a hinge at the front of the frame, and cartridges could then be inserted, or ejected by using a rod which unscrewed from the butt-cap.

The six-shot, single-action, Devisme revolver was a type also shown at the 1867 Exhibition, and based on a muzzle-loading revolver developed around 1855 by the same maker. In this centre-fire version the centrally mounted hammer from the muzzle-loading weapon was retained, but the frame was hinged at the lower edge of the standing breech. In the 12-mm. "*Pistolet d'Arcon*" shown on Plate 30, the hammer had to be half-cocked, and a key at the front of the frame given a quarter-turn to allow the barrel to tilt down; like the fist pistol, cartridge ejection was by means of a separate rod. This was carried beneath the barrel of the revolver, but has been lost from the specimen shown.

The inventor sold both models from his premises at 36 Boulevart des Italiens, Paris, and considerable prominence was given to the *cartouche impermeable* designed for them.

The revolver patented by W. CLARK (q.v.) also had a hinged frame, but, in general, the "break-open" revolver was principally designed to eject its cartridge automatically on opening, and this type of arm is the first for consideration here.

Section II: Part 1—"Break-open" revolvers

This method of automatic extraction was much favoured in England and America, but any consideration of Appendix II will show that this system cannot be solely identified with the famous names of SMITH & WESSON or P. WEBLEY & SON.

In the United Kingdom (as abroad) a number of break-open revolvers were patented, but the market absorbed a variety of arms for which there was either no traceable British patent protection, or which were outright copies of patented designs. Thus Plate 31 shows German and Belgian copies of a particular Smith & Wesson revolver, Plate 56 shows a Belgian improvement (by A. FRANCOTTE; q.v.) of a revolver now commonly attributed to C. PRYSE THE YOUNGER (q.v.), and Plate 35 shows another weapon of Continental manufacture, which is widely regarded as made for WESTLEY RICHARDS (q.v.).

As to patented arms (and in date order), Appendix II contains twelve relevant British extractor patents, namely; 2050/1865 (W. C. DODGE); 3622/1868 (W. TRANTER); 1510/1869 (SMITH & WESSON); 3557/1869 (W. TRANTER); 2107/1870 (A. SPIRLET); 2662/1872 (C. F. TACKELS); 2777/1876 (O. JONES); 624/1878 (O. JONES); 922/1878 (P. MAUSER); 2161/1878 (A. T. DE MOUNCIE); 2855/1879 (W. TRANTER); 5143/1881 (T. W. & H. WEBLEY). For the purposes of this Chapter the patents of Mauser, de Mouncie or Tackels need little attention, and that of Spirlet is sufficiently described in Appendix II. Embodiments of these designs were uncommon whilst the patents were current, and lack of space must limit notice of them.

PAUL MAUSER's revolvers were normally hinged at the top of the frame, and used a special system for rotating their cylinders. The lock was linked to a stud sliding to and fro beneath the cylinder, and this stud rotated the latter, as it travelled, by engaging in suitable slots on the circumference of the cylinder wall. A pocket version is shown in Plate 33, but the arms were apparently conceived as service revolvers and larger weapons were more common. Company interest in their promotion ceased on the formal adoption of the M/80 and M/84 "Commission" pistols earlier described, but the single-action solid-framed weapon on Plate 33 showed that a serious attempt was made to produce a pistol sturdy enough for issue.

A. T. DE MOUNCIE (q.v.) abandoned his patent (after it had been sealed) by failing to file a Complete Specification to it. The patent application was for a revolver lock and a manually operated star extractor worked by a stud protruding from a slot. The Provisional Specification was not illustrated, but it could be read as describing both the basic idea for the automatic extractor used on the revolver shown in Plate 57, and the type of barrel latch used in the "LeVaux" revolver on Plate 49.

Captain TACKELS showed an automatic extractor in his Complete

E

Specification, but did not claim protection for it. Presumably his Agent (J. PIDDINGTON : q.v.) either felt that the patents of DODGE (q.v.) and SMITH & WESSON (q.v.) anticipated any novelty in the feature, or that the European service trials of the arm, in 1871, had received too much publicity to permit claiming the device as new in Great Britain. However, the Complete Specification showed the extractor mechanism, quite plainly, as a horn hinged on the brow of the frame-hinge at which the barrel was pivoted. This horn projected up into the barrel lug to engage a stem on the extractor, and forced the latter upwards when the pistol was broken open. At a casual glance the system was very similar to the devices of other inventors mentioned in Appendix II, but the extractor plate did not snap back automatically into its recess in the cylinder face. On some pistols, the barrel had to be tipped back towards the breech in order to retract Tackels's extractor, but in others a spring flipped the barrel backwards sufficiently to seat the extractor and permit reloading.

The "Le Vaux" revolver shown in Plate 49 presents something of a problem in identification today, and remarks about the barrel latch (made in regard to Br. Pat. 4163/1876 of DE MOUNCIE; q.v.) should be noticed. The specimen shown probably dated from about 1880, but it embodied the old Nagant lock (shown in Plate 25), which was in the public domain as early as 1868.

For convenience, the first two extractor patents of W. TRANTER (q.v.) have already been noticed in Chapter III, with the bulk of his revolvers. Strictly, they anticipated the basic idea of SPIRLET (q.v.) and MAUSER (q.v.) for hinging the barrel at the top of the frame and operating a star-shaped cartridge extractor by suitable means. Spirlet's method is described in Appendix II, and Tranter accomplished the same end with hinged levers or a manually operated rack.

Tranter did not produce many weapons under his patents of '68 and '69, but his last revolver (under Br. Pat. 2855/1879) was more widely known, and was a sturdy, hinged-frame, self-extracting weapon of the type shown in Plate 34. Bond mentioned and illustrated this arm in his treatise of 1884, but his remarks yielded little detail about the lock mechanism. His plate revealed "Tranter's Self-extracting Revolver" as a ·450 centre-fire weapon with a 6-in. barrel and rebounding hammer. The barrel and frame were latched together by a thumb-operated pivoted hook (on the left rear of the frame), which engaged a lug protruding from the side of the top strap. A notch in the hammer brow backed up the latch, by engaging the end of that strap when the hammer fell. All of these details can be seen in Plate 34, and it should also be noted that the revolver attributed to the Westley Richards

Company which is shown in Plate 35 had the same notched hammer face.

Apart from their patents 2050/1865 (W. C. DODGE: q.v.) and 1510/1869 (see Appendix II) the SMITH & WESSON company gave little regard to patent protection for their extractor mechanisms, in Great Britain. The inventions of Schofield (U.S. Pat. 138047 of 1873), D. B. Wesson (U.S. Pat. 158874 of 1875), Wesson & Bullard (U.S. Pat. 187689 of 1877) or J. H. Bullard (U.S. Pat, 227481 of 1880) had no equivalent British protection. Such a policy was curious in a firm renowned for its shrewd handling of patents and its concentration upon self-extracting revolvers during the closing years of the period.

Thus, the American authority A. C. Gould (in the 1888 edition of his book) remarked that "all of the revolvers now made at the factory of Smith & Wesson are after this model", i.e. the "break-open", self-extracting weapon, and he listed the models then current, as follows:

"New Model Army, No. 3; weight $2\frac{1}{2}$ lb.; centre-fire; calibre ·44 in.; 6-shot; $6\frac{1}{2}$-in. barrel." This arm was (as the name suggested) an improved version of the original No. 3 "American" revolver shown in Plates 29 and 66, which is discussed in Appendix II under Br. Pat. 1510/1869. The "New Model" was introduced in 1878, and the design benefited from experience gained in manufacturing the Schofield and Russian Government revolvers; a specimen of the latter arm appears in Plate 31. Norton noticed the New Model No. 3 glowingly in the 1880 edition of his book, and credited the factory with a daily output of 150 weapons, as against "other sizes 140 per diem". As a matter of incidental interest, he also mentioned that the factory, ". . . when fully occupied with orders", could profitably employ over 600 hands.

"New Model Navy, No. 3; double-action; centre-fire; calibre ·44 in.; 6-shot: weight $2\frac{3}{16}$ lb.; 4-in., 5-in. and 6-in. barrels." This arm was actually the third of the Smith & Wesson double-action revolvers, which had been introduced around March, 1880, to compete with the solid-frame, double-action Colt arms. A specimen is shown in Plate 34, and the scope of the relevant British Patent (that of J. H. WESSON) is mentioned in Appendix II.

"New Model ·38, No. 2; weight 16 oz.; centre-fire; calibre ·38 in.; 5-shot; $3\frac{1}{4}$-in.; 4-in. and 5-in. barrels, and a similar double-action model weighing 2 oz. more." This single-action weapon had been introduced in 1876 (following discontinuance of the old rim-fire top-hinged pocket arms) as "Smith & Wesson's New Model '38' Pistol", or the "·38 Automatic Ejecting Revolver", and is shown in Plate 31. It had a stud-trigger, without guard, and an improved model appeared in

1877; the rebounding hammer was designed by D. B. WESSON (q.v.) and may be seen in Fig. 7. The double-action version (referred to by Gould) came out in 1880, and embodied the double cylinder bolt protected by J. H. WESSON's Br. Pat. 5569/1881, which held the cylinder locked under all circumstances except when actually cocking the arm. This weapon was, in fact, the first of the double-action Smith & Wesson models.

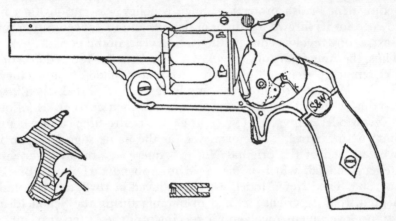

FIG. 7. *D. B. Wesson's Rebounding Hammer.*
Drawings from the Complete Specification to Br. Pat. 4831/1877. A few of the weapons made under the equivalent U.S. Patent rebounded to a half-cock bent. (See Chapter IV.)

"New Model ·32 No. 1½; weight 12½ oz.; centre-fire; calibre ·32 in.; 5-shot; 3-in. and 3½-in. barrels, and a similar double-action model weighing 14 oz." This revolver also appeared in 1878 and was similar in appearance and mechanism to the single-action ·38, except for using a "bird's head" butt design. It was immensely and deservedly popular. The double-action model appeared in July 1880, also without the "bird's head" grip, and was another pocket version of the New Model Navy earlier mentioned, which it anticipated by a year.

"New Model Hammerless Safety Revolver, centre-fire; calibres ·32, ·38 and ·44; weight, in ·38 calibre, 18½ oz.; with barrels of different lengths." This revolver was very new indeed when Gould mentioned it, and is now more generally known to collectors as the "lemon squeezer" pistol. A safety lever on the back-strap of the butt prevented firing unless the weapon was correctly gripped; since the hammer was completely shrouded, and struck a separate firing-pin in the standing breech, accidental discharge of this self-cocking arm was almost impossible. The ·44 calibre version was never produced commercially, despite Gould's mention of it.

"New Target Revolver, single-action; centre-fire; calibre ·32; 6-shot; weight $2\frac{12}{16}$ lb.; barrel $6\frac{1}{2}$ in." Like the New Model Hammerless, this revolver had been introduced in 1887, and was another development from the single-action New Model Army No. 3. It was undoubtedly one of the finest target revolvers ever produced commercially, and chambered a special cartridge known as the "·32–44 S. & W. Centre-Fire". A similar ·38 44 Target Revolver appeared in the same year, and these two pistols (with the "New Model Army No. 3", and a single-action ·44–40 "Frontier" revolver) saw out the remainder of the century in the catalogues of Smith & Wesson or their agents.

In England, a hinged-frame revolver was adopted by the services in 1880, and this Enfield cavalry weapon (shown in Plates 49 and 50), was based on O. JONES's Br. Pats. 2777/1876 and 624/1878 (as to its extractor mechanism) and made at the R.S.A.F., Enfield, until finally superseded in 1889. However, a comparison between Plate 72 and Fig. 8 will show that the lock mechanism of the revolver was not invented by Jones, but was that protected under Br. Pat. 5031/1878 by M. KAUFMANN and J. WARNANT (q.v.).

The version of the weapon most commonly found today is the Mark II, Model 1882, but Mark I, Model 1880, revolvers will be encountered. Both should have had a safety device (approved in 1887) fitted during their service lives, and Mark II pistols had a cylinder brake embodied in their loading-gates. Dogmatic identification of Mark I or Mark II revolvers is seldom easy by casual inspection. Dowell has listed the differing features of the two Marks, but actual specimens tend to disregard this tidy classification. Thus the weapon illustrated in Plates 49 and 50 was an uneasy compromise. At first blush, it appeared to be a Mark II 1882 Model, but was actually dated "1881". Conversely, it had the R.S.A.F. Enfield monogram of the Mark II pistol and also had that Mark number on the frame. As a Mark II revolver, however, it should neither have had the chequered butt now fitted, nor the Mark I, Model 1880, foresight on its Mark II barrel. In such circumstances, it seems best to describe the pistol in general terms, and to leave detailed identification to the experts. A curious short-barrelled pistol shown in Plate 32 so far defies explanation, but it is included to bolster the view that Enfield revolvers were not entirely confined to the two Marks commonly accepted.

In brief, the ·476 centre-fire service revolvers were six-chambered, had Henry-rifled $5\frac{7}{8}$-in. barrels, were gate-loaded, and weighed 2 lb. $8\frac{1}{2}$ oz. The hammer bore a conventional bent to engage the

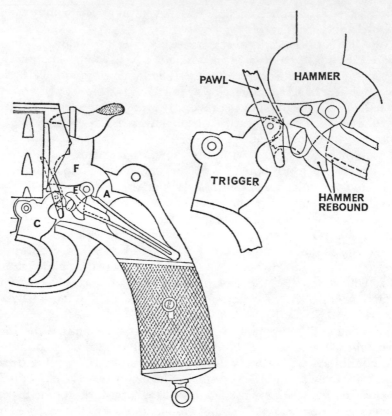

FIG. 8. *Kaufmann & Warnant's Revolver Lock.*
(Br. Pat. 5031/1878.)

The lock is admitted to be an improvement upon DE MOUNCIE'S Br. Pat. 3206/1876 (see Fig. 17), and a comparison with Plate 72 will demonstrate its adoption for use in the Mark 1 "Enfield" Service revolver.

The refinement over the earlier lock lies in the use of the pivoted lever "E" to connect the cylinder rotating pawl with the lower arm of the mainspring. Since this pawl is also linked to the trigger by its pivot, the pressure of the mainspring thus serves in place of separate trigger and pawl springs.

The internal lump on the lower end of the pawl serves to push back the hammer if the trigger is pulled when the hammer is down, and if the latter is cocked by thumb conventional bents hold it at full-cock.

trigger when cocked by the thumb, and the self-cocking part of the mechanism may be grasped by reference to Figure 8. The small arm linked to the lever "E" (which can be seen in Plate 72) assisted in rebounding the hammer and in preventing accidental firing by a blow on the hammer when "at rest". A further improvement to Kaufmann & Warnant's lock lay in reshaping the lug in which the lower limb of the mainspring rested, and in providing a small coil-spring at the rear of the trigger. This spring acted on the cylinder pawl to assist the trigger in returning to the "at rest" position.

Latterly, the loading-gates embodied a safety feature similar in function to that adopted (in 1887) for the Swiss SCHMIDT M/1882 officers' revolver, and in design to that earlier protected by M. KAUF-MANN (q.v.) as Br. Pat. 3913/1881. Here, with the gate ajar, the Enfield could not be cocked, or, if the hammer was already cocked, the gate could not be opened for loading. Since the Schmidt and Enfield revolvers embodied distinct lock mechanisms, the safety feature was, of course, arranged by different methods respectively.

Before leaving the lock-mechanism of this revolver, mention must be made of a minor refinement protected by J. CARTER's Br. Pat. 16638/1888 (q.v.). This claimed an additional sear (fitted in a vertical slot at the rear of the trigger guard) which engaged a bent in the hammer-belly when the hammer rebounded after firing. The idea was not new (Smith & Wesson had abandoned such a fusion ten years earlier), and is mentioned only because the Enfield revolver was specifically claimed as suitable in the patent, but was superseded so shortly afterwards.

Carter was an Action Filer, at Mona Terrance, Bracebridge Street, Aston, who patented several important revolver improvements used by P. WEBLEY & SON (q.v.), and he would presumably be fully aware of the order secured by that firm (in July 1887) to supply the Mark I Webley revolver to the British Government. His rebounding hammer patent was maintained until 1901 because it also protected a different safety feature used in the Mark I Webley pistol, but the inclusion in it of a refinement to the moribund Enfield design, by a man in his position, is difficult to explain.

Although the parentage of its lock has not been generally acknowledged, the cartridge extraction system of the Enfield revolver has always been conceded to the patents of O. JONES (q.v.). However, the test-bed for this system provided yet another puzzle. Jones's Br. Pat. 2777/1876 (the first) covered his basic idea only, and provided for the barrel/frame latch to be drawn backwards by the right thumb, and the barrel then tipped down in the conventional "break-open" manner. However, instead of causing a star-shaped extractor to rise at the rear of the cylinder, this tipping of the barrel drew the cylinder forward off its axis pin and left the cartridge-cases caught by their rims on an extractor fixed to the standing breech (see Plate 50). The interesting feature of this first patent was that it showed a small single-action revolver, and this weapon Bartlett illustrated again (in 1883) with the comment that "the cartridge ejector is the invention of Mr. Owen Jones, of Philadelphia, but is not *now* manufactured in the United States". This remark certainly suggested that the arm had been made, but specimens have not been reported in any major collections.

Owen Jones's second British Patent (624/1878) went no further towards suggesting the source from which the quite distinctive Enfield revolver's shape and appearance originally sprang. The patent was one of improvement on the inventor's Br. Pat. 2777/1876, but the pistols illustrated as embodying the extractor appeared to be single-action "Army"-sized weapons similar to those made by Messrs. Forehand & Wadsworth of Worcester, Mass., U.S.A.

To infer any connection between Jones and Messrs. Forehand & Wadsworth on such slight evidence would be useless, but it is worthy of note that Jacob Rupertus (the arms manufacturer earlier noticed, and an associate of Sullivan Forehand and Henry C. Wadsworth) was still in business in Philadelphia in the mid-1870's, and that someone called John K. Rupertus witnessed U.S. Pat. 151882 of 1874 for Owen Jones. This patent has neither place here, nor any traceable British equivalent, and it is mentioned only to support a possible Jones/Rupertus connection, prior to the former's arrival in England. Briefly, the patent protected a double-barrelled revolver with a spare cartridge cylinder encased in its butt. Turning over the barrels and exchanging cylinders permitted use of "projectiles (i.e. cartridges) of different sizes in the same revolver".

This type of ingenuity characterized Jones's designs, and his Br. Pat. 624/1878 included a claim for a "Tool-tube" to be screwed into the front of the revolver frame, and aligned beneath the barrel. This tube contained a double-ended screwdriver, which could be held in the tube cap, and a sectional cleaning rod. Considerable opposition was apparently encountered by this patent, since W. R. LAKE (q.v.) had to file a Disclaimer and Memorandum of Alteration for many features, on May 6th, 1880. The "tool-tube" was one of the casualties here, and the Enfield revolver (which could have embodied it) had instead the separate "Implement, Pistol Revolver, B. L. Enfield pattern; Marks I and II" noticed by Dowell.

What was left of the second patent protected various methods for constructing or operating Jones's extractor and covered features actually used in the Enfield revolver, both for linking cylinder and barrel, and for latching barrel to frame.

One interesting idea in the original patent (which was not embodied in the Enfield) was a proposal for selective cartridge extraction. Here, the blow of the hammer not only fired the primer but also forced part of the cartridge case to distort and thus engage the extractor. In this way, only fired cases were extracted on breaking the revolver. In the event, a rather more sensible method was adopted for this selective feature. Thus the patent provided for the cylinder to be drawn forward just far enough for a fired case to clear its chamber. Any loaded round remained in the weapon, since its bullet still projected into the cylinder, and the cartridge would thus be picked up again when the weapon was closed.

Harsh words have been uttered about the Enfield, and various *ad hoc* refinements to the lock did not suggest that the design was ever very satisfactory. Certainly, as Plate 72 should reveal, the general workmanship of the specimens examined was rarely good enough for satisfactory operation of such a design. Perhaps the most balanced comment on the weapon was made by Major H. E. C. Kitchener, in 1886, when he wrote that "the pull-off is good, the weapon appears to me inaccurate and clumsy".

This brief study of the principal hinged-frame, self-extracting revolvers must inevitably close with the Webley series, but a few weapons by others makers remain to be noticed. In the main, such arms tended to be copies of the principal designs, but some originality can be seen.

SMITH & WESSON arms (both single and double-action) were extensively copied. In the single-action series, the duplicates by Ludwig Loewe of Berlin were justly famous. This firm used machinery apparently identical to that made for arms manufacturers by Messrs. Pratt & Witney of Hartford, Conn., and the quality of these copies echoed the excellence of the true Smith & Wesson arms. The copy shown in Plate 31 was a thoroughly dependable arm.

Truly execrable versions came also from Belgium and Spain, but Orbea Hermanos of Eibar did produce some reasonable single-action arms of Smith & Wesson type, and the rim-fire Belgian weapon shown in Plate 31 was identical in appearance to centre-fire copies of these arms. A. FRANCOTTE (q.v.) turned out some tolerable double-action pistols of "New Navy" type, and the Austrian M/77 "system Smith & Wesson" revolver will be noticed in Chapter V.

In England, the "Kynoch" revolvers designed by H. SCHLUND (q.v.) broke new ground by their lock designs, but appear to have been derivative as to their cartridge extraction mechanisms. Tradition links these arms with operations in W. TRANTER's factory following his retirement, but positive proof of this claim remains lacking. The majority of the Kynoch pistols were clearly marked "Kynoch Gun Factory, Aston", which certainly suggested proximity to W. Tranter's factory at

Aston Cross. Confirmation that the former was housed in the latter is still wanting, but some circumstantial evidence can be shown for a connection between the men most obviously interested. Thus Kynoch, Schlund and Tranter were later associated in a company which traded briefly as "The Aston Arms Co. Ltd." from March 1889 to July 1891. The stated objective was to develop a patented projectile owned by the two first-named, and no specific reference to patented arms manufacture appeared in that Company's Memorandum of Association; however, the transaction certainly established a connection between the three men and could have followed an earlier partnership.

The Kynoch revolver received favourable review in "Engineering", on January 15th, 1886, and was offered to the Metropolitan Police, on February 11th, in three models. All were six-chambered, double-action, central-fire, weapons embodying the lock mechanism protected by Henry Schlund's Br. Pat. 9084/1885, and with double-triggers of Tranter type (see Plate 1).

Model No. 1 had a 6-in. barrel, and was available (at £3 15s.) in calibres ·476, ·455, ·450 and ·430.

Model No. 2 had a 5-in. barrel, in calibres ·400, ·380, ·360, or ·320, and retailed for two shillings less than the No. 1.

Model No. 3 was in ·300 or ·297–230 (Morris) calibres, had a 3-in. barrel, and sold for £3.

This particular series clearly owed a debt to Tranter designs, quite apart from their double-trigger mechanism, although the lock itself followed the inventor's patent, and had all components mounted on an easily removable internal plate. A milled nut on the right of the frame being undone, the butt then pulled off and gave access to detach mainspring and rebound lever. The remainder of the mechanism could then be removed, by pulling the trigger-guard first downwards and then backwards.

As to "Tranter features" specifically appearing in them, the catch on the extractor, the lifter and release for that component, and the hammer rebound, were virtually identical to those features shown in W. TRANTER's Bt. Pat. 2855/1879. It will be recalled that "Tranter's Self Extracting Revolver" was made under that patent, and Table II shows that it was allowed to lapse in the year that this Kynoch/Schlund revolver appeared. Naturally enough, H. SCHLUND's Br. Pat. 9084/1885 skirted these features in its Specification, and claimed only the barrel/frame latch, the self-cocking lock-mechanism and the dismount system.

H. A. SCHLUND's Br. Pat. 11900/1886 was for improvements to the previous patent by providing for automatic closure of the barrel/

frame latch and for lock modifications permitting the two triggers to be completely enclosed by the trigger-guard. In this patent, the Tranter extractor features were again shown but not claimed, and when Kynoch revolvers are encountered today they are likely to be of the pattern protected here. Two specimens are shown on Plate 33, and it should be remarked that the barrel latch was operated by a thumb-piece at the top rear of the action body.

It is a matter for regret that a tidy Kynoch/Tranter connection cannot be shown, but the operations of George Kynoch, M.P., are obscure in many details even today. All that can really be said at the date of writing is that William Tranter died in 1890, and that The Aston Arms Co. Ltd. folded up in 1891, on the instance of the chief debenture holder. Kynoch died in February, 1891, and the writer has never traced a reference to the Aston factory in any reports by G. Kynoch & Co. Ltd. (the company which followed the close of his personal reign at Witton) regarding the various factories. In these circumstances it is probable that the "Gun Factory" was a personal venture by George Kynoch, which was based in the old Tranter establishment and ended with the death of the two men responsible for it.

For obvious reasons this Chapter ends with the hinged-frame, self-extracting revolvers of P. WEBLEY & SON (q.v.).

The terminal year for this period of study saw the introduction of a Mark I Webley revolver (see Plate 49) as the standard weapon for the British Armed Forces, and marked the effective end of all native competition for the quantity revolver market here.

Major Dowell has shown that this competition did not die immediately, but "Artifex & Opifex" stated no more than the truth in commenting on the activities of the Company which succeeded Messrs. P. WEBLEY & SON. "It is also worth mentioning," they wrote, "that for years past there has been in the whole of the British Empire only one manufacturer of revolvers, and that for some years the Webley-Scott Co. have had the sole monopoly, the Government having discontinued the production of revolvers in the ordnance factories."

Dowell traced these revolvers exhaustively, starting with a hinged frame self-extracting pistol marked "Webley's Patent", which was retailed by Edmund Woods around 1870. Early as this dating may appear there is no reason to question it. An extractor of this type could not be patented by C. F. TACKELS (q.v.) in 1872, which suggests that it was an acceptable alternative to SMITH & WESSON's patent of 1869 (q.v.) for the rack-operated extractor. Even if the idea is rejected that Tackel's extractor was wholly unprotected by his patent,

Table II shows that his whole design shortly passed into the public domain, to become freely available to P. Webley & Son (or anyone else) after 1875.

Dowell identified the next hinged frame design as the "Webley-Pryse" weapon, distinguished for most collectors by the barrel/frame latch to be seen in Plates 34 and 56. He pointed out that this arm was sold by P. WEBLEY & SON, in competition with similar revolvers by other makers, and the remarks in Appendix II upon C. PRYSE THE YOUNGER should also be studied, on the strength to be given to any claim for the latter as father of the basic design.

J. H. Walsh (in 1884) illustrated "Webley's British Army Extractor, No. 4 Pattern" as a ·455 calibre pistol with a 5½-in. barrel, and a specimen is shown in Plate 34. This arm was the classic example of the "Pryse" revolver, with a rebounding hammer, half-fluted cylinder (double bolted and with a turn-button cylinder release on the left of the barrel), but it lacked any roller-bearing on the rear sear, which the purists now identify with this arm. W. W. Greener, in the original (1881) edition of his most famous book, described the weapon simply as the "Self-extracting Safety Revolver". He illustrated a revolver with the "Pryse" barrel latch, but with an unfluted cylinder which was not apparently double-bolted. The brow of the hammer was indented to engage the top frame strap as a weak, additional barrel latch, and the overall picture was closer to the "Westley Richards" arm shown on Plate 35 than to the ordinary Pryse revolver. His comment upon the pistol was that "the improvement mainly consists in the method of making fast the barrel and chambers to the pistol body and in the employment of a rebounding cock", and he added that "large quantities of these revolvers are made in Belgium in imitation of our 'Bulldog' and 'Irish Constabulary' models". Greener made no specific mention of a version by P. WEBLEY & SON, but stated that "the English Army Revolver made upon this system we believe to be the most efficient revolver produced and the easiest to manipulate". Described as a 6-chambered, ·450 revolver, weighing 31 oz. with a 5½-in. barrel, this weapon sounded very similar to the Webley No. 4, shown in Plate 34.

There is no point in attempting any detailed breakdown here of the various "Pryse" models and versions. Dowell noticed models in calibres ·32, ·38. ·44, ·450, ·455 or ·577, and versions by Bonehill, Francotte, Horsley, Webley and Wilkinson. As he revealed the lock mechanisms to these "Pryse" revolvers, one basic distinction appeared. The British-made versions embodied the lock mechanism which Pryse himself disclaimed in his patent as being "of the ordinary kind", and it is on these arms that references were stamped to "STANTON & CO. JOINT PATENTS" with a "C" prefixed number. In the revolvers which he attributed to FRANCOTTE, and other Continental makers, a different lock mechanism appeared, being almost identical to that found in the Swiss Schmidt M/78 service revolver earlier mentioned. The Francotte-Pryse revolver shown in Plate 56 has this lock, and the absence of any sear projecting through the rear of the trigger-guard can be noticed. It was this sear which formed the principal external identification for British-made revolvers of this type.

To the present writer it would appear quite reasonable tentatively to label all these Continental revolvers as coming from Liège. The barrel latch (whether in twin or single lever form) was popular with makers there, and the Schmidt lock was developed from a basic design by C. F. GALAND (q.v.) of that town. A. FRANCOTTE, of Liège, catalogued over 150 different types of revolver in the years immediately following our period, and of the 21 self-extracting designs, nine embodied the Pryse-type barrel/frame latch.

In association with the later "Pryse" revolvers, Dowell next recognized the "Kaufmann" and "Improved Government" Webley hinged-frame pistols. The patents of M. KAUFMANN (q.v.) are described in Appendix II, and it is only necessary to state here that his Br. Pat. 4302/1880 claimed the lock mechanism used in Webley's "Improved Government Pattern" ·455 revolvers, which were illustrated by Bond and Walsh in 1884, and are shown here in Plate 35. It must be accepted that the locks used in these revolvers were of Continental inspiration, and it is interesting that KAUFMANN figured as applicant for British patents protecting both the R.S.A.F. Enfield revolver lock, and this very beautiful commercially competitive design, with only five lock components. Since J. WARNANT (q.v.) joined with him in the Enfield revolver lock patent, it can be assumed that the commercial revolver owed something to the same source. The debt to DE MOUNCIE's Br. Pat. 3206/1876 (q.v.) is much in point on this suggestion. This patent was assigned to Kaufmann as a necessary preliminary to securing the latter's Enfield revolver lock patent, and was itself merely an improvement of the combined trigger/pawl spring shown in Br. Pat. 2308/1872, by C. F. GALAND (q.v.) of Belgium. A link between Kaufmann and the Belgian makers seems firmly established.

Dowell identified six British Patents as relevant to the "Webley-Kaufmann" and "Improved Government" revolvers, namely 5031/1878; 4302/1880; 3313/1881 and 3913/1881 (by Kaufmann or his patent agent), together with 5143/1881 and 542/1883 from the Webley brothers, Thomas William and Henry. However, this identification does not appear to be wholly accurate, particularly as to 5031/1878, which was strictly relevant only to the Enfield service pistol.

Br. Pat. 4302/1880 was, of course, in point as protecting the lock mechanisms actually used in the "Webley-Kaufmann" and "Improved Government" arms, and Br. Pat. 3313/1881 covered the rather weak, three-piece, barrel latch used on the "Webley-Kaufmann" pistols. This was a tranverse button latch entirely contained in a reinforce at the rear of the top strap, and can be seen in Plate 35.

Br. Pat. 3913/1881 was not really relevant to these models, despite Dowell's mention of it. The patent protected a loading-gate which automatically freed the cylinders of solid-framed revolvers when open, and permitted rotation of the cylinder for loading or unloading. It had no application for hinged-frame pistols of the true Kaufmann type, although it was embodied in the solid-frame Webley shown first in Plate 23.

Thomas William and Henry Webley's Br. Pat. 5143/1881 covered the cartridge extractor mechanism used on both "Webley-Kaufmann" and "Improved Government" revolvers, which was noted with particular approval by both Bond and Walsh for its self-extracting feature and anti-friction mount. Henry Webley's Br. Pat. 542/1883 protected the barrel/frame latch used on the "Improved Government" revolvers. This was an improved version of Kaufmann's weak 1881 latch, by which a thumb-piece pivoted on the left of the frame unbolted the latch, instead of the press-button system originally patented. It can be seen in Plate 35.

If Walsh is to be believed now, one further patent should be added to Dowell's list, since the former referred to "Carter's Patent Safety Cylinder Locking Bolt" as being embodied in the "Improved Government" revolver.

J. CARTER (q.v.) secured Br. Patents 1820/1884 and 2555/1884 for two different methods of bolting the cylinder against accidental rotation, which might have caused the revolver to be blown open, if chamber and barrel were slightly mis-aligned on firing. Both patents were illustrated as applied to revolver mechanisms of the British "Pryse" type, but the second design was adaptable to the "Improved Government" pistol lock, and Walsh's words suggested that this was done.

In 1885 another hinged frame Webley was introduced with a quite different lock mechanism and a new type of barrel/frame latch. Both refinements were patented by H. WEBLEY and J. CARTER (q.v.), as

Br. Pat. 4070/1885 and can be studied in the Webley "W.G." revolver illustrated in Plate 73. It will be observed that the latch is the famous "stirrup" type used on all Webley revolvers since the supersession of the Kaufmann designs. The revolver lock shown dated after 1888, but the long rebound bar operated by the lower limb of the mainspring was taken from this patent.

Dowell identified an earlier Webley "W.G." revolver, which he labelled as the "Model 1882". The present writer is at a loss to account for the weapon on which that authority based this dating, if it can be definitely shown as made according to Carter's patent. This protection was secured in 1885 (and it is not stated to be a communicated design), so that it is difficult to see how it was secured if the lock and barrel latch were in commercial circulation in England three years earlier. The length of time for which the patent was maintained (see Table II) demonstrated its value, and it would be illogical to suppose that it would go unchallenged if another maker knew it to have been revealed in 1882.

It is a matter of record that a Webley "Model Government Extractor" revolver was shown to the *Field* newspaper on December 16th, 1882, again on March 10th, 1883, and, once more, on March 29th, 1884. However, it seems likely that this weapon was not, in fact, the arm patented by Carter in 1885 (see Plate 35), and that the *Field* was more probably shown revolvers embodying the earlier improvements mentioned above, by KAUFMANN and the WEBLEY brothers.

The last Webley revolver of concern here was, of course, the Mark I Government Model shown in Plate 49. The weapon illustrated is a demonstration weapon and the lock mechanism could be studied through the apertures milled in both sides of the frame. Dowell recorded that this revolver was produced in 1886, accepted for the Armed Forces in mid-1887 (with an initial contract for 10,000 pistols), sealed as a pattern arm in November of that year, and finally approved in 1892. The original revolver was a ·442 Metford-rifled six-chambered arm, weighing about 35 oz. and with a 4-in. barrel; subsequent production runs were made in ·476 and ·455 calibres.

The *Field*, in mid-1889, featured a savage exchange of letters dated May 25th and June 29th, over the parentage of the "stirrup" barrel latch used in this Mark I revolver and in the "W.G." weapons, protected by H. WEBLEY and J. CARTER's Br. Pat. 4070/1885. Edwinson C. Green laid claim to designing and introducing this latch in 1883, to which P. Webley & Son offered a stinging rebuttal. Their reply is of interest as outlining the differences between the Mark I and its predecessors. Thus, they alleged, the frame hinge joint was enlarged; a simplified and more robust extractor lever used; and a single screw secured the cylinder axis to the barrel.

Curiously, no specific mention was made, in their reply, to the 1885 Webley-Carter patent for the disputed barrel latch, and only oblique reference was made to the hammer blow, which slammed the latch shut if it was not correctly seated on firing.

The omission of any reference to this long-lived patent was odd, for Webley's letter then mentioned two patented refinements under loose references to "Patent No. 1886" and "Patent No. 1888" which had no traceable reference to any firearms patent number. The first patent referred to a "smoke ferrule" or anti-fouling device, and could be fairly safely identified as W. J. WHITING's Br. Pat. 1923/1886 (q.v.). The second patent related to "a safety lock formed upon the pawl of the lock action, the object of which is to prevent the discharge . . . by the hammer being accidentally knocked down when in the rebounded position", and these words were taken verbatim from the Provisional Specification to Br. Pat. 16638/1888 of J. CARTER, which has already been mentioned in relation to the Enfield pistol. The invention relevant here was specifically claimed and illustrated for "revolver firearms which have the lock or firing mechanism known as Webley's Pistol Mark I". The improvement consisted in a lump projecting upon the inside of the cylinder rotating pawl over the front end of the main-spring auxiliary lever. This lever rebounded the hammer after firing, and the pawl lump bolted the lock "at rest", to prevent depression of the hammer by any accidental blow.

Section II: Part 2—"Automatic" and other designs, without hinged frames
This Chapter is inevitably a rag-bag of designs, some of which never achieved commercial exploitation, and although principal attention is given to self-extracting arms recognized in ordinary collections, brief preliminary mention of one unsuccessful British patent must first be made. The principle which it demonstrated flowered commercially in 1889.

The classic design for a sturdy alternative to hinged-frame extraction is the solid-frame weapon with a side swinging cylinder even today, and A. ALBINI's Br. Pat. 838/1869 should be studied in Fig. 9 as an early example of this approach.

Competing British Patents were lacking, and although W. Mason (a designer then associated with E. REMINGTON & SONS; q.v.) had anticipated Albini's idea with his U.S. Patent No. 51117 of 1865, the lead was not accepted in England and no ideas emerged here to compete with Albini's system.

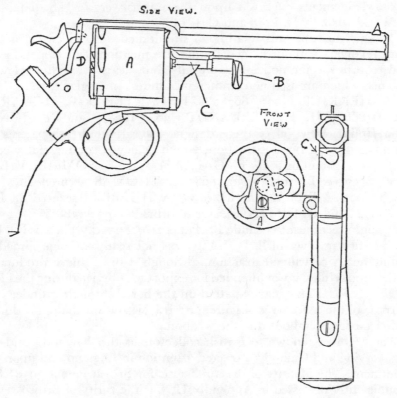

FIG. 9. *Albini's Cartridge Extractor.*

Pulling forward "B" brings a reduced section of the centre rod opposite the frame slot "C" and also withdraws the rod from an inner housing at "D".

The cartridge cylinder "A" may then be swung out to the right, as shown, and the cartridges extracted by pressing "B". This operates a star-shaped extractor mounted on the centre rod at "D" and embedded in the rear of "A" to push out the cartridges by their rims.

In America, however, Mason remained interested in the side-swinging cylinder, and when COLT's PATENT FIRE ARMS MANU-FACTURING CO. (q.v.) turned their attention to this design, he duly developed a fully automatic system for them, in which the extractor was actually operated by the outward lurch of the cylinder on its crane. U.S. Patents Nos. 249649 and 250375 of 1881 resulted, but were not eventually adopted by that Company. When the swing-out cylinder Colt pistol eventually arrived (as the ·38 U.S. Navy Model of 1889), it retained a crane mount for the cylinder, but the extractor was manually operated by a press-button protruding at its front. The only patent

F

acknowledgements engraved upon these arms were to U.S. patents of 1884 and 1888, by H. Lord and C. J. Ehbets.

Those British patents relating to simultaneous cartridge extraction from revolvers without hinged frames are mentioned in Appendix II, and require specific notice here in only four cases. The other relevant patents, which aroused no commercial interest in England, were those of W. HERRICK (1007/1867); C. H. CARTER & T. RICHARDS (3222/1868); H. HILLEBRANDT (3943/1868); and T. JONES (1992/1869). Deletion of these designs leaves four British patents for simultaneous cartridge extraction, which achieved commercial success and merit attention; C. F. GALAND and A. SOMMERVILLE (q.v.) secured Br. Pat. 3039/1868; J. THOMAS secured Br. Pat. 779/1869; J. MERWIN and M. & W. A. HULBERT secured Br. Pat. 277/1878; and H. DIMANCEA secured Br. Pat. 9973/1885.

It might seem just to include Br. Pat. 2210/1865 (q.v.) in this list, but the pin-fire revolver of P. POLAIN was not really a design aimed at simultaneous cartridge extraction, although it did achieve production in Belgium. Unless it was intended for export to America during the life of ROLLIN WHITE's master-patent on the bored through cylinder, the purpose of the inventor is obscure, and it is significant that an ordinary rod-ejector was embodied in the weapon.

The revolvers known to British collectors as the "Galand" and the "Somerville and Galand" attracted attention in England and upon the Continent. The identity of the applicants for British Patent 3039/1868 is sufficiently discussed in Appendix II, but the rarity of British revolvers on this system should not blind collectors to the attention which the design received abroad. The Galand revolver seen in Plates 47 and 48 was the pattern shown by Schmidt as the M/70, a strong runner-up in the Swiss revolver trials of 1871 and widely marketed on the Continent. The method for operating the extractor is made clear by Plate 48, and it may be seen that the extractor lever forms part of the trigger-guard.

The Liège-proved weapon illustrated was chambered for six 12 mm. centre-fire "welt-rimmed" Perrin cartridges, and had a $4\frac{9}{10}$-in. barrel marked "Galand, Paris". It was serially numbered 11397, and the butt was modified to accept a detachable carbine stock. A more rare 7-mm. version in Plate 56 (Serial 12751) had the same marking, but has survived "in the white" (i.e. unfinished) and the 3-in. barrel was unrifled.

The lock mechanism used in both of these weapons was that shown in Plate 36, and can be identified with that shown in Plate 25; it was illustrated, but not claimed, in one design covered by Br. Pat. 3039/1868 and is today known as the "Nagant" lock. A decade later, it was to be embodied in the Belgian M/78 Nagant service revolver, and it was also used in the LeVaux weapon shown in Plate 49.

Plate 36 is taken from Von Sauer's book, published in 1876, the text of which dealt with Galand's pistol (under the title of *der ruſſiſche Ordonnanzrevolver*) in considerably greater detail than that devoted to other cavalry arms shown on the same Plate. No mention was made as to the date when this weapon was approved by the Russian Imperial Government, but the adoption must have occurred during deliveries of the competing Smith & Wesson hinged-frame cavalry revolver. These began in 1872 and continued until 1877. Parsons reveals that around 150,000 Smith & Wesson revolvers were made for the Russians, but no similar details are known as to the scale of issue for the Galand pistol. Presumably, this 35-oz. side-arm was intended for service with un-mounted personnel, but the only specific reference by Von Sauer was to a Naval issue.

As the notes in Appendix II will show, British development of the Galand revolver was probably in the hands of "THE BRAENDLIN ARMOURY CO. LTD." (q.v.), despite the appearance of revolvers (using Galand's extractor) which were marked "Galand and Sommerville". In fact, Galand patented three methods for operating his ex-tractor, but only two of them have been so far observed in British pistols. W. W. Greener illustrated one of these as "Galand and Somerville's [*sic*] Patent Self-Extracting Central-Fire Revolver" in 1871, and the version which he showed was illustrated in Galand's 1868 patent. Apparently available in ·450 and ·380 calibres, it was machine-made, and Greener observed that "the workmanship is very good". In these revolvers (see Plate 37), the short operating lever for the extractor ended (and was latched) at the front of the barrel lug, and did not give a leverage equal to that on the Continental version.

The third extractor design in the Specification used a longer lever, but this rested along one side of the frame instead of acting as a trigger-guard. Again, a star extractor attached to the standing breech was used, and a specimen marked "Galand & Sommerville" is shown in Plate 37.

The Complete Specification, however, gave pride of place to a weapon similar to the Continental Galand, but with a two-piece top-strap joining barrel to standing breech for extra rigidity. The lock was not claimed, but the illustration was clear enough to confirm use of the mechanism shown in Plate 36, and the Continental disc extractor.

The two "Galand & Sommerville" revolvers shown in the Specifica-tion had quite a different lock mechanism, which was similar to that used on the Tranter revolvers shown in Plate 68. A distinctive horn on the rear of the trigger appeared in both drawings, and was one of the features of many "Galand & Sommerville" pistols (see Plate 37) along with the use of a star-shaped extractor in place of the Continental disc.

It is not clear how long the Galand lasted as a commercial proposition, either in England or on the Continent. The British patent was maintained for its full life, and Greener still mentioned the design in the 1881 edition of his greatest work. However, the extraction system was not one that could be cheaply made and it is difficult to see how it competed with the hinged frame designs perfected in the late '70's. In fact, like the two weapons next to be described, it probably owed much of its success to the aggressive sales policy adopted by the promoters.

J. THOMAS's revolver is sufficiently described in Appendix II, but possible variants demand notice here. The weapon illustrated in Plate 37 was representative of the model normally encountered, but it should be borne in mind that two other simultaneous extraction systems were also claimed in the patent.

System One used the long frame of a normal Thomas revolver, but neither barrel nor cylinder were dragged forward to extract the cartridges. Instead, a thick hinged breech-block (like an oversized loading-gate) was swung out sideways from behind the cylinder, and the extractor could then be levered rearwards to empty the chambers. System Two had a short conventional frame aperture, but the barrel could be turned through 90° on the cylinder axis pin. When pulled forward on the pin, a hook at the rear of the top strap dragged the cylinder forward too, and the cartridges were extracted by a plate anchored to the standing breech. The similarity of this method to that used by T. JONES (q.v.) will be noted.

The last revolvers of detailed concern were the Merwin & Hulbert series protected here by Br. Pat. 277/1878, in the names of MERWIN, J., HULBERT, M., and HULBERT, W. A. (q.v.). Something is said (in Appendix II) of the patentees, and the official report on the unsuccessful 1878 U.S. Army tests for their single-action cavalry revolver (see Plate 38) has been too well summarized, by John E. Parsons, to bear repetition here.

The Abridgement of their British Patent Specification stated that the improvement related to revolvers in which the cartridges were extracted by moving the cylinder and barrel longitudinally on a central pin projecting from the butt (i.e. the standing breech). The lock mechanism and cylinder-bolt were disclaimed, however, as being "of usual construction".

The cylinder rotated in front of a circular standing breech, and the loading-gate was unusual in that it slid down for loading, instead of being hinged or pivoted. In the centre of the standing breech was a "grooved boss" (i.e. the extractor) which trapped the rims of the cartridges when barrel and cylinder were drawn forward, and a rim round the standing breech steadied the cartridges against this boss.

Cylinder and barrel were linked by a segmental flange on the latter, which engaged a collar formed around the axis pin hole in the cylinder, and the barrel lug fitted over this long cylinder axis pin to engage a slot in the end of the frame when the weapon was latched for firing. A spring bolt just forward of the trigger guard locked the barrel in this position.

To unload the weapon, this spring bolt was released and the barrel turned over on the cylinder axis pin. A key in the barrel lug fitted a groove in that axis pin; and the inner end of the groove was helical in form. As a result, when the barrel was turned over, the key and groove cammed it forward and this caused the cylinder to follow in train and started the cartridges from the chambers. The two components were then slid forward along the axis pin until the barrel key hit the end of its groove, by which time the cartridge-cases had cleared the cylinder.

Complicated as all this may sound, the weapon was easy to use and the extractor proved to be powerful and effective.

The barrel-securing key was on a pivoted spring-loaded mount and could be levered clear of the axis pin groove to allow complete removal of the barrel. An additional safety-key was fitted at the front of the pin, which could only be taken out with the barrel in a position not achieved during ordinary working conditions.

The whole design was an admitted mishmash of features taken from various American patents, eight of which were acknowledged on the barrels of the Model 1876 "Army" revolvers. Only one of these features (U.S. Pat. 187975 of 1877) appeared recognizably in the British Patent, and was the invention of W. A. Hulbert. It protected the flange around the standing breech, which located the cartridges on to the extractor plate.

The "Army" revolver was a hefty 42-oz. pistol with a single-action mechanism and a 7-in. barrel; it chambered six ·44–40 WCF cartridges. The U.S. Ordnance Board at Springfield were not sufficiently impressed with the design to recommend adoption, but it was energetically promoted to secure a fair prominence in the commercial market. Thus Norton featured two models in the 1880 edition of his book, as the ·44 "New Army" weapon without a topstrap connecting barrel and frame, and the "New ·38 Revolver" with such a refinement.

Merwin, Hulbert & Co. merely promoted and distributed these

pistols, which were made for them by the "Hopkins & Allen Mfg. Co." of Norwich, Connecticut, and the association apparently continued throughout the period. Catalogues of the late 1880's featured "M. H. & Co's. Automatic Ejecting Revolvers" and single-shot rifles alongside Hopkins & Allen's hinged-frame ejector revolver and their cheap "XL" pistols and shotguns. The Merwin & Hulbert revolvers thus illustrated were double-action pocket weapons in ·32 S. & W., ·32 Long or ·38 centre-fire calibres, embodying a simplified barrel latch and a top strap to the frame. All were fitted with a folding thumb-piece to the hammer, on a pattern developed by Hopkins & Allen.

Mentioned briefly in the catalogues were ·44 calibre revolvers "also in single action", but the Model 1876 single-action weapon was probably obsolete by the early 1880's, since advertisements featuring the "Automatic" Merwin Hulbert (with top frame strap) appeared in 1882.

If any compliment were required for a weapon quite complicated in construction, the manufacturers must have appreciated the comment of Stelle & Harrison, in 1883. "The Automatic (Merwin, Hulbert & Co.)," they wrote, "is so simple in its arrangements as to need no directions for assembling or taking apart."

For other revolvers of nominal concern here, the briefest of notes must suffice.

The revolver of H. DIMANCEA (q.v.) is sufficiently described in Appendix II, as a weapon in which the cylinder and barrel swung out to the left and were drawn forward to extract the cartridges. The design was principally noteworthy for its ingenious lock mechanism, with firing-pin and cylinder-bolt pin riding in horizontal frame slots in place of pivoted hammer or bolt. (See Plates 52 and 53.)

Unpatented in England, but of considerable theoretical interest, were the Sharps revolver, M/73, and the similar Schmidt weapon, M/74. These arms, on which the barrels pivoted about a vertical pin to operate the automatic extractor, are noticed in the remarks upon C. SHARPS (q.v.).

Finally, a listing of automatic, but not simultaneous cartridge extraction patents for revolving arms may prove of service to the reader. Not all of these designs related to revolving pistols, but reference to the notes upon the individual inventors should outline the principle of their patents.

299/1866	C. MASON
2004/1871	E. JOHNSON
2500/1875	E. HENARD
3266/1877	J. A. CROCKER

87/1880	T. SEDERL
5613/1881	J. H. McLEAN
16078/1884	W. FLETCHER & H. A. SILVER
5607/1888	G. H. SCHNEE

CHAPTER V

SERVICE ADOPTION AND COMPETING WEAPONS

NATURALLY, the El Dorado sought by every revolving arms manufacturer and designer would be an official order for the armed forces of his country. This would not necessarily be large in quantity, for many standing armies were surprisingly small, but the cachet of formal adoption meant valuable publicity for civilian markets and a steady backbone of modest production runs to keep military stores topped up against the needs of war (and drill-wastage!) were always welcome.

By 1888, many countries had approved revolver pistols for troops and officers carrying holstered arms, and (by reference to their Model-years) the date of their formal adoption or issue can be tabulated:

AUSTRO–HUNGARY

(1) Troopers' revolver, GASSER (Mod. 1870) 11-mm. centre fire. A Model 1882 solid-framed weapon was under test.

(2) Infantry Officer's revolver, GASSER-KROPATSCHEK (Mod. 1873), 9-mm. centre-fire.

(3) Troopers' revolver, system SMITH & WESSON (Mod. 1877), 11-mm. centre-fire.

BELGIUM

(1) Troopers' revolver, system CHAMELOT-DELVIGNE (Mod. 1871), 11-mm. centre-fire.

(2) Officers' revolver, system NAGANT (Mod. 1878), 9-mm. centre-fire.

(3) N.C.O.s', trumpeters' and artillery revolver, system NAGANT (Mod. 1883), 9-mm. centre-fire. (The Nagant weapons also found favour in the armies of Brazil and Argentine.)

DENMARK

(1) Troopers' revolver, LEFAUCHEUX-FRANCOTTE (Mod. 1882), 10·9-mm. centre-fire.

(2) Officers' revolver, LEFAUCHEUX-FRANCOTTE (Mod. 1886), 9-mm. centre-fire.

N.B. A new revolver of 7·5 mm. calibre was under study from 1885, presumably prompted by the Swedish NAGANT (Mod. 1885) experiments, but not adopted until 1893.

ENGLAND

Issue revolver (Army & Navy) "PISTOL, REVOLVER, B.L., ENFIELD MARK II, ·476 CALIBRE" (centre-fire), in course of supersession by the MARK I, ·442 GOVERNMENT MODEL revolver to sealed pattern of November 8th, 1887, submitted by P. Webley & Son of Birmingham.

It would appear (since the necessary ammunition for them was not yet formally obsolete) that the Mark II and III models of the "ADAMS's, REVOLVER, B.L., ·450 CALIBRE" were still in limited issue. (See Plates 24, 49 and 50.)

FRANCE

(1) Naval issue revolver, LEFAUCHEUX (Mod. 1870), 11-mm. centre-fire.

(2) Troopers' revolver, CHAMELOT-DELVIGNE (Mod. 1873), 11-mm. centre-fire.

(3) Officers' revolver, CHAMELOT-DELVIGNE (Mod. 1874), 11-mm. centre-fire. (See plate 26.)

GERMANY

(1) Troopers' revolver, COMMISSION (Mod. 1880),* 11-mm. centre-fire.

(2) Officers' revolver, COMMISSION (Mod. 1884),* 11-mm. centre-fire.

ITALY

(1) Cavalry troopers' revolver, system CHAMELOT-DELVIGNE ET SCHMIDT (Mod. 1872), 10·4-mm. centre-fire. (See Plate 26.)

(2) Officers' revolver, system CHAMELOT-DELVIGNE (Mod. 1879), 10·4-mm. centre-fire.

(3) Gendarmerie revolver of unidentified type or calibre. The author believes it to have been a GASSER design, but manufactured by LEFAUCHEUX.

NORWAY

(1) Cavalry/Artillery, Troopers' revolver, LEFAUCHEUX (Mod. 1864) 11-mm. pin-fire.

* Single-action weapons. Some authorities refer to "M/79" or "M/83" in describing. (See plate 26.)

(2) Officers' revolver, LEFAUCHEUX (Mod. 1864)* 11-mm. pin-fire.

(3) Officers' & N.C.O.s' revolver, NAGANT (Mod. 1883), 9-mm. centre-fire.

RUSSIA

Issue revolver, SMITH & WESSON (Mod. 1878),† ·44 calibre centre-fire. (See Plate 31.)

> N.B. An earlier self-extracting revolver identical to the GALAND weapon (q.v.) in 11-mm. Perrin centre-fire calibre may still have been in issue (See Plate 36.)

SPAIN

(1) Troopers' revolver, LEFAUCHEUX (Mod. 1863), 11-mm. pin-fire.

(2) Officers' revolver, system SMITH & WESSON (Mod. 1884)‡ 11-mm. centre-fire.

SWEDEN

(1) Troopers' revolver, LEFAUCHEUX-FRANCOTTE (Mod. 1871), 11-mm. centre-fire.

(2) Officers' revolver under study (based on NAGANT and SCHMIDT design of 1885) for a 7·5 mm. centre-fire cartridge.

SWITZERLAND

(1) Troopers' revolver, system SCHMIDT (Mod. 1878), 10·4-mm. centre-fire.

Revolvers on system CHAMELOT-DELVIGNE ET SCHMIDT (Mod. 1872), in 10·4-mm. centre-fire (or the earlier rim-fire cartridge), possibly still in issue in some numbers.

(2) Unmounted Officers' revolver, SCHMIDT (Mod. 1882), 7·5-mm. centre-fire with Rubin copper-jacketed bullet.

TURKEY

Issue revolver, system SMITH & WESSON (Mod. 1882) 7·5-mm. centre-fire.

UNITED STATES

Issue revolvers (Regular Army)

(1) COLT'S REVOLVER, calibre ·45-in., i.e. the single-action, Model 1873 pistol for the ·45–28–230 centre-fire cartridge. (See Plate 21.)

---

* Two distinct models available at choice; single-action or double-action.
† Single-action weapon.
‡ Double-action revolver made by the Orbea Bros. at Eibar,

(2) SCHOFIELD-SMITH & WESSON REVOLVER, Calibre
·45″. Two versions were in issue (Mods. 1874 and 1875) using the
·45–28–230 centre-fire cartridge. The weapon was a refinement of the
single-action self-extracting SMITH & WESSON'S ARMY REVOL-
VER, Calibre ·44″. (Mod. 1869.) This latter pistol and its ·44–25–225
centre-fire cartridge were in limited issue during the 1870's and used up
in service. (See Plate 29.)

> *N.B.* The REMINGTON REVOLVER (Mod. 1875), a single-
> action pistol using a commercial Remington ·44-in. centre-
> fire cartridge, was tested by a U.S. Ordnance Board in 1876.
>   Serious differences of opinion exist as to whether or not U.S.
> Government purchase and issue followed. The virtually con-
> clusive evidence of American authority John E. Parsons is
> against such issue. (See Plate 67.)

As an extension of this Table, some notes are added upon the scale of
service issue for revolvers. These show that such weapons were not
generously distributed in England and Europe, and should dispel any
idea that Army revolvers from this period are common today. Limited
issue in 1865 suggests limited availability in 1965! Specialist works exist
to guide the serious student on this score, and the author proposes to do
no more than to quote the opinion of "Un Officer Superieur", an anonymous military writer in the early 1890's.

As to the British Enfield revolver, this author stated that the issue of
1882 was for arming Lancer cavalry (except as to sixteen men in each
squadron, who retained carbines); for cavalry sergeant-majors; for infantry N.C.O.s attached to the regimental sergeant-major; and for
general issue at need in the Navy. In weighing evidence from this
quarter, it is as well to record that he regarded the muzzle-loading Navy
Colt revolver, model of 1851, as only *"probablement retiré aujourd'hui"*
from active service in the British forces and described it at some length.

His notes upon the three revolvers in issue for the armies of the
Austro–Hungarian Empire suggested that the apparent logistical weakness of issuing two different revolvers to troops in the ranks actually
raised few problems. The same cartridge served for both pistols and the
so-called "system Smith & Wesson", model 1877, weapon (if a Plate of
it was accurate) was made up of as many basic Gasser, Model 1870,
forgings and components as possible. The result was a hinged frame,
break-open, self-extracting revolver (hence, presumably, "syst. S. &
W."), with a button-operated latch securing top strap to standing
breech, star-shaped cartridge ejector of Dodge/S. & W. type and a rebounding hammer. The cylinder was locked for firing by recesses

machined in its rear circumference, in place of the proud indexing lumps used on the earlier pistol (see Plates 27 and 28).

Issue here was to Uhlan units (thirty-two troopers in each squadron being excepted and armed with carbines); to cavalry N.C.O.s generally; to N.C.O.s and trumpeters of mounted bands; to N.C.O.s, corporals and gunners of horse-drawn artillery; to N.C.O.s in heavy artillery trains and naval petty officers; and to the trumpet-majors of "Chasseur" infantry units.

Sweden issued the "Lefaucheux-Francotte revolver, Model 1871" to cavalrymen, field-artillerymen and signallers, but the scale of issue was not clearly established. According to J. Hentsch (writing in 1879), the cavalryman then also had two heavy single-shot pistols in his saddle-holsters. The Norwegian equivalent was the "flankør" (smooth bore) and "studser" (rifled) pair issued to each horseman with a single attachable shoulder stock for each pair. Hentsch suggested that these Swedish pistols were breech-loaders of Remington-type (employing a buck-shot or multi-ball cartridge at need), but the recent work upon Norwegian hand firearms, by Skaar & Nielsen, made no mention of such weapons for their army. A series of makeshift conversions from flintlock to percussion are shown in it and von Sauer (writing in 1876) certainly regarded such a weapon as being in active service for Sweden and illustrated it. (See Plate 36.)

The year 1887 appears to have been the year when Sweden decided to put her house in order on this matter of service hand-guns, and to study seriously the revolving ammunition-feed principle for them. The Gasser-Kropatschek (Austrian), Nagant (Belgian) and Schmidt (Swiss) issue weapons were considered, along with a native Swedish (Husqvarna) design and a lighter 9-mm. Warnant weapon. Thirty revolvers were ultimately ordered to be made up for trial (based on the Nagant and Schmidt designs) and experiments with them saw out the period. The resultant weapon was not formally adopted in Scandinavia until 1893, and was in 7·5 mm. centre-fire calibre like the Schmidt arm. It appears to have been made in Belgium principally, but smaller numbers were made in Sweden and Norway, presumably under licence. The unidentified applicant for Br. Pat. 8331/1888 (T. F. TÖRNELL; q.v.) may have had a possible connection with this design, purely on the strength of his unusual name, the dating of his application and the general configuration of the revolver shown in his Complete Specification.

The whole matter of the scale upon which revolving arms were issued within the various armies cannot be explored further here, but the writer hopes that enough has been said to show that the revolver manufacturer who secured an order for an approved side-arm for service issue gained no "licence to print money" with it. Obviously enough, there were important exceptions to this rule where large conscript armies had to be armed (as for Leopold Gasser in Austria–Hungary, and Smith & Wesson or Remington of America on securing Russian, Turkish or Egyptian Government orders), but the general reward in peaceful years cannot have been large.

As an examination of Appendix II will show, efforts at producing rotating feed mechanisms for rifles, stout enough for field service, were unremittent throughout the period. One or two systems achieved commercial success in bolt-action weapons, but the classic infantry rifle of Gras or Mauser type would not adapt to such a refinement. Even in 1894, a Continental writer mourned the existence of but one practical rotary magazine, *imagine par l'armurier autrichien Spitalsky* (see Plate 63), for coarse arms of this description. He pointed to Bavaria, as a State in which the rotary feed system found no favour even as a weapon of personal defence, for N.C.O.s and pistol-armed O.R.s in that army still carried the Model 1869 single-shot Werder pistol, with its huge rifle-sized (albeit reduced-charge) 11-mm. cartridge. Similarly, even in Belgium, cradle of the cheap revolver industry, the gendarmeric side-arm was a NAGANT-designed double-barrelled pistol at the close of the period, and the Scandinavian cavalry pistol have already been noticed.

This lukewarm official attitude to the revolver (and other arms employing a similar ammunition feed) was not so widely shared by travellers, householders and wrongdoers. A wide variety of revolving pistols served their devotion to this type of hand-gun. However, even in this market mistrust, or honest conviction, produced weapons that were either a compromise solution or an outright competitor, and at the outset of the period Captain Majendie remarked upon "a noticeable novelty" at the Paris Exhibition of 1867, which demonstrated this mistrust.

The same novelty was exhibited by Lefaucheux, by Le Page et Chauvot, and by other Liège makers, and it also appeared in the Italian collection; it was a sword with a revolver in the hilt. Majendie wrote of it that "the pistol is so arranged that the trigger falls within the sword-guard, and the fire is delivered parallel to the blade of the sword. These revolvers, said to be used by the officers of the Italian Army in large numbers, are invariably adapted for copper cartridges containing their own ignition, either pin or central fire". This kind of attempt to combine two weapons suggests a basic mistrust of both. The revolver-sword never caught on in England, although the designs of

A. MICHELONI (q.v.); W. DAVIS (q.v.); and R. HOWARD (q.v.) showed that the idea was explored here.

Naturally enough, other combination weapons were designed, and the two pin-fire revolvers in Plates 39 and 40 are examples of this same approach. The "L. DOLNE" weapon sketched in Fig. 10 was another idea, and further combination designs are noticed in relation to J. C. CAMPBELL; P. A. MATHIEU & J. F. GEVELOT; and C. F. GALAND & A. SOMMERVILLE (q.v.).

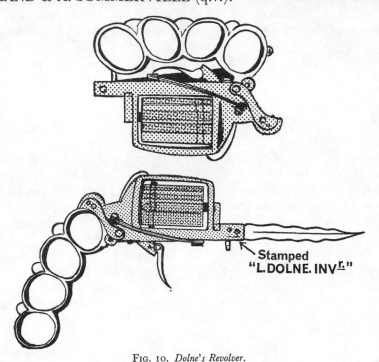

Stamped
"L. DOLNE. INV.ᵣ"

FIG. 10. *Dolne's Revolver.*
Top : Folded, as a knuckleduster.
Lower; Unfolded, for use as a revolver or dagger.

The significance of these arms does not lie in universal adoption (they are all rare), but in the attitude of mind that fathered them.

Issue revolvers were disliked on two counts in the armies of Europe, as a weapon too complicated for satisfactory use by private soldiers, and also as a temptation to N.C.O.s and officers to seek opportunity for its use. The reasoning went that such personnel were likely to forget their *raison d'être*, of commanding and directing troops, in favour of personal combat and wastage of ammunition.

This tradition died hard, and (in 1887) W. Witte recorded field issue of revolver ammunition, by the Imperial German Army, as only six cartridges for the weapon and six for the pouch.

In general, British military literature echoed this view and it is refreshing to read H. A. Leveson's book (published in 1871), in which some sound practical comment was offered. An indication that this author backed his words with experience can be gathered from his comment that "in practising with the revolver, the hand and the eye ought to be accustomed to act together, the trooper looking steadily at the object with both eyes open, and firing without sighting along the barrel".

It must be admitted that Leveson's ideal cavalryman was probably over-weaponed, for he recommended that the revolver be suitably reinforced. "In the off holster [he wrote] it is advisable to carry a double-barrelled, breech-loading pistol of the same calibre as the rifle and taking the same cartridge-cases, but loaded with only half the charge of powder . . ."

"The Old Shekarry" (as Leveson styled himself) recommended service adoption for a heavy calibre, centre-fire revolver "recently brought out by Messrs. Vaughan & Co.", but the identity of this pistol is so far untraced. A surprising, but quite sensible suggestion was made that the weapon be holstered at the back of the trooper's waist-belt, butt towards the right, where it could readily be grasped.

Throughout our period, the revolver suffered continual criticism over the gas-leak occurring between cylinder and barrel. The British Patents of F. DREVENSTEDT; E. HENARD; H. PIEPER; A. POLLAK; and W. STRINGFELLOW; recorded attempts to overcome this defect.

More serious competition came from the multi-barrelled pistols, sold by such makers as Charles Lancaster or T. Bland and Son in the closing decade of our period. Sired by the ancient "horse pistol" (and later double-barrelled developments by Westley Richards and others), such holster weapons first appeared as serious competitors to the metallic cartridge revolver in rim-fire embodiments offered by Beidermann, Grünbaum and others at the Paris Exhibition of 1867.

A specimen of the classic Lancaster design appears in Plate 42, but the patents of other inventors may be noticed to evidence the competition offered by multi-barrelled arms during our period, and (in date order) we have protection for C. SHARPS (207/1859); J. GRÜNBAUM (610/1866); T. RICHARDS & C. H. CARTER (3222/1868); W. TRANTER (3171/1875); A. MARTIN (1531/1880); H. A. A. THORN (1242/1881); T. W. & H. WEBLEY (5143/1881); H. A. A. THORN (213/1882); J. DICKSON the younger & A. G. MURRAY

(873/1882); H. A. A. THORN (3089/1882); G. H. NEEDHAM (4693/1883); A. CHUCHU (11201/1884); A FRANCOTTE (15891/1885); T. BLAND & F. CASHMORE (16969/1887).

It is true that not all of these designs were developed, and also true that some were not intended for military use. However, a contemporary searcher would certainly have encountered six weapons protected by these patents.

Christian Sharps's four-barrelled pocket pistol appeared in rim-fire calibres ·22, ·300 or ·32 and in very large numbers. It was made by Sharps, or his associates in Philadelphia, and by Lawden and Wade in England. The inventor developed the design continuously until his death in 1874, and the weapon was a formidable competitor to the pocket revolver (see Plate 41).

William Tranter's barrel bolt and extractor were principally applied to small-calibre, single-barrelled target arms, but multi-barrelled embodiments are known.

Martin's pistol (or "The Martin-Marres-Braendlin Mitrailleuse Pistol", as it was titled by its makers) probably owed more notoriety to its mention by Greener than to popularity or production in quantity. By the original (1881) edition of his book, Greener described "Martin's Patent Mitrailleuse Pistol" as expected to appear on the market in the course of the next few months. Versions were to be offered with four or six barrels, each of which had a separate striker and spring. A single trigger was connected to a vertical spindle with projecting studs on it, so that by pulling the trigger the strikers were cocked and fired in rotation. The ·450-in. cartridges were joined in groups (by thin metal retaining plates) appropriate to the number of barrels. This permitted simultaneous loading and unloading of all barrels, and Greener trumpeted that the weapon's advantages might "eventually occasion it to supersede the revolver entirely".

In the 1896 edition of his book Greener actually illustrated the "Mitrailleuse Pistol", as a four-barrelled weapon clearly marked "THE BRAENDLIN ARMOURY CO. LTD." (q.v.). With respect to this distinguished author, the present writer feels that the pistol shown owed something to the patent of A. FRANCOTTE (q.v.), whatever internal debt might have been due to A. Martin.

Whichever design fathered the weapon shown, Greener said of it that "the shock of the recoil prematurely discharges a second barrel, and this defect would alone prevent it coming into general use". Certainly, the pistol is rare by comparison with our next design.

Lancaster's pistols (see Plate 42) were made under the patents of H. A. A. THORN (q.v.), and principally appeared in ·450, ·455 and

·476 calibres, being commonly rifled with the original Charles Lancaster's oval-bored rifling. Whether in double or four-barrelled embodiments, the arms used Thorn's original revolving striker-mechanism of 1881, but the later versions used a firing-pin integral with the revolving striker to replace the older system of a firing-pin for each barrel.

Chuchu's pistol (a four-barrelled rim-fire weapon, normally in ·22 calibre) embodied a rotating firing-pin of Lancaster type, but struck it with a conventional self-cocking hammer. The barrels could be folded parallel with the underside of the action body, when the weapon was to be carried in the pocket, and their latch could also be folded down over the cartridge chambers to stop the cases from falling out. The extractor stem protruded at the muzzle of the barrels, and a tap on the button emptied the chambers.

Bland's four-barrelled pistol was chambered for the ·455 service revolver cartridge and embodied a combined rotating firing-pin and gas check, which was struck by a self-cocking hammer. The design was well received, but came too late in the day to attain real popularity.

As another competitor to the revolver, magazine pistol designs by BATE and KRNKA may be studied in Figs. 2 and 3. Similar weapons were developed by Schulhof, Seidl and others in the late 1880's, but lacked the rotary features that prompted mention of the two first named.

To conclude these brief notes, it remains only to notice the "harmonica" pin-fire pistols patented by A. E. JARRE (q.v.) in 1871. The nickname is modern, and springs from the magazine system in which a row of loaded barrels passed transversely beneath the hammer.

G

CHAPTER VI

LIGHT ORDNANCE, MACHINE-GUNS AND RIFLES

THE arms briefly and selectively dealt with in this Chapter might, perhaps, be strictly considered outside the scope of this study, but reference is made to them because they incorporated the revolving ammunition feed principle.

Easily the most important of all the designs discussed in this Chapter were the guns of Gatling, Hotchkiss, and Christophe & Montigny, though there were other designers whose machine-guns and light ordnance were of considerable interest. In date order, there were the patents of E. WALKER (3453/1867); P. J. J. NOËL (450/1868); T. J. CRANMER & W. P. MOFFATT (3164/1868); L. W. BROAD-WELL (2474/1870; 250/1871; 380/1871); J. P. TAYLOR (1686/1871); J. TRAWNICZEK (2865/1871): J. VINE *et al.* (2010/1872); J. P. TAYLOR (1549/1873; 2811/1873); L. BAILEY (1703/1876); H. DEFTY (3766/1877); D. W. C. FARRINGTON (1935/1878); J. F. TROTTER (497/1879); D. W. C. FARRINGTON (3338/1879); G. PACE (4378/1880); J. H. McLEAN (5613/1881): E. FABRE & A. TRONCHE (15771/1888). In addition (at the very outset of the period) the "battery gun" design of SIR JOHN LILLIE was apparently under study, and it is proposed to deal here with the guns and cannon patented by R. J. GATLING, B. B. HOTCHKISS, and L. CHRISTOPHE & J. MONTIGNY.

The machine-gun invented by Richard Jordan Gatling was originally patented in America, during 1862, as a weapon using paper cartridges and ordinary percussion caps. The cartridges were loaded in capped, separate metal firing chambers, which were wedged up to mate with the barrels for firing. Each of the six ·58 calibre barrels in the revolving bundle had a firing-bolt, and a manually-turned crank-handle rotated this bundle to cock and fire each bolt.

The first Gatling guns were made for their inventor by contractors in Cincinnati, Ohio, but a new design was conceived, during their manufacture, to use metallic rim-fire cartridges.

Gatling did not manage to interest the Union Army in adopting his paper-cartridge guns officially, but a few weapons saw active service during the American Civil War on the initiative of individual officers.

Between 1865 and 1866, manufacture switched to new hands in Philadelphia, and during this period the classic Gatling machine-gun emerged. This was the first model commercially produced to use rim-fire cartridges which chambered in the barrels and not in separate firing chambers.

Gatling's Br. Pat. 790/1865 presumably described this gun, and a four-barrelled, water-cooled embodiment is described in the Complete Specification.

Turning a crank-handle rotated the barrels by a gear train engaging the central shaft on which they were mounted, and the breech end of this shaft carried the bolt cylinder, the cartridge carrier, and the bolts which loaded, fired, extracted and ejected the cartridges.

As the barrels revolved, the cartridges dropped into their carrier from a feeder on top of the gun, and spiral cam surfaces engaging each bolt forced it back on to a firing spring for release against the cartridge head. Firing occurred as each barrel reached the "five o'clock" position in its circuit.

In August 1866, Gatling secured U.S. Army adoption for his ·58-calibre rim-fire gun, and (in 1868) 1-in. calibre rim-fire and ·50 centre-fire weapons were also approved. During this period Gatling changed manufacturers for the last time, and from 1867 until 1886 COLT'S PATENT FIRE ARMS MFG. CO. (q.v.) manufactured for him exclusively in America. (See Plates 43 and 44.)

The gun now settled to a basic ten-barrel, air-cooled design, and manufacturing licences were granted under the Austrian and British patents (790/1865; 3341/1869, in the latter case). In England, Gatling's licensee was the "Sir W. G. Armstrong Company" of Newcastle upon Tyne (as represented by Messrs. Cruddas, Noble, Rendel and Westmacott), who secured the concession in 1870. Their ·45-calibre, centre-fire gun was introduced into the British Army in 1872, as improved by Br. Pat. 2954/1871.

Gatling machine-guns using solid-drawn, centre-fire cartridges proved almost incredibly robust and reliable. One trial in America (during 1873) cleared 100,000 rounds of ·50 ammunition through an M/65 gun and virtually without incident.

By the date of appearance for "THE GATLING GUN, LIMITED" (q.v.) the gun was in use by America, Britain, China, Egypt, France,

Japan, Morocco, Russia, South America and Turkey. The relevant British patents of R. H. BRANDON and J. G. ACCLES (q.v.) may be noted in the remarks upon that Company, and inventions of G. O. KINNE (2463/1870) and L. W. BROADWELL (2474/1870) are also in point.

During our period the possible rate of fire climbed steadily from the early 300–500 rounds per minute and, by 1880, nearly 1,200 rounds per minute could be cleared by a 90-lb., five-barrelled, ·45 calibre light Gatling.

Although no part of our study here, it is worth recording also that one experimental Gatling attained a fire-rate of 3,000 rounds per minute. This gun was patented in America (in 1893), and Gatling embodied an electric motor to rotate ten ·30-calibre barrels.

Needless to say, service requirements seldom demanded fire-power even at the level attainable manually.

In the United Kingdom, the official Small Bore Machine Gun Committee laid down three basic requirements, during 1880, which had to be satisfied before any machine-gun would be accepted for test.

Firstly, a capable rate of firing at 400 rounds per minute.

Secondly, the gun breech to remain closed for one-third of a second (or as accepted by the Committee) to handle any cartridge hanging fire.

Thirdly, rapid firing of 1,000 continuous rounds without overheating the barrels.

It will be clear from what has already been said, that the Gatling gun had little to fear from these requirements, although the competing (and non-revolving) Gardner gun carried the day, when that Committee reported early in 1881.

As mentioned, the Gatling gun was capable of development in heavy calibres, but the revolving weapon now primarily remembered in the field of light ordnance was the invention of another American, Benjamin Berkley HOTCHKISS (q.v.).

The British patents for the Hotchkiss revolving cannon appeared as Nos. 3017/1878 and 4454/1879, but the design was developed in France primarily, with the main factory at Paris employing more than 1,000 hands by 1885.

Only the barrels of the Hotchkiss revolved, and were backed by a heavy recoil plate pierced by the firing-pin. The shells were loaded into a tube on the left side of the gun and transferred to the barrels by a loading piston. Subsequently, the round was finally seated by an incline on the recoil plate against which the cartridge heads bore during rotation of the barrels.

Bartlett described the firing cycle quite succinctly. "A plunger [he wrote] forces one cartridge nearly into barrel number one, at the upper left-hand side of the gun, at the same time a reciprocating extractor is withdrawing a spent shell from barrel number five, at the lower left-hand side, and while barrel number four is in firing position at the bottom of the gun, directly under the sights, the barrels being locked for the instant. A pull at the trigger fires the piece, and releases the barrels from their locked position. Barrels number two and three contain their cartridges, the cartridge in number two started slightly forward from the position in which it was left by the loading plunger, and that in number three nearly home in its chamber."

The light Hotchkiss threw an 18-oz. shell, and could fire eighty-rounds in a minute. Range was something over two miles, and short-range penetration of an inch of steel plate was claimed. The heaviest model threw $2\frac{1}{2}$-lb. shells over nearly four miles at a rate of some thirty in a minute.

The light gun was adopted by the French Navy, and a Dutch test demonstrated the value of the weapon against torpedo boats, with a target moving at 16 m.p.h. hit forty times.

This 18 oz. shell was ribbed internally and shattered into 1-oz. fragments on impact, making it both an admirable anti-personnel round, and useful against light hulls.

A number of ingenious mountings were developed (and purchased by many European powers) and the cannon owed much of its popularity to these refinements. The solidity and reliability of the breech mechanism was another strong sales point.

Although not a revolving machine-gun, the "Montigny Mitrailleuse" is noticed here as a weapon somewhat similar to the classic Gatling in outward appearance, which has been so long remembered as the Continental competitor to the revolving feed.

The Montigny weapon is sometimes known as a "volley-gun", and consisted of thirty-seven rifled barrels, jacketed into a bundle. An iron firing-chamber, suitable bored, fed metallic centre-fire cartridges simultaneously into each barrel, when a supporting breech-block was cranked home behind it.

On turning this separate loading-crank, the firing-pins were cocked behind each barrel, and could be released at will by turning another (firing) crank.

The gun was conceived in 1851, but was not offered to the French forces until 1867, when J. MONTIGNY and L. CHRISTOPHE (of Belgium) offered their improved version to Emperor Napoleon III. The relevant British Patent was No. 3553/1867.

As modified by Colonel de Reffye, of the Meudon Arsenal, an improved 25-barrelled gun went into action during the Franco–Prussian War of 1870. Too complicated for field service, and tactically mishandled to boot, the weapon failed miserably.

The design was hastily corrected (see Plates 45 and 46) and the Model 1870 discarded the slow loading-crank in favour of a toggle-joint lock for supporting the breech. The massive firing-chamber block was also reduced to a slim plate of manageable thickness and weight, but all modifications were in vain.

Damned by its reputation, the design went to the scrap-heap and took with it the French confidence in machine-guns of any sort.

During the war it had been handled like a piece of light artillery, and it was this sort of weapon that the French sought and found in the Hotchkiss cannon.

To conclude this Chapter, mention must be made of those arms fired from the shoulder, which embodied revolving features.

Very few weapons of this type achieved production in quantity, and the details set out in Appendix II are considered to be sufficient in a study of this type.

In this listing of relevant British patents (by date order), some duplications will be observed from the Chapter devoted to self-extracting revolvers. The inclusion of these designs is deliberate. Some inventors (G. H. SCHNEE is an example) patented systems for both long arms and pistols.

In date order, we have the following British Patents: W. PALMER (1592/1862); A. WYLEY (1785/1864); B. BURTON (2059/1864); S. H. ROPER (182/1867); E. L. STURTEVANT (798/1867); J. J. KRAFFERT (1259/1867); C. F. & J. E. de DARTIEN (778/1870); E. JOHNSON (2004/1871); W. R. EVANS (2261/1873); E. JOHNSON (1722/1875); J. D. GREENE (2241/1875); E. HENARD (2500/1875); 111/1876); J. A. CROCKER (3266/1877); OEST. WAFF. GES. (1272/1878; 1960/1878); J. WERNDL (3878/1878); D. B. WESSON (4614/1878); P. GAY & H. GUENOT (197/1879); J. WERNDL (2840/1879); A. SWINGLE (2965/1879); T. NORDENFELT (5324/1880); J. J. ATKINSON & J. NEEDHAM (716/1881); F. MANNLICHER (2915/1881); W. STRINGFELLOW (5564/1881); J. H. McLEAN (5613/1881); J. WERNDL (712/1882); F. DREVENSTEDT (1823/1882); J. WERNDL (1982/1882; 229/1883); G. de OVERBECK (3411/1883); W. W. COLLEY (5163/1883); O. SCHOENAUER (5793/1884); G. SHEPHEARD (2214/1885); AUSTRIAN SMALL ARMS MFG. CO. (7989/1885); L. &. S. S. YOUNGHUSBAND (3047/1886); L. ARMANNI (8131/1886);

10587/1886); J. SCHULHOF (9066/1886); E. A. SALVATOR (12686/1886); R. C. ROMANEL *et al.* (9998/1887); J. SCHULHOF 10423/1887); F. MANNLICHER (632/1888); G. H. SCHNEE (5607/1888); R. C. ROMANEL *et al.* (6994/1888); J. SCHULHOF (10286/1888); E. FABRE & A. TRONCHE (15771/1888); A. LINDNER (17159/1888).

APPENDIX I

Patents

THIS Appendix contains a listing of all relevant British patents and details of their duration. It should be noted at the outset that the "Patentees" in Tables I and II were not always the inventors of weapons or devices patented; in many cases they were professional Patent Agents acting on behalf of other men, taking the laborious paperwork and assigning the patent to its inventor after grant.

A patent in the United Kingdom, for the purposes of this book, was a grant from the Crown by "Letters Patent" to the person who applied for such patent in respect of some manner of new manufacture. It conferred on him the sole right of making, using, or selling the patented article during the period for which the right was granted.

Under an Act of Parliament dated 1852 the period of protection could last for up to fourteen years from the date of application, provided that renewal fees were paid at stipulated intervals. The initial fee for a British patent was £25, followed by renewal fees of £50 before the end of the third year and £100 before the end of the seventh year. If the renewal fees were not paid on time, the patents became void and public announcement of their voidance was officially made in the *London Gazette* or the *Official Journal of Patents*.

In 1883 a new Act was passed which made it possible to renew the patent annually after the third year. There were smaller individual fees which, nevertheless, increased in amount periodically as the years passed. Thus, in both the following Tables, the nearer a patent approaches its statutory fourteen years' limit the more likely it is to have enjoyed some commercial success and the more likely to warrant the researcher's increasing attention. No official mention was made on the expiry of a patent at the end of its statutory fourteen years.

An application for a patent had to be accompanied by a Provisional Specification. This merely outlined the claims of the inventor, and served to protect his basic idea until a Complete Specification was filed. Some of the patentees listed in the Table never filed a Complete Specification, and merely used the application as a provisional protection (of six months' duration) in which to decide whether or not to complete their patent. It was, of course, always open to the patentee to file a Complete Specification with his application if the invention was sufficiently developed and he desired to secure his patent speedily.

The right of monopoly was only granted, however, on condition that each patentee filed at the Patent Office a Complete Specification of his invention which particularly described the nature of it and in what manner it was to be "performed". The purpose of this Complete Specification was to ensure that the public should know, during and after the period of monopoly, precisely how the invention worked.

The Complete Specification was, therefore, a highly detailed document, describing in close detail the nature, manufacture or purpose of the invention concerned. These Specifications were, and still are, open to public scrutiny and constitute an immense treasury of information about the weapons and devices so protected; and even the shorter Provisional Specifications can yield valuable information. Copies of these Specifications can still be bought on payment of a small fee, but as they are not classified by subject the reference value of Tables I and II, which together present the essential patent details contained in these Specifications, will be apparent to collector and researcher.

Table I sets out termination dates, through *voidance* or *expiry*, of all British revolver patents secured before 1865 which survived into the period 1865–1879—although during this period there were, in fact, no revolver patents surviving after 1874. Table II sets out patents actually secured between 1865 and 1888 and their termination dates. The object of both Tables is to suggest the probable source of a firearm or mechanism that may bear only a retailer's name and to help in dating weapons carrying a patentee's name. In some cases, improvements on a Table I invention will be found in Table II.

Some warning must be given on the use of the patent dates in these Tables when attempting to date weapons by reference to them. With rare exceptions, every British patent had to be sealed within fifteen months of its stated date. This meant that when Letters Patent had been granted to the patentee the document had to be taken by him to the appropriate office to be officially sealed and the fee paid, and this had to be done within fifteen months of the date of the grant. Failure to have the document sealed and the formalities cleared within this period ended that particular attempt to secure protection. Once Letters Patent had been granted, however, the invention could be freely discussed and revealed to possible developers without fear of having the idea pirated or stolen.

It follows, therefore, that the practical development of a patented weapon may well have occurred some years after the date of the patent. As an example, the recent researches of Major W. C. Dowell show that Messrs. Fletcher and Silver were still working in October, 1887, on the *pattern* Webley revolver embodying their British Patent No. 16078, dated December 6th, 1884.

In compiling Table II, the date of the voidance of patent protection was preferred to a termination date based on the renewal fee payments because not until the *London Gazette* or the *Official Journal of Patents* had published that a patent was void was it safe for anyone to use a formerly patented idea. Until the *publication* of voidance, the inventor could still belatedly maintain his patent by paying the overdue renewal fee, under penalty for his tardiness. The following notes will assist when studying the Tables.

"V" = Voidance.   "E" = Expiry

FIELD OF INVENTION. The descriptions in this column are my own and are
    not necessarily taken from the official title.
PATENTEE. The individual in whose name an application for a patent was
    filed was deemed by the Patent Office to be the Patentee. Thus
    if an inventor conducted his own application it was his name that
    appeared in the records as Patentee. Alternatively, if he instructed a
    professional Patent Agent to act for him it was the Agent's name that
    was so recorded. In such instances, the practice was for the Agent to
    assign the patent to the inventor after grant.
COMMUNICATION FROM. Whenever an Agent acted for an inventor the pub-
    lished patent contained the words "A communication from . . ."
    followed by the inventor's name. In these Tables, where this occurred
    the name in the "Patentee" column is that of the Agent; that of the
    inventor is in the column on the extreme right.

In column IV of Table II, those entries which are not followed by (V) or (E) are the expiry dates of Provisional protection.

TABLE I

Termination dates of British revolving arms patents granted prior to January 1st, 1865, and surviving into the period of this book.

Voidance or Expiry Date	Patentee	Patent Number and Year	Field of Invention	Communication from
1865				
Feb. 12th (E)	J. P. Lindsay	2013/1864	Firearm locks	
Feb. 24th (E)	R. Adams	13527/1851	Rifles and revolvers	
Mar. 8th (V)	J. Deane (Jun.)	626/1862	Breech-loading revolvers	
Apr. 12th (E)	I. Williams	2513/1864	Revolver embodied in sabre	A. Micheloni
May 24th (V)	W. Harding	1159/1858	Revolver—both lock and assembly	
May 27th (V)	W. Palmer	1592/1862	Revolving cartridge feed	

TABLE I (continued)

	Voidance or Expiry Date	Patentee	Patent Number and Year	Field of Invention	Communication from
1865					
	July 19th (V)	W. Tranter	2067/1862	Revolver locks and assembly. Ramrods. Rifle barrel	
	July 20th	T. Bailey	1634/1858	Revolver locks and assembly. Ramrod	
	Aug. 22nd (V)	D. Moore	2351/1862	Revolver and its rim-fire cartridge	
1866					
	Jan. 22nd (V)	C. Sharps	207/1859	Repeating firearms—multi-barrelled	
	Jan. 26th (V)	J. Kerr	242/1859	Revolver	
	Mar. 5th (V)	W. Clark	628/1863	A revolver	A. Guerriero
	Apr. 9th (V)	A. V. Newton	902/1863	Lance and "pepperbox" firearm combined	J. C. Campbell
	May 19th (V)	J. H. Johnson	1251/1863	Revolver for use with metallic cartridges	A. Pollak
	July 23rd (V)	G. Davies	1844/1863	Revolver	C. Sharps
	July 27th (V)	W. Tranter	1862/1863	Revolver locks, loading-gates and lever cartridge ejectors	
	Aug. 11th (V)	Sir. J. S. Lillie	1985/1863	Revolving battery gun	
	Sept. 12th	W. Clark	2250/1863	Revolver for metallic cartridge	T. J. Vail
	Oct. 5th (V)	A. V. Newton	2263/1859	Revolver and metallic cartridge	From Perrin & Delmas
	Nov. 7th (V)	J. K. Hoyt	2768/1863	Revolver and metallic cartridges	B. F. Joslyn
1867					
	Jan. 28th (E)	W. Tranter	212/1853	Rammer and lock mechanism for a revolver	
	Mar. 3rd (E)	S. Colt	535/1853	Revolver	
		S. Colt	538/1853	Revolver	

TABLE I (*continued*)

Voidance or Expiry Date	Patentee	Patent Number and Year	Field of Invention	Communication from
1867				
Mar. 12th (V)	C. E. Wallis	624/1864	Double-loaded percussion revolver. Sixteen charges in eight chambers	
Apr. 7th (V)	W. Clark	880/1860	Muzzle-loading percussion re-revolver	The Starr Arms Co.
July 16th (V)	A. Wyley	1785/1864	Breech-case or chamber	
Aug. 19th (V)	B. Burton	2059/1864	Breech-chamber and cartridges	
Sept. 28th (V)	J. Jongen	2383/1864	Lock and cylinder for revolver using percussion caps	
1868				
July 12th (V)	J, Adams	1758/1861	Revolver and cartridges	
1869				
Apr. 15th (V)	F. A. Le Mat & C. F. Girard	1081/1862	Lock and main-spring linkage for revolvers	
Dec. 26th (V)	W. Clark	3452/1862	Revolver to be attached at will to infantry rifles	P. A. Mathieu & J. F. Gevelot
1870				
Aug. 16th (E)	W. Tranter	1913/1856	"Single-action, double-action and triple-action" revolver locks	
1871				
Nov. 7th (E)	J. Adams	2824/1857	Frame construction, locks and ramrods for revolvers	
1872				
Dec. 17th (E)	J. Kerr	2896/1858	Revolver locks	
1873				
No relevant	expiries traced			
1874				
Apr. 10th (E)	J. Rigby & W. N. Norman	899/1860	Breech-loading guns; pin-fire cartridges; loading of revolvers	
1875–1879				
No relevant expiries traced				

TABLE II

British Letters Patent (for revolving arms or rotary ammunition-feed devices). 1/1/1865–31/12/1888 with dates of expiry or publication of voidance in the Official Journal of the Commissioners of Patents.

	Dates of Patent	Patent Nos.	Patentees	Expiry or Voidance dates	Field of Invention	Communication from
1865						
	Feb. 4th	309	S. W. Wood	16/2/1872(V)	Revolver, front loading	
	Mar. 9th	659	W. Clark	15/3/1872(V)	Radial revolver pistol	S. A. Noël & F. Gueury
	Mar. 21st	790	R. J. Gatling	21/3/1879(E)	"Battery gun"	
	Apr. 12th	1046	T. J. Mayall	19/4/1872(V)	Rammers and cartridges	
	July 20th	1889	W. Tranter	20/7/1879(E)	Revolver cylinder	
	Aug. 4th	2027	H. A. Bonneville	4/2/1866	Revolver lock	P. Drivon & C. J. Biron
	Aug. 4th	2030	T. W. Webley	4/2/1866	Hammer for revolvers	
	Aug. 7th	2050	W. C. Dodge	14/8/1868(V)	Revolver cartridge extractors	
	Aug. 15th	2108	J. Broun	15/2/1866	Includes revolvers	
	Aug. 28th	2210	P. Polain	4/9/1868(V)	Revolver	
	Dec. 16th	3258	A. V. Newton	25/12/1868(V)	Cartridges; includes a revolver to use the cartridge	S. Crispin
1866						
	Jan. 31st	299	W. R. Lake	31/7/1866	Revolver cartridge extractor	C. Mason
	Feb. 28th	610	D. L. Cohn	31/8/1866	Multi-barrelled firearms with revolving firing mechanism	J. Grünbaum
	Apr. 7th	997	E. T. Hughes	16/4/1869(V)	Revolvers	J. B. Doolittle & G. O. Downing
	July 28th	1959	J. Adams	8/8/1873(V)	Cartridges, machinery and revolvers	

(i) W. Tranter's double-trigger percussion revolver, in 54 bore calibre, No. 19530T

(ii) W. Tranter's single-trigger percussion revolver, in 54 bore calibre, No. 15932T

(iii) Beaumont-Adams double-action percussion revolver, in 54 bore calibre, No. 100,076C

(iv) Colt single-action "Navy" percussion revolver, in .36 calibre. London manufacture. No 39632.

PLATE 1   TOWER COLLECTION

(i) Colt single-action "Army" percussion revolver, in ·44 in. calibre. Model 1860. No. 210

(ii) "Wedge-frame" Webley percussion revolver, in ·44 calibre. Retailed by "Webley & Sons, London". No. 3025

(iii) Starr Arms Co. double-action percussion "Army" revolver, in ·44 calibre. No. 17841. (After Br. Pat. 880/1860

(iv) Kufahl needle-fire revolver in ·38 calibre. No. 1866. Made by F. Drevse of Sommerda. (After Br. Pat. 13,994/1852)

PLATE 2   TOWER COLLECTION

PLATE 3

Top : Cased "Deane's Patent" optional percussion or rim-fire revolver, in
·32 cal. No. 15,507P. 132 D.H.D. Retailed by Deane & Son, London Bridge.
Lower : Six shot "Army" revolver in ·450 centre-fire calibre. A permanent
conversion from percussion. Embodies W. Harding's patented features, but
is Birmingham proved. No number or retailer's name.

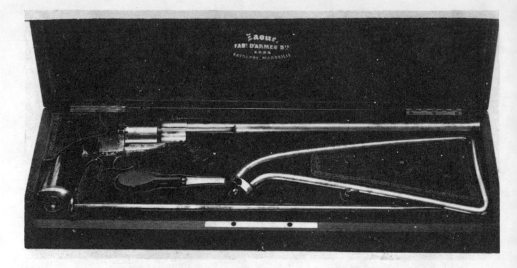

PLATE 4

Six shot, single-action, 11 mm. pin-fire revolver, retailed by ZAOUE of Marseilles. 11-inch barrel (with folding sights) and detachable stock. (*Wallis & Wallis, Lewes*

PLATE 5

Five shot, double-action, 5 mm. pin-fire revolver, embodied in purse. "Frankenau's Patent". No. 269. *Wallis & Wallis, Lewes*

PLATE 6

Twelve shot, 9 mm. pin-fire revolver. No maker's name. Birmingham proof. Serial Number 1000

(i) Double-barrelled, double-action, 20-shot pin-fire revolver in 7 mm. calibre. Marked "E. Lefaucheux"

(ii) Self-cocking six-shot pin-fire revolver, in 12 mm. calibre. Marked "Chamelot Delvigne"

(iii) Nameless double-action 20-shot pin-fire revolver, in 7mm. calibre. Double-barrelled, like the "Lefaucheux" pistol, but with single hammer.

PLATE 7   TOWER COLLECTION

(i) Single-barrelled, double-action, 20-shot pin-fire revolver in 7mm. calibre. Marked "J. Chaineux"

(ii) Two nameless self-cocking pin-fire "fist-pistols" or "coups de point". Note ejector rods in butts.

(iii) Seven-shot, double-action pin-fire revolver, in 12 mm. calibre. Marked "A. Fagnus", and retailed by Charles Kerr, Stranraer.

PLATE 8   TOWER COLLECTION

(i) Smith & Wesson's No. 2, six-shot, single-action rim-fire ·32 revolver. No. 57770

(ii) Smith & Wesson's No. 1, seven-shot, single-action rimfire ·22 revolver. No. 106154. (Barrel tipped up to show method for removing cylinder)

(iii) British copy of Smith & Wesson's No. 2 revolver. Un-numbered. Retailed by Walter Scott, Birmingham.

(iv) British copy of Smith & Wesson's No. 2 revolver. Un-numbered. Retailed by J. Smith, Birmingham.

(v) British copy of Smith & Wesson's No. 2 revolver. Retailed by J. Lang, Cockspur St., London. No. 1341

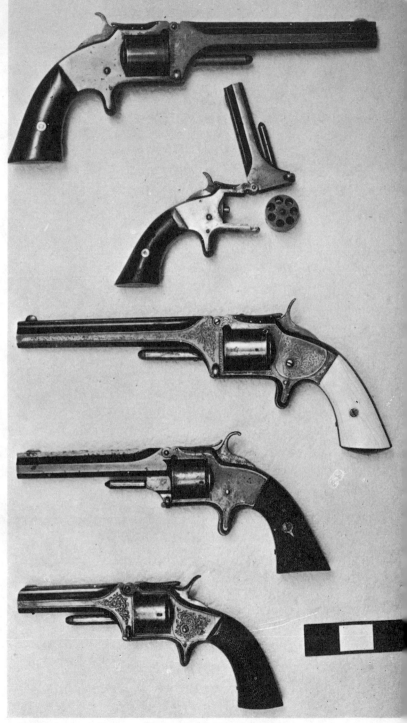

PLATE 9   TOWER COLLECTION

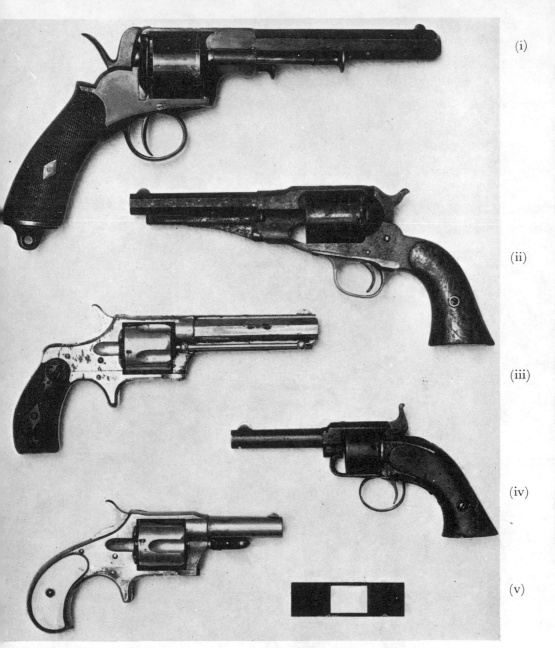

PLATE 10   TOWER COLLECTION

(i) Single-action ·45 "Army" rim-fire revolver, marked "Webley's Patent"

(ii) Single-action Remington "New Model Police" ·36 cal. revolver, converted from percussion to rim-fire ·38

(iii) Single-action Remington "New Line Revolver No. 3", in ·38 rim-fire cal.

(iv) Single-action ·32 rim-fire revolver, made under James Warner's patent of 1857. An infringement of Rollin White's U.S. master-patent (q.v.)

(v) Single-action Remington "New Line Revolver No. 4", in ·38 rim-fire cal.

(i) Five-shot, single-action Colt ·38 "New Line House" revolver, in ·38 centre-fire calibre. The "Cop & Thug" scene popular with collectors can be seen on the grip. Serial No. 22382

(ii) Seven-shot, single-action Colt. ·22 rim-fire "New Line Pocket Revolver". No. 44749

(iii) & (iv) Two single-action seven-shot Allen & Wheelock ·22 rim-fire pocket revolvers. Ethan Allen infringed Rollin White's U.S. master patent (q.v.) with a very similar pistol.

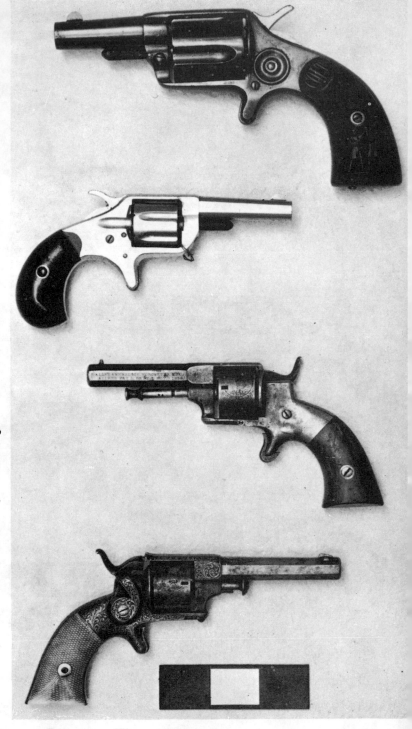

PLATE 11 TOWER COLLECTION

PLATE 12

Six shot, single-action, Belgian revolver. No. 1175. Marked "Mariette Bvte."
32 rim-fire calibre. Three inch barrel is smooth-bored. (*Photograph from
Messrs. Wallis & Wallis, Lewes.*)

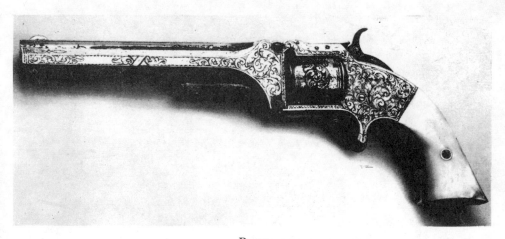

PLATE 13

Six shot, presentation engraved and silver-plated Smith & Wesson revolver.
6 inch barrel. Model No. 2, in ·32 rim-fire calibre. No. XX4. (*Photograph
from Messrs. Wallis & Wallis, Lewes.*)

PLATE 14

Four shot Colt "House" revolver, in ·41 rim-fire calibre. No. 3943. London proved and retailed. Three inch barrel. The "Clover Leaf" cylinder can be adjusted to present a flat profile, suitable for carrying in the pocket.

(Photograph from Messrs. Wallis & Wallis, Lewes.)

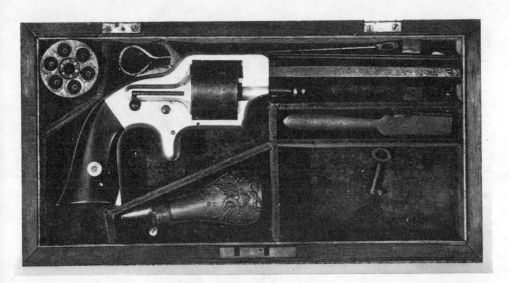

PLATE 15

Six shot, single-action "Army" revolver in optional percussion or cup-primer ·42 calibre. Made by Plant's Mfg. Co., New Haven, Conn. Retailed by Merwin & Bray, New York. No. 5935

PLATE 16

Nameless self-cocking "Birmingham" rim-fire revolver in ·380 cal. Made from components designed for cheap percussion revolvers, but not a conversion. The lever ejector is similar in form and operation to the rammers used on muzzle-loading revolvers.

PLATE 17 Colt "Navy" revolver, Model of 1851, converted to use A. Thuer's cartridge. New York barrel address. Serial No. 168611 L. Conversion No. 79. (*Photograph from Messrs. Wallis & Wallis, Lewes.*)

PLATE 18 Colt five-shot "Small Frame Conversion" revolver in ·38 rim-fire calibre. The weapon is nickel-plated and serially numbered 8194. It was almost certainly made as a cartridge arm. (*Photograph from Messrs. Wallis & Wallis, Lewes*)

PLATES 19 & 20

John Adams' Army Revolver, Mark 1. This was originally a London Armoury Co. Ltd., Model 1857 Beaumont-Adams percussion pistol, in 54 bore (No. B.3663. 19077R.). It has been converted to the Mark 1 weapon, in ·450 centre fire. No. 465. Conversion date June, 1869.

(i) Six-shot, single-action, Colt Army revolver, Model of 1873, in ·450 centre-fire calibre. No. 17900

(ii) Six-shot, double-action, Colt Army revolver, Model of 1878, in ·450 centre-fire calibre. No. 18715

(iii) Six-shot, double-action, Colt "Lightning" revolver, in ·38 centre-fire calibre. No. 39719

(iv) Six-shot, double-action, Colt Army revolver, Model of 1878, in ·450 centre-fire calibre. No. 14216. Adapted for Silver & Fletcher's Safety Hammer (under Br. Pat. 16,078/1884) and marked "Patent No. 119"

PLATE 21   TOWER COLLECTION

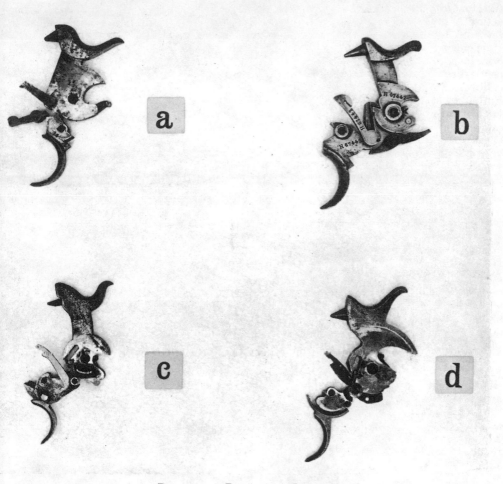

PLATE 22   REVOLVER LOCKS

(a) Single-action (from M/84 German Service revolver), half-cocked to
    show trigger tipping cylinder-bolt out of engagement.
(b) Double-action, Chamelot-Delvigne lock from French M/73 Service
    revolver.
(c) Double-action, from Colt "Lightning" revolver. Cylinder bolt wanting.
(d) Double-action, from Colt M/78 Army revolver. (All springs removed, for
    clarity)

(i) Double-action Army revolver, by P. Webley & Son, in ·450 centre-fire calibre. Embodies M. Kaufmann's safety gate (Br. Pat. 3913/1881). No. 77418

(ii) Double-action "Webley No. 5" or "New Army Express" revolver in ·450 centre-fire calibre. No. 973

(iii) Double-action Webley "R.I.C. No. 1, ·450/·455″·, Model 1883 revolver. No. 4785

(iv) Double-action Model 1867 Webley Royal Irish Constabulary revolver in ·450 centre-fire calibre. Marked "Stockport Police No. 5". No serial number.

PLATE 23   TOWER COLLECTION

(i) Double-action, John Adams', Model 1867 Army revolver (Mark II) in ·450 centre-fire calibre. No. 1980. (Contrast with Mark I revolver in Plates 19 and 20).

(ii) Double-action "Constabulary" revolver in ·450 centre-fire calibre. Embodies W. Tranter's ejector-rod to Br. Pat. 3622/1868. No. 200.

(iii) Double-action "Army" revolver of Continental type, but marked "Thornton's Patent", and Birmingham proved. Embodies features of Br. Pat. 5504/1881. No. 517

(iv) Double-action Continental Army revolver of Chamelot Delvigne type, marked "Pirlot Freres a Liege". F. 954

PLATE 24   TOWER COLLECTION

PLATE 25

E. Nagant's revolver lock mechanism, as embodied in a Model 1873 Dutch service revolver, by De Beaumont of Maastricht.

PLATE 26 TOWER COLLECTION

(i) Single-action M/80 German Trooper's revolver, in 11 mm. centre-fire calibre. Made by F. Dreyse, of Sommerda. No. 5825

(ii) Double-trigger German Officer's revolver, based upon the single M/84 pistol, and in 11 mm. centre fire calibre. Made by Dreyse. Front trigger cocks the hammer, rear trigger drops it. No. 2634

(iii) Double-action Italian Chamelot Delvigne Army revolver, M/72, in 10·4 mm. centre-fire calibre. Marked "Glisenti, Brescia". No. V.438

(iv) Double-action Chamelot-Delvigne French Service revolver, M. 74, in 11 mm. centre-fire calibre. Marked "St. Etienne. S. 1884". No. J.15233

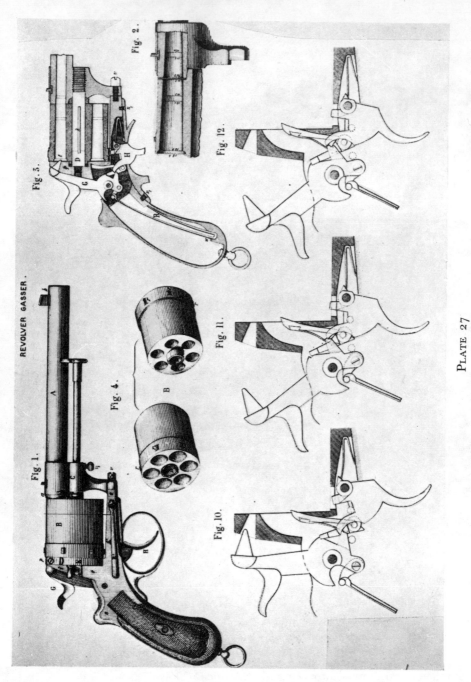

PLATE 27

Detail of Gasser M/70 Army Revolver. (Plate from Colard's "Les Armes Portative en Autriche-Hongrie", 1874)

PLATE 28

(i)   Model 1870 "revolver du troupe", by L. Gasser. Service cavalry revolver for Austria-Hungary.

(ii)   John Adams' Model 1872 "Army" revolver, embodying the rod-ejector protected by Br. Pat. 2258/1872

(iii)   Model 1873 Dutch Army revolver by "De Beaumont, Maastricht". (See Plate 25, for lock mechanism)

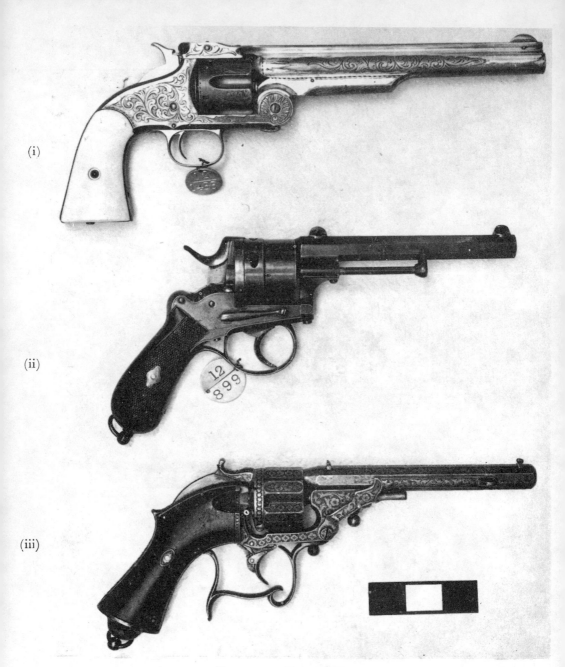

PLATE 29   TOWER COLLECTION

(i)   Model 1869 Smith & Wesson "American Model" revolver, in ·44 centre-fire calibre. No. 21185

(ii)   British copy of the Model 1870 Gasser army revolver, in ·44 rim-fire calibre. Retailed by J. H. Crane, London

(iii)   French double-action centre-fire revolver, possibly converted from percussion. Cylinder and back-plate remove for loading. About ·44-calibre. Marked "Pidault & Cordier Inventeur Bvte"

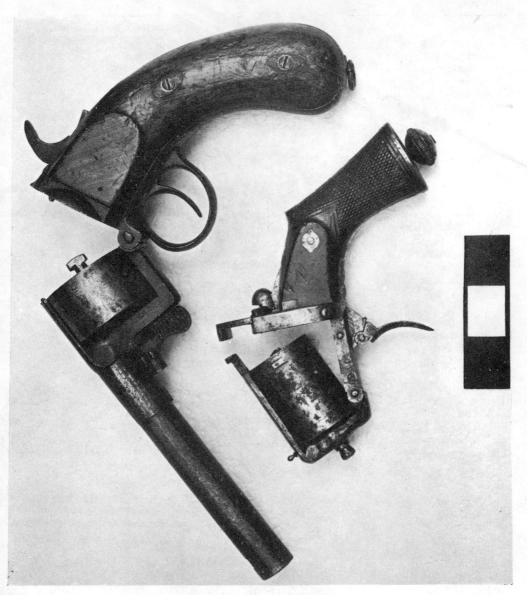

PLATE 30   TOWER COLLECTION

Left: 12 mm. "Pistolet d'Arcon", by Devisme of Paris. Single-action lock.
Belgian proof. No. 253. *Right:* 7 mm. "Pistolet de Poche" by Devisme of
Paris. Self-cocking lock. London proof. No. 118. Note ejector rod screwed
into butt. Both weapons took centre-fire cartridges

(i) Single-action Smith & Wesson "Russian Model". Cal. ·44 cavalry revolver. No. 28414. Russian barrel markings

(ii) Single-action German copy of the Smith & Wesson "Russian Model" cavalry revolver. ·44 cal. No. 618. Made by Ludwig Loewe, Berlin.

(iii) Single-action Smith & "Wesson New Model 38 No. 2" revolver, embodying the hammer rebound protected by D. B. Wesson's Br. Pat. 4831/1877. No. 63469

(iv) Single-action rim-fire copy of the Smith & Wesson "Russian Model" revolver. Made in Belgium, and marked "Russian Model. Smith & Wesson. New York". No. 19482

PLATE 31   TOWER COLLECTION

PLATE 32 TOWER COLLECTION

Unidentified model of the "Pistol, Revolver, B. L. Enfield". Embodies extractor patents of O. JONES (*q.v.*), with lock mechanism of M. KAUFMANN & J. WARNANT (*q.v.*). No external marks, and has features of both Mk. I and Mk. II service revolvers. Possibly a police weapon. ·476 cal.

(i) ·476 cal. Kynoch double-action revolver. No. 367. Embodies features of H. A. SCHLUND'S BR. Pat. 11,900/1886

(ii) ·380 version of the Kynoch revolver. No. 537

(iii) Solid-framed version of P. MAUSER's revolver, with single-action lock. Uses cylinder rotating grooves

(iv) Double-action ·32 top-hinged self extracting pocket revolver by P. MAUSER (*q.v.*). Embodies the features of Br. Pat. 922/1878

PLATE 33   TOWER COLLECTION

(i) ·44 double-action Smith & Wesson revolver, embodying cylinder bolt from J. H. WESSON's Br. Pat. 5569/1881

(ii) ·450 double-action, hinged frame, self-extracting "Army" revolver embodying W. TRANTER's Br. Pat. 2855/ 1879. Marked "W. Tranter's Patent". No. 4119

(iii) Smaller version of (ii), but not numbered or marked

(iv) "Webley's No. 4" revolver in ·450 centre-fire cal. No. 2319. Shorter barrel than standard. Commonly known as the "Pryse" revolver. (See Br. Pat. 4421/1876)

PLATE 34
TOWER
COLLECTION

(i) "Webley-Kaufmann" self-extracting "Army" revolver, in ·450 calibre. No. 33. Embodies features of Br. Pats. 4302/1880 & 3313/1881

(ii) "Webley-Kaufmann" or "Improved Government" revolver, in ·450 calibre. No. 349. Embodies features of Br. Pats. 4302/1880 and 542/1883

(iii) Webley Model 1885 "W.G" revolver in ·455 calibre. Embodies lock and barrel latch from Br. Pat. 4070/1885

(iv) Double-action, self-extracting, ·450 revolver of "Pryse" type. No. 2335. Attributed to Westley Richards

PLATE 35   TOWER COLLECTION

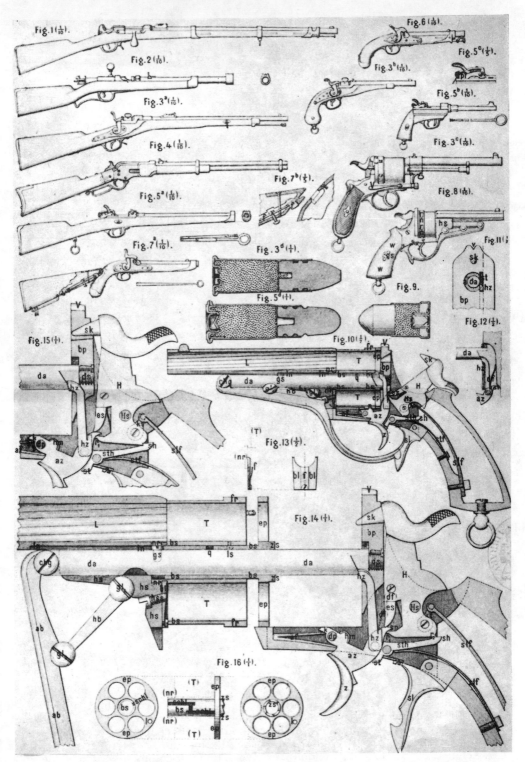

PLATE 36   Detail of Galand's Self-extracting revolver, as "der ruffiche Ordonnanz-revolver" from von Sauer's "Grundriss der Waffenlehr". 1876. Compare with Plate 47, and note the Perrin cartridge shown in Fig. 9 herein.

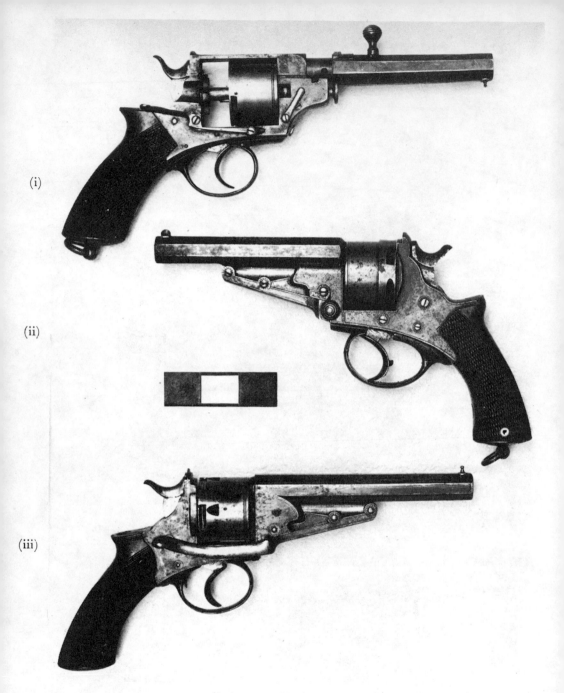

(i)

(ii)

(iii)

PLATE 37   TOWER COLLECTION

(i) J. Thomas's Patent Self-Extracting Revolver, in ·450 calibre. Retailed by
S. Grant, London. No. 250. (Note that barrel has been turned to the "extract"
position. The most common version made under Br. Pat. 779/1869.
(ii) Galand & Sommerville's Patent Self-Extracting revolver, in ·450 calibre.
Retailed by H. Holland, London. No. 579. The most common version made under
Br. Pat. 3039/1868, having the short front-latched lever
(iii) Galand & Sommerville revolver, in ·450 calibre. Retailed by J. D. Dougall. Rare
side-lever version

PLATE 38 McCARTHY COLLECTION

Merwin & Hulbert single-action "Army" revolver, in '44 calibre. No. 1172. Made by the Hopkins & Allen Mfg. Co., Norwich, Conn. (See Br. Pat. 277/1878)

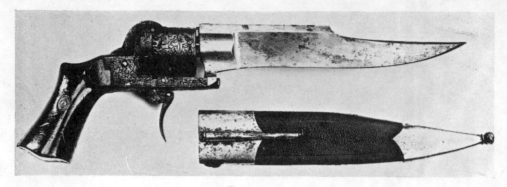

PLATE 39

Six shot 7 mm. pin-fire knife revolver, marked "Invention LeFaucheux, Paris", and there patented by Dumonthier. Overall length eleven inches.

PLATE 40

Six shot 9 mm. pin-fire knife revolver. No makers name. Serial No. 35. Overall length 13? inches. *Wallis & Wallis, Lewes*

(i) Tipping & Lawden's version of C. Sharps' four-barrelled pistol. ·30 rim-fire calibre. Made under Br. Pat. 207/1859

(ii) C. Sharps' four-barrelled pistol, in ·22 rim fire calibre. Shown with barrel drawn forward to load

(iii) 7 shot, single-action, "First Model ·22 Calibre Colt" revolver. No. 10684

PLATE 41   TOWER COLLECTION

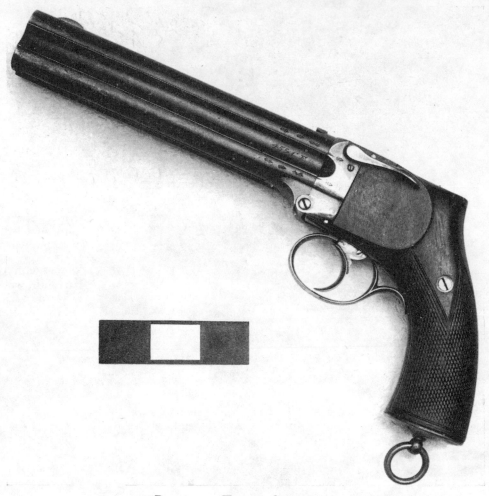

PLATE 42   TOWER COLLECTION
Charles Lancaster (H. A. A. Thorn) four-barrelled holster pistol, in ·455
centre-fire calibre. No. 22. Made basically to Br. Pat. 1242/1881.

PLATE 43

Gatling Machine Gun, as tested by the British Army and illustrated by
Leveson, in 1871

PLATE 44

Rear view of Gatling Gun shown on Plate 43. This was apparently not a Colt
manufactured gun, and the workmanship was criticized.

PLATE 45

"Montigny's Mitrailleuse", as tested by the British Army, and illustrated by
Leveson in 1871. Note charging plate in soldier's hand.

PLATE 46

Rear view of the Montigny Mitrailleuse, shown on Plate 45. This was the improved
gun, and the breech lever (which superseded the original breech crank) can
be seen

(i) Webley percussion revolver, converted to centre-fire metallic cartridge.

(ii) Galand's Self-Extracting Army Revolver

(iii) F. Martin & Cie's Patent Revolver

(iv) LeFaucheux Pin-Fire Rod Ejecting revolver

PLATE 47   CARTRIDGE EXTRACTION SYSTEMS. (CLOSED)

(i) Webley percussion revolver, converted to centre-fire metallic cartridge

(ii) Galand's Self-Extracting Army Revolver

(iii) F. Martin & Cie's Patent Revolver

(iv) LeFaucheux Pin-Fire Rod Ejecting revolver

PLATE 48   CARTRIDGE EXTRACTION SYSTEMS (OPEN)

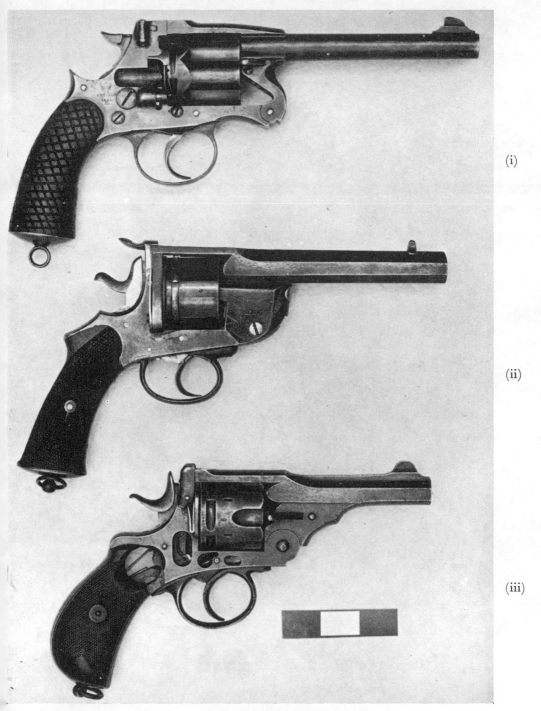

(i)

(ii)

(iii)

PLATE 49   CARTRIDGE EXTRACTION SYSTEMS (CLOSED)
  (i) Mark II Enfield Service Revolver (O. Jones' Patent)
  (ii) Le Vaux Self-Extracting Revolver
  (iii) Mark I Webley Service Revolver

(i) Mark II Enfield Service Revolver (O. Jones' Patent)

(ii) Le Vaux Self-Extracting Revolver

(iii) Mark I Webley Service Revolver

PLATE 50   CARTRIDGE EXTRACTION SYSTEMS (OPEN)

PLATE 51   REVOLVERS RETAILED BY "DEANE & SON"

(Left) 1. ·450 Constabulary revolver. Maker unknown   (Right) 2. ·450 "Tranter's Patent" Army Revolver
(Middle) 3. 54 bore "Deane-Harding" percussion revolver   (Lower) 4. ·380 Pocket revolver. Maker unknown

AUTHOR'S COLLECTION

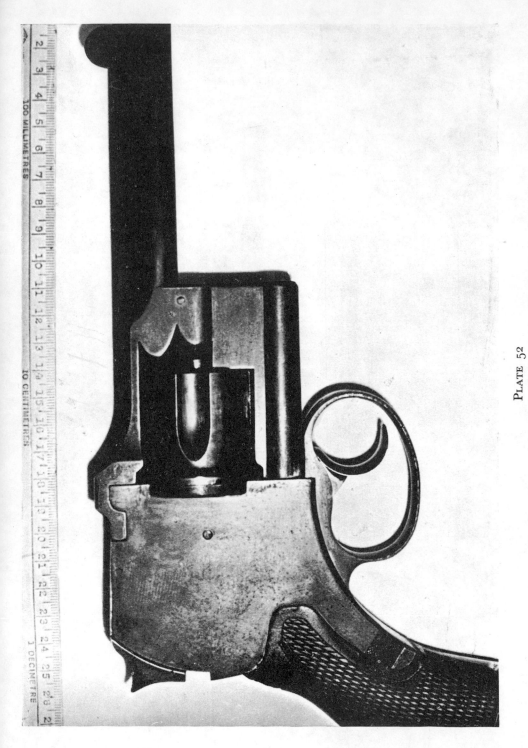

PLATE 52

H. Dimancea's Patent Revolver, as made by the "Gatling Arms & Ammunition Co. Ltd.", of Birmingham

PLATE 53

Barrel legend from the Dimancea revolver featured in Plate 52. Signed specimens are rare in the United Kingdom

PLATE 54

Five chambered smooth-bored revolver, in ·500 centre-fire calibre. Retailed by Boss & Co., London, but stamped "W. Tranter's Patent". No. 61897. Possibly suggested by W. C. Dodge's Br. Pat. 772/1879

PLATE 55   TOWER COLLECTION

S. W. Silver & Co's "New Patent, Solid Frame, Self Extracting Revolver. "The Expert" (Reg'd)", in ·450 centre-fire calibre. Embodies safety-hammer and extractor mechanism from Br. Pat. 16,078/1884. (See Fig. 14). Built on Webley M/83 R.I.C. revolver No. 34779. Silver & Co's No. 231

PLATE 56

(i)   ·380 centre-fire "Pryse-type" pocket revolver, retailed by Dickson, Edinburgh. Made by A. FRANCOTTE

(ii) ·380 centre-fire, top-break, self-extracting pocket revolver, after "Hill's Patent". (See Plate 27). No. 5. Made by A. BRAENDLIN

(iii) 7 mm. centre-fire pocket revolver, by Galand, Paris No. 12751. Self-extracting mechanism to Br. Pat. 3039/1868

PLATE 57   DETAIL OF EXTRACTION IN REVOLVER (ii), PLATE 26

Top : Barrel unlatched, and tilted back on frame hinge. *Bottom :* Barrel tilted to limit, until hinge at forward end of barrel strap operates extractor (by claws engaging studs on side of extractor shaft)

Plate 58

Six shot ·45 centre-fire "Army" revolver, No. 935, retailed by the "London Armoury Co., London", i.e. by James Kerr & Co., (*q.v.*). Note a similar trade "Constabulary" revolver of lesser quality, retailed by "Deane & Son", as shown in Plate 51(1). (*Photograph from Messrs. Wallis & Wallis, Lewes*)

PLATE 59

Cased pair of muzzle-loading, Model 1857, Colt pocket revolvers. Cal. ·31. London retailed. The lid-plaque and high serial numbers (12865/8) show the long popularity of the percussion system. *Wallis & Wallis, Lewes*

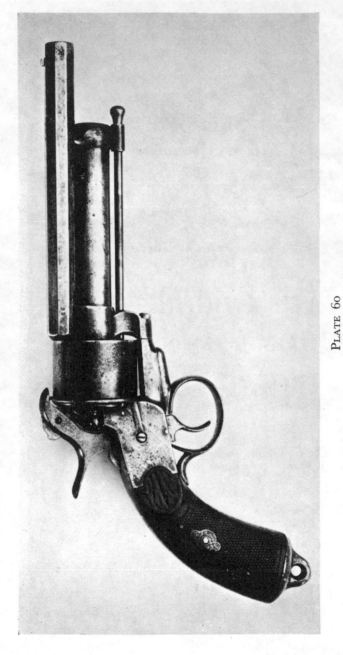

PLATE 60

Nine-shot, 9 mm. pin-fire Le Mat revolver, with ·65 smooth-bore shot barrel beneath. Serial No. 65. Hinged hammer nose for selective firing. (*Photograph from Messrs. Wallis & Wallis, Lewes*)

PLATE 61

Nine-shot, 9 mm. centre-fire Le Mat revolver, with 14 mm. centre-fire shot-barrel
beneath. *Wallis & Wallis, Lewes*

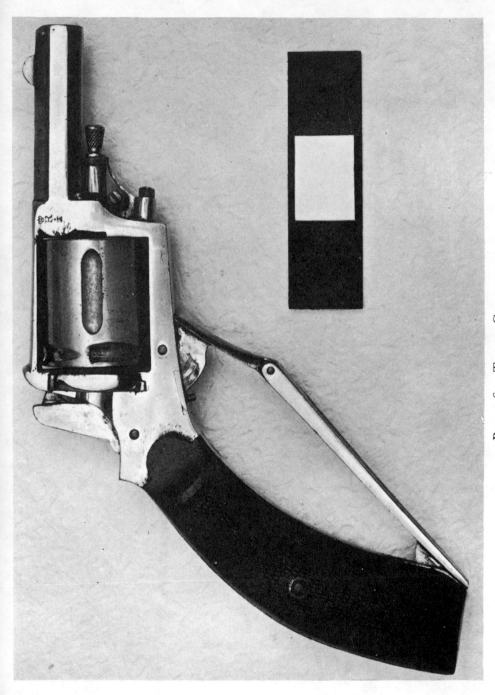

PLATE 62   TOWER COLLECTION

Self-cocking pocket revolver, with bar-trigger. Belgian manufacture. ·380 centre-fire
calibre. No number. Suggested embodiment or imitation of G. H. Needham's Br. Pat.
4693/1883

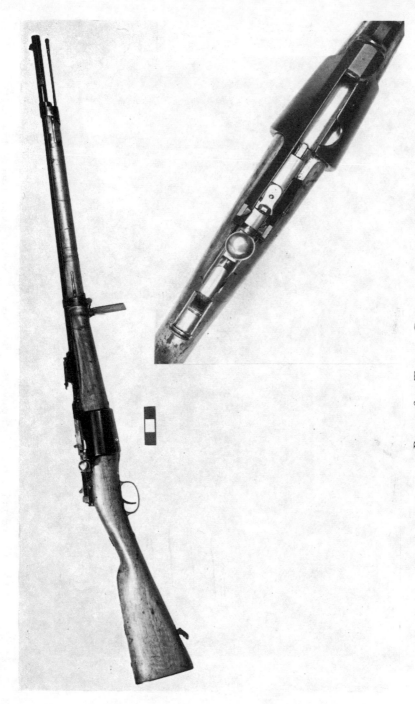

PLATE 63   TOWER COLLECTION

Austrian infantry rifle, and detail of revolving magazine. Marked "Spitalsky. Steyr. 1883", and numbered "3". Believed embodiment of J. Werndl's Br. Pat. 229/1883

PLATE 64

·44 percussion Colt, Model 1860, revolver No. 156660. New York barrel address, but
London proved and cased. Thuer conversion ring No. 91. (Note re-loading accessories
in case). *Wallis & Wallis, Lewes*

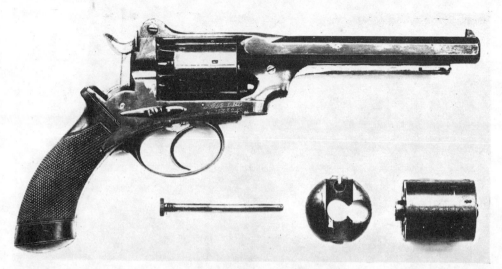

PLATE 65   54 bore percussion/·44 rim-fire "Deane's Patent" revolver. Percussion cylinder in position; rim-fire cylinder and conversion plate on right. Rod ejector screws into butt. Serial No. "Deane-Harding 15432P. DHD 92". *Wallis & Wallis, Lewes*

PLATE 66   Six shot ·44 Smith & Wesson No. 3, single-action, "American Model" revolver. No. 27065. Patent dates to Aug. 24th, 1869 on barrel. The detachable shoulder stock was not a normal accessory with this Model. *Wallis & Wallis, Lewes*

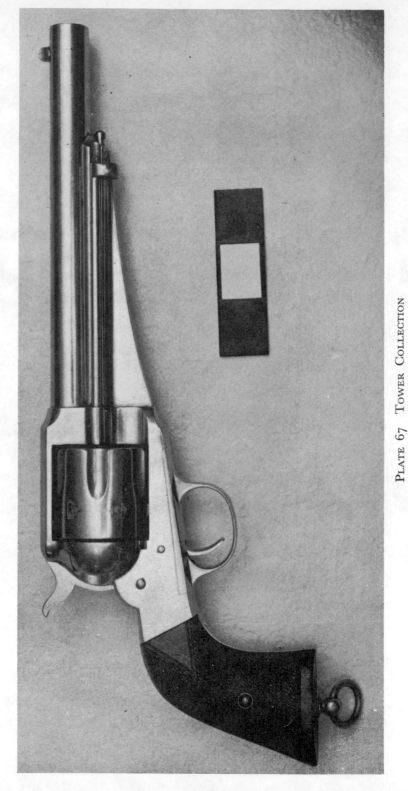

PLATE 67   TOWER COLLECTION

Single-action Remington Model 1875 Army revolver, in ·44 calibre. No. 1831. Embodies spring-loaded rod-ejector protected by Br. Pat. 2579/1875

Plate 68

Left: Seven shot, single-action "Tranter's Patent" pocket revolver. ·32 rim-fire cal. No. 8125. Retailed by J. H. Crane, Royal Exchange, London. *Centre:* Six shot, double-action "Tranter's Patent" Army revolver, Model 1863. Cal. ·44 rim-fire. No. 5578. Retailed by W. B. Barrett, Burton-on-Trent. *Right:* Six shot, double-action "Tranter's Patent" Army revolver, Model 1868. Cal. ·45 centre-fire. No. 5766. Retailed by Deane & Son, London Bridge. *Lower:* Five shot, double-action "Tranter's Patent" pocket or house-defence revolver. Cal. ·380 rim-fire. No. 7346. Retailed by F. T. Baker, Fleet St., London

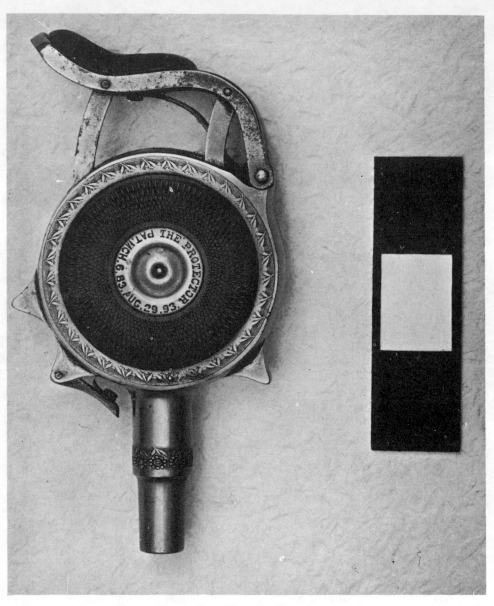

PLATE 69   TOWER COLLECTION

Seven shot "Chicago Protector" pistol, after J. E. Turbiaux's Br. Pat.
2731/1882. Made by the Chicago Firearms Co. No. 10038. Probable date
after 1893

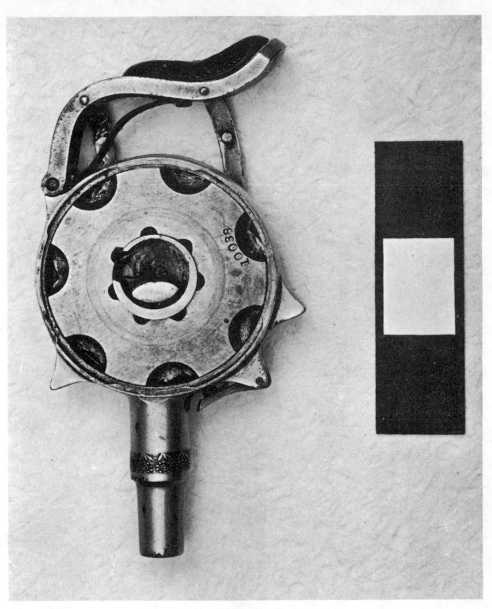

PLATE 70   TOWER COLLECTION

Internal view of "Chicago Protector". The ·32 cal. cartridges lie in the radial "chambers", and are fed up to the barrel and fired there, in turn, as the pistol is squeezed, in the fist, successively

PLATE 71

Left: E. M. PERRY COLLECTION. Six-chambered, twelve shot, self-cocking percussion revolver, to C. E. Wallis Br. Pat. 2248/1863

Right: J. B. BELL COLLECTION. Six-chambered, twelve-shot, self-cocking percussion revolver, to C. E. Wallis Br. Pat. 624/1864. (The forward row of nipples are concealed by the protective band)

PLATE 72

Detail of Kaufmann/Warnant lock mechanism used in the "Enfield"
Service revolver. Compare with Fig. 12

PLATE 73

Detail of Webley "stirrup" barrel latch, and trigger rebound lever, claimed
in H. Webley and J. Carter's Br. Pat. 4070/1885. (The actual pistol post-
dates 1888)

TABLE II (continued)

	Dates of Patent	Patent Nos.	Patentees	Expiry or Voidance dates	Field of Invention	Communication from
1866						
	Aug. 17th	2113	W. Tranter	17/8/1880(E)	Revolver locks	
	Sept. 10th	2326	E. Harlow	17/9/1869(V)	Revolvers	
1867						
	Jan. 24th	182	J. H. Johnson	20/1/1874(V)	Revolving cartridge carrier for single-barrelled long arms	S. H. Roper
	Mar. 19th	798	E. L. Sturtevant	25/3/1870(V)	Includes revolving magazine in rifle-butt	
	Apr. 3rd	1007	W. R. Lake	15/4/1870(V)	Revolver cylinder	W. Herrick
	May 1st	1259	J. J. Kraffert	1/11/1867	Needle rifle with rotary magazine	
	May 3rd	1299	J. G. Rollins	3/11/1867	Ejector for revolvers	R. Drew
	June 1st	1625	T. Poultney	10/6/1870(V)	Ejector/firing-pins for revolvers	
	Aug. 1st	2228	W. Tranter	12/8/1870(V)	Revolver locks	
	Oct. 22nd	2961	J. Adams	22/10/1881(E)	Improvements to 1959/1866	
	Dec. 4th	3453	E. Walker	16/12/1870(V)	Rotary loading of ordnance	
	Dec. 13th	3553	L. Christophe & J. Montigny	13/12/1881(E)	The "Montigny Mitrailleuse"	
1868						
	Jan. 28th	285	W. Tranter	3/2/1871(V)	Revolver	
	Feb. 10th	450	A. M. Clark	17/2/1871(V)	Battery gun and cartridges	P. J. J. Noël
	June 23rd	2018	M. H. Downing	30/6/1871(V)	Needle-fire nipple applicable to revolvers	

H

TABLE II (continued)

	Dates of Patent	Patent Nos.	Patentees	Expiry or Voidance dates	Field of Invention	Communi- cation from
1868	June 27th	2066	R. Warry	27/12/1868	Application of invention to "revolvers" is claimed but not made clear in this provisional specification	
	Oct. 5th	3039	C. F. Galand & A. Sommerville	5/10/1882(E)	Revolver pistol and a firearm similar to 3452/1862	
	Oct. 13th	3131	F. A. Le Mat	22/10/1875(V)	Revolver	
	Oct. 15th	3164	W. R. Lake	27/10/1871(V)	Battery gun	T. J. Cranmer & W. P. Moffatt
	Oct. 21st	3222	T. Richards & C. H. Carter	21/4/1869	Cartridge extractor for pistols	
	Nov. 28th	3622	W. Tranter	10/12/1875(V)	Jointed firearms	
	Dec. 24th	3843	H. Hille- brandt	24/6/1869	Revolver cartridge extractor of "star" shape	J. Hille- brandt
	Dec. 31st	3981	F. A. K. W. von Oppen	12/1/1872(V)	"Thuers" conversion system for revolvers and another cartridge ejector for same	Colt's Pt. Fire Arms Mfg. Co.
	Dec. 31st	3987	W. E. Newton	12/1/1872(V)	Revolver and the special cart- ridges for it. Front loading	E. H. & A. P. Plant & A. Hotchkiss
1869	Jan. 14th	118	A. M. Clark	26/1/1872(V)	Includes a revolver cartridge	J. F. Gévelot

TABLE II (*continued*)

Dates of Patent	Patent Nos.	Patentees	Expiry or Voidance dates	Field of Invention	Communication from
1869					
Mar. 13th	779	J. Thomas	24/3/1876(V)	Cartridge extractors for revolvers	
Mar. 19th	838	A. Albini	29/3/1872(V)	Revolvers	
May 17th	1510	W. R. Lake	26/5/1876(V)	Revolver cartridge extraction and lock refinement	Messrs. Smith & Wesson
July 2nd	1992	T. Jones	12/7/1872(V)	Revolver frame	
Nov. 19th	3341	A. M. Clark	19/11/1883(E)	Improvement to battery gun; see 790/1865 of Table II	R. J. Gatling
Dec. 9th	3557	W. Tranter	15/12/1876(V)	Includes an improvement on 3622/1868	
Dec. 30th	3774	J. Stanton	10/1/1873(V)	Safety locks for firearms, including revolvers	
1870					
Mar. 16th	778	H. W. Hammond	Void for want of final specification. Date uncertain but protection after 16/6/1871 unlikely.	Revolving firearms	C. F. & J. E. de Dartien
Apr. 16th	1119	P. J. X. Günther & J. A. C. de Latouche	16/10/1870	Revolver construction	
July 27th	2107	J. Piddington	8/8/1873(V)	Revolver cartridge extraction	A Spirlet
Sept. 12th	2463	A. V. Newton	21/9/1877(V)	Battery gun	G. O. Kinne
Sept. 14th	2474	L. W. Broadwell	21/9/1877(V)	Cartridge feed for battery guns	
Dec. 1st	3154	A. M. Clarke	12/1/1873(V)	Revolvers with two cylinders	C. J. Linberg & W. J. Phillips

TABLE II (continued)

	Dates of Patent	Patent Nos.	Patentees	Expiry or Voidance dates	Field of Invention	Communication from
1871	Jan. 31st	250	T. J. Smith	31/1/1885(E)	Battery guns	L. W. Broadwell
	Feb. 15th	380	T. J. Smith	27/2/1874(V)	Battery gun mounting	L. W. Broadwell
	June 27th	1686	B. J. B. Mills	3/7/1874(V)	Battery guns	J. P. Taylor
	July 29th	2002	J. H. Johnson	9/8/1878(V)	Repeating small arms (not revolving)	A. E. Jarre
	July 31st	2004	E. Johnson	Provisional protection refused	Repeating firearms (revolving)	
	Sept. 23rd	2509	W. Tranter	2/10/1874(V)	Includes cartridge extractor (improvement to 3622/1868)	
	Oct. 25th	2865	W. R. Lake	25/4/1872	Battery gun cartridge feed	J. Trawniczek
	Nov. 3rd	2954	A. M. Clark	3/11/1885(E)	Battery guns (improvement to 790/1865 and 3341/1869)	R. J. Gatling
	Nov. 28th	3218	T. J. Smith	28/5/1872	Revolvers and other firearms. (Loading-gate, hammer and lock improvement to 3131/1868)	F. A. Le Mat
	Nov. 29th	3224	T. J. Smith	29/5/1872	Rifling of barrels	F. A. Le Mat
1872	Jan. 3rd	21	P. Giffard	15/1/1875(V)	Includes compressed air revolvers and battery guns	
	Jan. 16th	129	G. H. Wilson	16/7/1872	Safety devices	

TABLE II (continued)

Date of Patent	Patent Nos.	Patentees	Expiry or Voidance dates	Field of Invention	Communication from
1872					
May 27th	1605	C. E. Wallis	27/11/1872	Revolver with two hammers	
July 3rd	2010	J. Vine, the elder. J. Vine, the younger. J. Brown & J. A. Skinner	3/1/1873	Battery gun	
July 29th	2258	J. Adams	8/8/1879(V)	Revolver cartridge ejection	
Aug. 2nd	2308	C. F. Galand	13/8/1875(V)	Revolvers and other small arms	
Sept. 7th	2662	J. Pidding-ton	17/9/1875(V)	Self-ex-tracting revolver	C. F. Tackels
1873					
Apr. 15th	1362	A. Browne	15/10/1873	Revolvers	C. F. A. Bas-set
Apr. 29th	1549	B. J. B. Mills	5/5/1876(V)	Battery guns (improve-ment on 1686/1871)	J. P. Taylor
May 20th	1827	H. Adams	26/5/1876(V)	Safety ap-pliance for revolvers	
June 30th	2261	W. R. Evans	9/7/1880(V)	Magazine rifle	
Aug. 26th	2811	B. J. B. Mills	1/9/1876(V)	Battery gun	J. P. Taylor
1874					
Oct. 1st	3353	O. Alten-dorf	1/4/1875	Safety de-vice for re-volvers and other small arms	A. Fagnus & Co.
1875					
Feb. 13th	534	L. Dolne	13/8/1875	Revolver-butts	
May 8th	1722	E. Johnson	8/11/1875	Magazine feed for rifles	
June 18th	2241	J. D. Greene	28/6/1878(V)	Magazine feed for rifles	

TABLE II (continued)

	Dates of Patent	Patent Nos.	Patentees	Expiry or Voidance dates	Field of Invention	Communication from
1875	July 12th	2500	E. de Pass	12/1/1876	Repeating firearms	E. Hénard
	July 20th	2579	W. R. Lake	26/7/1878(V)	Cartridge ejector-rod for revolvers	E. Remington & Sons
	Sept. 10th	3171	W. Tranter	22/9/1882(V)	Safety locks and devices (not for revolving arms)	
1876	Jan. 11th	111	E. de Pass	11/7/1876	Refinement of 2500/1875	E. Hénard
	Feb. 3rd	445	W. R. Lake	14/2/1879(V)	Revolver	E. P. Boardman
	Mar. 30th	1381	A. A. Pope	11/4/1879(V)	Air pistols	A. C. Carey
	Apr. 21st	1703	W. R. Lake	21/4/1890(E)	Battery gun	L. Bailey
	July 7th	2777	W. R. Lake	7/7/1890(E)	The Enfield revolver	O. Jones
	Aug. 14th	3206	T. de Mouncie	14/8/1890(E)	Revolver	
	Oct. 26th	4163	T. de Mouncie	26/4/1877	Revolvers	
	Nov. 15th	4421	C. Pryse the younger	23/11/1883(V)	Revolvers	
1877	Feb. 12th	588	F. A. Le Mat	23/5/1884(V)	Revolver hammer	
	Mar. 8th	928	J. Stanton	19/3/1880(V)	Rebounding hammer for gun locks. Revolvers *not* claimed	
	Aug. 28th	3266	J. A. Crocker	3/9/1880(V)	Double-barrelled gun with revolving cartridge chambers	
	Sept. 5th	3375	F. Wirth	17/9/1880(V)	Revolver in purse	O Frankenau
	Oct. 10th	3766	H. Defty	22/10/1880(V)	Machine-gun	
	Dec. 7th	4644	W. Davis	6/6/1878	Combined sword and revolver	
	Dec. 19th	4831	W. R. Lake	27/3/1885(V)	Rebounding revolver hammer	D. B. Wesson

TABLE II (*continued*)

	Dates of Patent	Patent Nos.	Patentees	Expiry or Voidance dates	Field of Invention	Communication from
1878						
	Jan. 22nd	277	J. Merwin, M. &. W. A. Hulbert	28/1/1881(V)	Revolver	
	Feb. 14th	624	W. R. Lake	26/5/1888(V) but heavily curtailed by Disclaimer 6/5/1880	Revolver (improvements on 2777/1876	O. Jones
	Mar. 7th	922	J. H. Johnson	7/3/1892(E)	Revolver	P. Mauser
	Mar. 30th	1272	A. M. Clark	15/7/1891(V)	Revolving magazine for bolt-action rifles	Osterreichische Waffenfabriks-Gesellschaft
	Apr. 18th	1561	B. J. B. Mills	24/7/1885(V)	Horseman's magazine for revolvers	R. White & A. W. Wheeler
	May 14th	1935	W. R. Lake	20/5/1881(V)	Machine-gun	D. W. C. Farrington
	May 15th	1960	A. M. Clark	21/8/1885(V)	Detachable revolving rifle magazine	Osterreichische Waffenfabriks-Gesellschaft
	May 30th	2161	A. T. de Mouncie	30/8/1879(V)? (No final specification filed)	Revolvers	
	July 30th	3017	W. Morgan-Brown	30/7/1892(E)	"Revolving cannons" or machine-guns	B. B. Hotchkiss
	Sept. 16th	3645	W. J. Hill	16/3/1879	Revolver locks	
	Oct. 2nd	3878	A. M. Clark	8/1/1886(V)	Magazines for bolt-action rifles	J. Werndl
	Nov. 13th	4614	W. R. Lake	25/11/1881(V)	Magazine revolver-rifle	D. B. Wesson
	Dec. 9th	5031	M. Kaufmann & J. Warnant	20/3/1889(V)	Revolver locks (improvement on 3206/1876)	
1879						
	Jan. 17th	197	P. Gay & H. Guénot	27/1/1882(V)	Magazine firearms	

TABLE II (continued)

Dates of Patent	Patent Nos.	Patentees	Expiry or Voidance dates	Field of Invention	Communication from
1879					
Feb. 7th	497	J. F. Trotter	17/2/1882(V)	Machine-guns (improvement on 1703/1876)	
Feb. 26th	772	W. P. Thompson	26/8/1879	Smooth-bore revolvers	W. C. Dodge
July 11th	2840	A. M. Clark	21/7/1882(V)	Magazine rifles	J. Werndl
July 14th	2855	W. Tranter	22/10/1886(V)	Revolving and repeating small-arms and breech-closing arrangements for small-arms and ordnance	
July 22nd	2965	A Swingle	28/7/1882(V)	Lever-action magazine rifle	
Aug. 19th	3338	W. R. Lake	25/8/1882(V)	Machine-guns (improvements to 1935/1878)	D. W. C. Farrington
Oct. 22nd	4310	E. Nagant	3/11/1882(V)	Revolvers	
Nov. 1st	4454	B. B. Hotchkiss	1/11/1893(E)	Revolving cannon	
Dec. 24th	5266	W. R. Lake	24/6/1880	Revolvers	O. Jones
1880					
Jan. 8th	87	H. J. Haddan	8/6/1880	Automatic cartridge ejection for revolvers	T. Sederl
Apr. 14th	1531	A. Martin	21/7/1888(V)	Repeating small-arms (*not* revolving)	
May 11th	1936	C. Jacquelin	18/5/1883(V)	Combined walking stick and revolver	
June 21st	2505	T. Woodward & T. Woodward the younger	21/12/1880	Revolver safety lock-mechanism	

TABLE II (continued)

	Dates of Patent	Patent Nos.	Patentees	Expiry or Voidance dates	Field of Invention	Communication from
1880						
	Oct. 12th	4146	A. J. Boult	19/10/1883(V)	Combined walking stick and revolver	M. O'Mahoney
	Oct. 21st	4302	M. Kaufmann	6/2/1889(V)	Revolver locks	
	Oct. 27th	4378	G. Pace	2/11/1883(V)	Multitubular firearms	
	Dec. 18th	5324	T. Nordenfelt	18/6/1881	Bolt-action rifle and magazine	
1881						
	Feb. 19th	716	J. J. Atkinson & J. Needham	28/5/1886(V)	Repeating firearms and cartridges	
	Mar. 21st	1242	H. A. A. Thorn	21/3/1895(E)	"Lancaster" multibarrelled firearms	
	July 4th	2915	C. D. Abel	16/10/1885(V)	Bolt-action rifles and magazines	F. Mannlicher
	July 29th	3313	W. E. Gedge	5/11/1886(V)	Locking device for fastening barrel to breech on revolvers, etc.	M. Kaufmann
	Sept. 9th	3913	M. Kaufmann	22/12/1888(V)	Revolver cylinder-lock. Improvement to 4302/ 1880	
	Sept. 29th	4211	R. H. Brandon	13/1/1892(V)	Cartridge feed for machine-guns	Gatling Gun Co.
	Oct. 19th	4579	H. E. Newton	19/4/1882	Revolver and "hammerless" gun lock mechanism	Colt's Patent Firearms Mfg. Co. (Inc.)

TABLE II (continued)

Dates of Patent	Patent Nos.	Patentees	Expiry or Voidance dates	Field of Invention	Communication from
1881					
Oct. 20th	4602	H. E. Newton	20/4/1882	Includes revolver lock and loading-gate device	Colt's Patent Firearms Mfg. Co. (Inc.)
Oct. 26th	4689	H. E. Newton	26/4/1882	Revolver lock	as 4602/1881
Nov. 24th	5143	T. W. & H. Webley	24/11/1895(E)	Includes revolvers	
Dec. 12th	5420	W. H. Beck	12/6/1882	Safety device	Y. C. H. Tassel
Dec. 13th	5436	J. G. Accles	28/3/1894(V)	Machine-guns, etc.	
Dec. 16th	5504 5520	E. Bled E. Richoux & J. Warnant	26/3/1886(V)	Revolver locks	
Dec. 20th	5564	W. String-fellow	2/4/1890(V)	Firearms with horizontally revolving chambers	
Dec. 20th	5569	W. R. Lake	26/3/1886(V)	Revolver locks	J. H. Wesson
Dec. 22nd	5613	B. J. B. Mills	2/4/1886(V)	Firearms, machine-guns and cartridges	J. H. McLean
1882					
Jan. 16th	213	H. A. A. Thorn	27/4/1892(V)	Improvement to 1242/1881; possibly applicable to "Lancaster" pistols	
Feb. 14th	712	G. E. Vaughan	21/5/1886(V)	Improvement to 3878/1878	J. Werndl
Feb. 23rd	873	J. Dickson the younger & A. G. Murray	7/6/1893(V)	Improvement on 394/1880 (not included above)	
Mar. 28th	1489	L. Loewenthal & R. de R. Willoughby	28/9/1882	Sights	

TABLE II (*continued*)

Dates of Patent	Patent Nos.	Patentees	Expiry or Voidance dates	Field of Invention	Communication from
1882					
Apr. 17th	1823	S. P. Wilding	17/10/1882	Repeating firearms	F. Drevenstedt
Apr. 27th	1982	G. E. Vaughan	6/8/1886(V)	Improvements on 712/1882	J. Werndl
May 11th	2215	T. Gilbert	20/8/1886(V)	Sights	
May 25th	2495	W. H. Willats	25/11/1882	Bird scarer	
June 10th	2731	E. G. Brewer	24/9/1890(V)	Revolver to conceal in hand	J. E. Turbiaux
June 30th	3089	H. A. A. Thorn	8/10/1887(V)	Locks for multi-barrelled firearms	
Aug. 23rd	4038	R. Howard	23/2/1883	Sword and revolver combined	
1883					
Jan. 15th	229	G. E. Vaughan	23/4/1887(V)	Magazine improvements to 3878/1878 and 1982/1882	J. Werndl
Feb. 1st	542	H. Webley	14/5/1887(V)	Improvement on 3313/1881	
Apr. 21st	2043	H. Pieper	21/10/1883	Includes chamber adaptors for using small cartridges in revolvers	
July 10th	3411	G. de Overbeck	22/10/1887(V)	Magazine rifle	
Sept. 15th	4427	T. P. Wood	15/12/1884? (No final specification filed)	Electrically discharged firearms	
Oct. 2nd	4693	G. H. Needham	14/1/1888(V)	Bolt for securing barrels	
Oct. 30th	5163	W. W. Colley	30/1/1885? (No final specification filed)	Self-cocking revolving	

TABLE II (*continued*)

	Dates of Patent	Patent Nos.	Patentees	Expiry or Voidance dates	Field of Invention	Communication from
1883	Dec. 31st		THE PATENTS, DESIGNS AND TRADE-MARKS ACT, 1883, OPERATED FROM THIS DATE. ANNUAL RENEWAL FROM THE FOURTH YEAR BECAME POSSIBLE.			
1884	Jan. 1st	189	M. Kaufmann	14/4/1888(V)	Revolver cylinder lock	
	Jan. 21st	1820	J. Carter	21/1/1898(E)	Revolver trigger bolt	
	Feb. 1st	2555	J. Carter	1/2/1898(E)	Revolver cylinder lock	
	Mar. 22nd	5308	M. Kaufmann	30/6/1889(V)	Revolver stocks, etc.	
	Apr. 1st	5793	G. E. Vaughan	15/7/1891(V)	Bolt action rifle magazine	O. Schoenauer
	Aug. 5th	10944	C. McG. Bate	17/11/1888(V)	Repeating pistol	
	Aug. 12th	11201	H. H. Lake	24/11/1888(V)	Repeating pistol	A. Chuchu
	Dec. 6th	16078	H. A. Silver and W. Fletcher	18/3/1896(V)	Cartridge ejector and a safety device for revolvers	
1885	Feb. 17th	2214	G. Shepheard	29/5/1889(V)	Magazine for firearms	
	Mar. 31st	4070	H. Webley & J. Carter	31/3/1899(E)	The Webley "stirrup" revolver barrel latch	
	May 15th	5972	G. Envall	26/8/1891(V)	Revolver lock mechanism	
	July 1st	7989	G. E. Vaughan	15/10/1890(V)	Bolt action rifle magazine	Austrian Small Arms Mfg. Co.
	July 28th	9084	H. Schlund	13/11/1889(V)	The first "Kynoch" revolver	
	Aug. 22nd	9973	H. Dimancea	7/12/1892(V)	A revolver	
	Sept. 9th	10664	R. Paulson	25/12/1889(V)	Recoil and gas-operated firearms	
	Dec. 24th	15891	W. H. Beck	9/4/1890(V)	A four-barrelled pistol	A. Francotte

TABLE II (continued)

Dates of Patent	Patent Nos.	Patentees	Expiry or Voidance dates	Field of Invention	Communication from
1886					
Feb. 10th	1923	W. J. Whiting	25/5/1899(V)	Anti-fouling sleeve for revolvers	
Feb. 15th	2167	H. Pieper	28/5/1890(V)	"Gas-seal" revolvers	
Mar. 3rd	3047	L. & S. S. Young-husband	18/6/1890(V)	Repeating rifle	
June 18th	8131	L. Armanni	1/10/1890(V)	Automatic magazine gun	
July 12th	9066	J. Schulhof	28/10/1891(V)	Magazine rifle	
Aug. 18th	10587	L. Armanni	3/12/1890(V)	Includes revolver locks	
Sept. 18th	11900	H. A. Schlund	31/12/1890(V)	Improvement to 9084/1885	
Oct. 5th	12686	E. A. Salvator	21/1/1891(V)	Repeating rifle	
Nov. 3rd	14130	R. Paulson	18/2/1891(V)	Includes a gas-operated revolver	
1887					
July 16th	9998	R. C. Romanel, A. H. Williams & F. Martin	28/10/1891(V)	Magazine rifle	
July 26th	10423	J. Schulhof	9/11/1892(V)	Improvement to 9066/1886	
Aug. 11th	10974	A. Arbenz	25/11/1891(V)	Revolver safety device	Pirlot & Tresart
Dec. 9th	16969	T. Bland & F. Cash-more	23/3/1892(V)	Multi-bar-relled pistol lock	
1888					
Jan. 14th	632	F. Mann-licher	27/4/1892(V)	Rifle magazine	
Apr. 16th	5607	G. H. Schnee	27/7/1892(V)	Includes a rotary magazine	
Apr. 18th	5778	J. Carter & W. J. Whit-ing	18/4/1902(E)	Revolver lock mechanism	

TABLE II (continued)

	Dates of Patent	Patent Nos.	Patentees	Expiry or Voidance dates	Field of Invention	Communication from
1888						
	May 10th	6994	R. C. Romanel, A. H. Williams & F. Martin	24/8/1892(V)	Improvement to 9998/1887	
	June 7th	8331	T. F. Törnell	21/9/1892(V)	Revolver lock mechanism	
	July 16th	10286	J. Schulhof	2/11/1892(V)	Bolt-action rifle and magazine	
	July 23rd	10651	C. C. B. Whyte	9/11/1892(V)	Carrying revolvers	
	Oct. 1st	14088	K. Krnka	17/1/1894(V)	Bolt-action pistol and magazine	
	Nov. 1st	15771	E. Fabre & A. Tronche	15/2/1893(V)	Includes a repeating pistol	
	Nov. 16th	16638	J. Carter	27/2/1901(V)	Safety-lock for revolvers	
	Nov. 26th	17159	A. Lindner	15/3/1893(V)	Magazine rifle	

APPENDIX II

"WHO'S WHO"

ABEL, C. D. London Patent Agent, at 28 Southampton Buildings, Chancery Lane, in the 1880's. Acted for F. MANNLICHER (q.v.) in communicated B. Pat. 2915/1881, and probably for H. SCHLUND (q.v.) in Br. Pat. 9084/1885, and C. C. B. WHYTE (q.v.) in Br. Pat. 10651/1888.

ACCLES, J. G. Engineer and patentee of a rotary feeder for cartridge machines and for the Gatling machine-gun described in Chapter VI. In filing application for the patent relevant here (No. 5436/1881) gave address at 41 Craven Street, Strand, London, but also mentioned residence in Hartford, Conn. U.S.A. This town was, of course, the base for the COLT'S PATENT FIREARMS MFG. CO. (INC.) (q.v.) mentioned in Chapter VI as the manufacturers of Gatling guns, and may indicate that Accles was an employee of that company. He held other British, Belgian, French and German patents for cartridge-boxes, cartridges, gun carriages, and machine-guns prior to 1888, but none embodying the rotary feed principle. He was also associated with the Gardner Gun Company, which developed another manually operated machine-gun; the Gardner gun, however, had no rotary barrel group like that used in the Gatling.

ADAMS, H. Gunmaker, trading as "ADAMS AND CO." (q.v.) at 9 Finsbury Place South, and other London addresses, from the early 1870's. The business was substantial, and may have manufactured arms for J. ADAMS (q.v.). He also secured Br. Pat. 1827/1873 for a self-acting safety lever (mounted in the lower butt-strap) which locked the revolver hammer, except when the pistol was grasped properly in the hand. Probably related to J. ADAMS or R. ADAMS.

ADAMS, J. London gunmaker, and related to **R. ADAMS** (q.v.), probably as the younger brother. Served the "London Armoury Company (Limited)" during the late 1850's, in an uncertain capacity. His own venture as a revolver manufacturer is dealt with in Chapter IV, together with the subject matter of his Br. Pats. 2824/1857; 1758/1861; 1959/1866; 2961/1867; and 2258/1872.

ADAMS, R. Noted designer and patentee of revolver mechanisms in years preceding those of concern. First entered limelight in revolver field at Great Exhibition of 1851, as patentee (under English Pat. No. 13527 of that year) of the famous "Deane-Adams" self-cocking, muzzle-loading percussion revolver. This patent evolved into a master-patent in the field, since it covered the basic manufacturing principle of making revolver frames and barrels in one solid unit.

Control of this feature through maintenance of this patent for its full life (i.e. until 1865) gave Robert Adams and his licensees and associates virtual control of the British markets for quantity-produced revolvers, save for the formidable competition of the Colt weapon which employed a built-up barrel/frame assembly but was also machine-made in large quantities (see Plate I).

The muzzle-loading Beaumont-Adams percussion revolver (with a modification of the original Adams's 1851 lock-work, permitting cocking by the thumb, as well as firing by trigger-pull only) was adopted as one of the British Army issue revolvers and was still in issue in 1865 (see Plate 1, and also Chapters I and IV.

Robert Adams was also associated with the Clive family of Birmingham in the production of rifle barrels by machinery, and during the period of concern his interest in revolving weapons appears to have been marginal only, although his royalty income from earlier patents for revolvers and their manufacture was presumably considerable.

Through a retail shop (originally at 76 King William St., E.C., but later at 40 Pall Mall), and a wholesale warehouse and rifle factory at Henry Street, Bermondsey, he sold revolvers made by others. The Beaumont-Adams percussion revolver naturally led his stocks, but the so-called "wedge-frame" Webley pistol (shown on Plate 2) was also sold under his name. In addition, a few small-calibre rim-fire revolvers (similar to those shown in Plate 9) were also sold, but his source of supply for these is still unknown.

Robert Adams left the Pall Mall address in 1866 or 1867, and cannot be traced again as a London gunmaker. The disappearance of these businesses may have been connected with the difficulties encountered by the Consolidated Bank Limited during the 1866 "Black Friday" panic that followed the collapse of Messrs. Overend & Gurney. He appeared as a patentee of conventional firearms in the 1870's, and the likeliest suggestion upon his whereabouts after 1866 must be that he worked with the Company next to be considered.

ADAMS & CO. Trading name for HENRY ADAMS (q.v.) at 9 Finsbury Place South, E.C. (1870–80), and 32 Finsbury Pavement, E.C. (1881–95), but presumably in partnership with others. Claimed to be "Manufacturers and Contractors for . . . . . central and rim-fire also nipple revolvers of every kind and quality", but details of the firm's manufacturing capacity are still wanting. It seems logical, as earlier mentioned, that work was done for J. ADAMS and R. ADAMS (q.v.).

ADAMS'S PATENT SMALL ARMS CO. LTD. See Chapter IV.

ADAMS'S PATENT SMALL ARMS MANUFACTURING CO. See Chapter IV.

ALBINI, A. As a Captain in the Royal Italian Navy, he claimed domicile in Genoa, but gave 1 New Broad Street Buildings, London, as his address when applying for Br. Pat. 838/1869 for "Revolvers". This protected the use of a crane-mounted, side-swinging cylinder, and "star"- shaped cartridge ejector assembly for solid-framed revolvers. The idea was startlingly similar to the modern Colt revolvers, which that Company introduced in 1889 (see Chapter IV); however, the Complete Specification actually showed his invention as applied to J. ADAMS's (q.v.) Army revolver. The drawing in Fig. 9 was taken from the patent, and may be compared with the pistol in Plate 24.

No specimen of Albini's revolver has been traced in the form of J. ADAMS's revolver, but Major Dowell found a pistol, which he secured from the successors to P. WEBLEY & SON (q.v.), that embodied both the crane-mounted cylinder and the star extractor. This was based upon a Model 1867 Webley R.I.C. revolver (shown on Plate 23) and is further possible evidence for the Webley/Adams connection suggested in Chapter IV.

ALTENDORF, O. Partner in the firm of "ALTENDORF & WRIGHT", a firm of "Manufacturers and Merchants" in Birmingham. The firm acted for A. FAGNUS & CO. (q.v.) in securing provisional British patent protection for a revolver lock modification as Br. Pat. 3353/1874. HILLEBRANDT & ALTENDORF were a possibly associated partnership.

ALTENDORF & WRIGHT. See "ALTENDORF, O.".

ARBENZ, A. Engineer and Patent Agent at 107/8 Great Charles Street, Birmingham, who acted for the Belgian firm of PIRLOT & TRESSART (q.v.) in their Br. Pat. 10974/1887 for a revolver safety device.

ARMANNI, L. Gave his address as 321 High Holborn, London, W.C. to secure Br. Pats. 8131/1886, and 10587/1886 for two highly improbable semi-automatic weapons. The later (pistol) patent has been taken into Table 2 because it included a specific claim for application to revolvers, and the earlier weapon is also included because it embodied a rotary cartridge feed. Neither the pistol nor the long arm is known in any major collection today.

ATKINSON, J. J. Barrister at Law, of the Middle Temple, London, and joint patentee with J. NEEDHAM (q.v.) in Br. Pat. 716/1881. This protected the repeating firearm more particularly described in relation to the latter, who presumably made it.

AUSTRIAN SMALL ARMS MANUFACTURING CO. Communicated

subject matter to G. E. VAUGHAN (q.v.) to secure Br. Pat. 7989/1885 for a revolving cartridge magazine for bolt-action rifles. Assumed to be synonymous
with the "OESTERREICHISCHE WAFFEN FABRIKSGESELLSCHAFT", of Steyr,
Austria (q.v.), but the name may have concealed that of a British trading
partnership.

BAILEY, F. L. American inventor, from Indianapolis, Ind., who developed a
highly efficient "Battery Gun" of Gatling type (q.v.). In this weapon the revolving barrel cluster was drawn to-and-fro to chamber the cartridges for
firing, and the latter were linked into a belt. Bailey secured Br. Pat. 1703/
1876, through W. R. LAKE (q.v.) but did not apparently try to promote his
gun here. Improvements were patented by TROTTER, J. F. (q.v.).

BAILEY, T. Patentee (under Br. Pat. 1634/1858) of a most attractive, but
rarely encountered, muzzle-loading percussion revolver with a side-hammer
and two-part barrel/frame assembly. The inventor's reasons for maintaining the patent to its seventh year, when production seems to have been so
small, are not known.

BASSET, C. F. A. Parisian applicant (through A. BROWNE [q.v.]) for communicated provisional Br. Pat. 1362/1873. This covered a simplified revolver
lock-mechanism, and a rearward opening safety loading-gate for solid-
framed revolvers.

The lock was genuinely novel, and employed a coil spring to hold the
hammer at full-cock. A claim was also laid to the use of separate butt-cheeks
fixed to the frame.

BATE, C. McG. Lieutenant (Corps of Royal Engineers), residing at 128 West-
moreland Road, Elswich, Newcastle-on-Tyne, and patentee by Br. Pat.
10944/1884, of a manually-operated magazine pistol. The cartridges were
fed, bullet first, from a tubular magazine under the barrel into a rotating
breech-piece which then turned them forward (through 180°), for firing by an
external hammer. As can be seen from Fig. 2, the tubular magazine was one
of a bundle beneath the barrel. The bundle turned on an appropriate
spindle.

BECK, W. H. Consulting Engineer and Patent Agent at 139 Cannon Street,
London. Acted for Y. C. M. TASSEL (q.v.) in Br. Pat. 5420/1881 and, from 115
Cannon St., for A. FRANCOTTE (q.v.) in Br. Pat. 15891/1885.

BIRON, C. J. Co-applicant (with P. DRIVON, also of Belleville, France) for Br.
Pat. 2027/1865 as a communication to H. A. BONNEVILLE (q.v.) for improvements in revolver pistols. An "improved escapement" was proposed for
cocking the weapon and a "sort of star" on the rear of the cylinder was employed to effect rotation. As no drawings were filed with the Provisional
Specification, the principles are not wholly clear.

BLAND, T. Member of the firm of "Thomas Bland & Sons" and co-applicant (with F. CASHMORE [q.v.]) from 433 Strand, London, for Br. Pat. 16969/1887 on a striker mechanism for multi-barrelled pistols (see generally, Chapter V), The firm name, and its "flying bee" trade-mark, are found on a variety of conventional revolvers, particularly the self-extracting Army-sized weapons associated with the name of C. PRYSE, THE YOUNGER (q.v.). Prior to removal to 433, the firm was at 106 Strand, and finally removed to its present address in King William IVth Street.

BLED, E. Described as "of Paris, Gentleman", was co-applicant with E. RICHOUX and J. WARNANT (q.v.) for Br. Pat. 5504/1881 and 5520/1881 for improvements to revolver locks (see Fig. 6).

BOARDMAN, E. P. Manufacturer, from Lawrence, Mass., U.S.A., and patentee (through W. R. LAKE [q.v]) under Br. Pat. 445/1876 of a small unconventional pocket revolver with its trigger *on top* of the barrel. This weapon was marketed in the U.S. (under U.S. Pat. No. 172243 of 1876) but the writer had not seen a British specimen (see Fig. 4).

BONNEVILLE, H. A. Professional Patent Agent at the "British and Foreign Patent Offices", 24 Rue du Mont Thebor, Paris, and 38 Porchester Terrace, Bayswater, in the 1860's. Acted for C. J. BIRON and P. DRIVON (q.v.) in their provisionally protected 2027/1865 and for a number of other French applicants for British patent protection in other fields of invention.

BOULT, A. J. Engineer and Patent Agent with the firm of "WM. P. THOMPSON & CO." (q.v.) at 323 High Holborn, London and 6 Lord Street, Liverpool, when acting for M. O'MAHONEY (q.v.) in his Br. Pat. 4146/1880. Active until about 1914 for many other Colonial and foreign applicants in all fields of invention.

BRAENDLIN, F. A. Birmingham gun manufacturer trading as "Braendlin, Sommerville & Co." at 1, 2 and 3 Lower Loveday Street, with A. SOMMERVILLE (q.v.) when the latter sought Br. Pat. 3039/1868 jointly with C. F. GALAND (q.v.). See, further, THE BRAENDLIN ARMOURY CO. LTD.

BRAEDLIN, G. C. Junior associate (probably son or younger brother) of F. A. BRAENDLIN (q.v.) and Liquidator of "THE BRAEDLIN ARMOURY CO. LTD." (q.v.) in March, 1888.

BRAENDLIN ARMOURY CO. LTD. Limited liability company, incorporated March, 1871, to acquire the business of F. A. BRAENDLIN. It developed the "Mitrailleuse pistols" patented by A. MARTIN and A. FRANCOTTE (q.v.) which are discussed in Chapter V. Although liquidated as a limited liability company in March, 1888, the name appears to have continued in use as the trading style "Braendlin Armoury Co." thereafter.

During World War One, this later business was under the managership of C. E. Greener, brother of the famous W. W. Greener, and still in Loveday St. The matter is mentioned to avoid confusion over arms sold under this trading style and under post-1888 patents.

BRANDON, R. H. French Engineer and Patent Agent at 1 Rue Laffitte, Paris, and partner in the firm of "BRANDON & MORGAN-BROWN" (q.v.). Acted for the "GATLING GUN COMPANY" over Br. Pat. 4211/1881.

BRANDON & MORGAN-BROWN. Anglo-French engineering partnership and patent agency with offices at 1 Rue Laffitte, Paris, and at 38 Southampton Buildings, London, in the 1870's and 1880's, between R. H. BRANDON and W. MORGAN-BROWN (q.v.). The partnership apparently handled patents business for both the Gatling and Hotchkiss revolving machine-gun and cannon companies in France and the U.K. (see for example, filing addresses for Br. Pats. 3017/1878 and 4454/1879 (B. B. HOTCHKISS) and 4211/1881 (GATLING GUN CO.)), and may also have acted in Br. Pat. 2241/1875 (J. D. GREENE).

"BRITISH AND FOREIGN PATENT OFFICES." See, generally, "BONNEVILLE, H. A.

BREWER, E. G. Patent Agent at 33 Chancery Lane, London. Acted for J. E. TURBIAUX (q.v.) in Br. Pat. 2731/1882 for the pistol shown in Plate 31.

BROADWELL, L. W. Patentee, "of Vienna, Austria and Jermyn Street, London" under Br. Pat. 2474/1870 of a rotary cartridge-feeder claimed as suitable for the Gatling battery gun (see Chapter VI).
Subsequently (through T. J. SMITH: [q.v.]) secured Br. Pats. 250/1871 and 380/1871 for a revolving battery gun of "Gatling-type" but with barrels stationary at the actual moment of discharge, and a carriage for such guns giving lateral dispersal of fire during operation.

BROUN, J. (should possibly be correctly spelled "Brown, J."). Barrister-at-Law (of Ardgowan Square, Greenock, Renfrewshire) who sought provisional protection under No. 2108/1865 for projectiles and a revolver-loading mechanism by which the charge was pushed forward from each chamber successively, and then fired in the barrel. The basic idea seems similar to that developed by S. H. ROPER (q.v.).

BROWN, J. Co-applicant (with the J. VINES' and J. A. SKINNER) in Br. Pat. 2010/1872 for a provisionally protected battery gun, with stationary barrels and a revolving "feed-and-fire" loading mechanism. All applicants were "of Eastbourne, Sussex".

BROWNE, A. Patent Agent, in the firm "BROWNE & CO." of 85 Gracechurch Street, London. Acted for C. F. A. BASSET (q.v.) in Br. Pat. 1362/1873.

BURTON, B. Secured Br. Pat. 2059/1864 which was maintained into our period. Applications to "revolving firearms" were claimed but, in fact, interest was apparently confined to use of this breech-loading system and its metallic cartridges for rifles.

CAMPBELL, J. C. Patentee (by communication to A. V. NEWTON: [q.v.]) of Br. Pat. 902/1863, which survived into the period. The patent protected a combined lance and revolving firearm. A cluster of muzzle-loading barrels were mounted at the butt of the lance, and discharged in turn at the point of aim for the lance as they were manually rotated. James C. Campbell, of New York City, secured a similar patent as U.S. Pat. 39032/1863.

CAREY, A. C. American inventor, of Malden, Mass., and patentee (by communication to A. A. POPE: [q.v.] of improvements to breech-loading air pistols, under Br. Pat. 1381/1876. One refinement included a revolving cylinder pellet-magazine.

CARTER, C. H. Birmingham manaufacturer, easily confused with the designer next mentioned. With T. RICHARDS (q.v.), he secured provisional Br. Pat. 3222/1868. The unillustrated Provisional Specification described lever-cranked cartridge extractors for breech-loading pistols of the type mentioned in Chapter V, and the system may have been applicable to revolvers.

CARTER, J. John Carter described himself indifferently (in his Patents) as an "Action Filer" or "Pistol Action Filer", and gave addresses at 33 Ford Street, and Mona Terrace, Bracebridge Street, Aston Juxta, Birmingham. The latter address was also given by W. J. WHITING (q.v.), who was then a tool-maker, but later managing director of the Webley company. Carter's Br. Pats. 1820/1884, 2555/1884, and 16638/1888 were key patents for P. WEBLEY & SON (q.v.) in the period, and he also secured Br. Pats. 4070/1885 with H. WEBLEY (q.v.) and 5778/1888 with W. J. WHITING (q.v.) of equal interest to that Company. All were revolver patents, and are more particularly noticed in Chapter IV. Br. Pat. 4070/1885 was possibly the most valuable, and is illustrated in Plate 73; the famous Webley stirrup barrel latch, and the long trigger rebound lever used in so many Webley revolvers may be clearly seen. It is not uncharitable to assume that Carter had seen Br. Pat. 5504/1881 (see Fig. 6) in designing his rebound lever.

CASHMORE, F. Joint-applicant (with T. BLAND [q.v.]) in Br. Pat. 16969/1887, for a striker mechanism used in multi-barrelled pistols of the type noticed in Chapter V. The name had been well known before 1865, as associated with others in the manufacture of percussion revolvers; Paul Cashmore and Charles Pryse patented a revolver which was developed by George Daw of London. The family traded from Steelhouse Lane, Birmingham, for many years, and a pistol factory at West Bromwich was rumoured to have a considerable output.

CHRISTOPHE, L. A "Mechanician" of Brussels, Belgium, and joint applicant with J. MONTIGNY (of the same craft and domicile) for Br. Pat. 3553/1867 on a "Battery gun for firing volleys of Grape-shot", i.e. the basic patent for the "Montigny Mitrailleuse" (see further, Chapter VI, and Plates 45 and 46).

CHUCHU, A. Brazilian applicant (through H. H. LAKE, [q.v.]) for Br. Pat. 11201/1884 as to a four-barrelled folding pistol (see further, Chapter V).

CLARK, A. M. Noted British Patent Agent active through our whole period at 53 Chancery Lane, London. He seems to have practised in all patent fields for both British and overseas applicants. Secured communicated Br. Pats.: 450/1868 (P. J. J. NOËL [q.v.]), 118/1869 (J. F. GÉVELOT [q.v.]), 3341/1869 (R. J. GATLING [q.v.]), 3154/1870 (C. J. LINBERG and W. J. PHILLIPS [q.v.]), 2954/1871 (R. J. GATLING [q.v,]), 1272 and 1960/1878 (OSTERREICHISCHE W. GES. [q.v.]), 3878/1878 (J. WERNDL [q.v.]) and 2840/1879 (the same).

CLARK, W. British Patent Agent of equal note to A. M. CLARK and practising from the same address as the latter but principally in years preceding those of concern here. He had secured the Table I "communicated" revolver patents of A. GUERRIERO (q.v.), 628/1863; T. J. VAIL (q.v.), 2250/1863; "STARR ARMS CO." (q.v.) 880/1860; and P. A. MATHIEU and J. F. GÉVELOT (q.v.), 3452/1862, which survived, as shown there, into our period, and also acted for S. A. NOËL (q.v.) & F. GUEURY (q.v.) in Br. Pat. 659/1865.

COHN, D. L. Merchant, of Islington, London. Secured provisional protection for J. GRÜNBAUM (q.v.) as to Br. Pat. 610/1866.

COLT, S. The name of this famous revolver designer (who died on January 10th, 1862) is included here only by reason of the survival of his Br. Pat. 535/1853 and 538/1853 until 1867 and, hence, their appearance in Table I. For the purposes of this book (since neither Patent was ever apparently developed in the United Kingdom) the activities of the undermentioned Colt Companies are those in point.

COLT'S PATENT FIREARMS MFG. CO. See, generally, Chapters I, III, IV and VI, and, specifically, F. A. K. W. VON OPPEN, G. O. KINNE, R. J. GATLING, "THE GATLING GUN COMPANY", and C. MASON.

COLT'S PATENT FIREARMS MFG. CO. (INC.) See, specifically, Chapter IV ; and, additionally, H. E. NEWTON in regard to British patent protection for revolvers. Since only provisional protection was sought in the three cases within our field, it is unlikely that any attempt was made formally to vest the patents in the Company.

COLLEY, W. W. Profession unknown, and gave address only as "of Camberwell, Surrey". Secured Br. Pat. 5163/1883 for a self-cocking revolving gun for military and sporting purposes, cocked, fired and revolved by a lever, which also extracted the empty cartridge-cases. Allowed his protection to become void, by failing to file a Final Specification after it had been sealed.

CRANMER, T. J. American inventor from San Francisco, Calif. Secured (with W. P. MOFFATT) communicated Br. Pat. 3164/1868 through W. R. LAKE (q.v.) for a breech-loading battery gun and magazine firearm.

CRISPIN, S. American inventor from New York City. Secured communicated Br. Pat. 3258/1865 through A. V. NEWTON (q.v.). The patent related generally to firearms using a peculiar metallic cartridge with its priming in an annular ring round the outside of the case. A revolver suitable for this cartridge was specifically claimed.

CROCKER, J. A. American inventor from Providence, Rhode Island. Secured Br. Pat. 3266/1877 for a *double-barrelled* gun combined with revolving charge chambers. A lever trigger-guard operated and locked the revolving chambers, cocked the hammers and extracted the fired cartridges.

Admirers of G. K. Chesterton and "The Flying Inn" please note. The writer had always regarded the reference therein to a repeating double-barrelled firearm as inane, until he saw this particular Specification!

DAVIES, G. Another active British Patent Agent, practising largely in the period immediately prior to 1865. Concerns us here as applicant for the communicated Br. Pat. 1844/1863 of C. SHARPS (q.v.) which survived into the period. He was also a Civil Engineer, and had offices at 1 Serle St., Lincoln's Inn, London, and 28 St. Enoch Sq., Glasgow, Scotland.

DAVIS, W. Inventor at "Parkrange", Westbury Park, Durdham Down, Bristol, of the "Davis combination sword" for which he sought provisional protection under Br. Pat. 4644/1877. (See Fig. 11.)

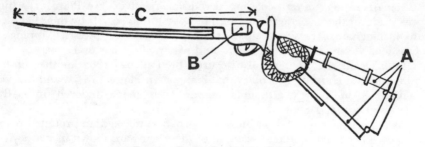

FIG. 11. *Davis's Combination Sword.*

An ordinary sword is combined with a six-chambered revolver, the sword-hilt answering for the revolver stock. The chambers "B" take Boxer cartridges. The steel scabbard "A" is formed in sections with stop hinges, and folds to form a rifle-stock at will. The weapon is sighted up to 100 yards, "more or less", the foresight "C" being taken from the point of the sword.

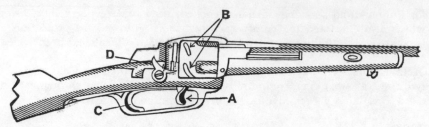

FIG. 12. *Four-Shot Revolving Shotgun.*
(De Dartien's Patent?)
"A" is the cocking spur for the lock and "C" is the firing trigger. "D" is a
safety-catch. The proud helical lugs "B" are engaged by "A" in its rearward
(i.e. cocking) travel, to rotate the cylinder.
    The Provisional Specification to the British Patent of De Dartien (q.v.) is not
illustrated. The Provisional Specification suggests that the unmarked weapon
here sketched (in the Lowe Collection) is made on the principle taught by the
inventor.

DE DARTIEN, C. F. & J. E. French applicants, from Strasbourg, France, for
Br. Pat. 778/1870, which they communicated to H. W. HAMMOND (q.v.)
but subsequently allowed to become void by failing to file a Final Specification.

   The patent related to the rotation of a revolver cylinder by helical peri-
pheral lugs machined to stand proud on its surface, instead of by means of the
conventional ratchet cut at the rear face of the cylinder. Fig. 12 is a sketch of
an unidentified revolver shotgun, from the Lowe Collection, which the
writer believes to be on this principle.

DEANE, J. & DEANE J. (JUN.) or "DEANE & SON". Two more survivors
from the previous era. The London merchant house of "Deane & Son"
specialized in the products of Birmingham and had a flourishing firearms
business as an inevitable part of this link. They actively promoted the
"Deane-Harding" muzzle-loading percussion revolver (see Plate 51) which
was made for them (under the patents of W. HARDING [q.v.]) by their licensees
in Birmingham. At various times, these licensees were Messrs. Tipping &
Lawden, Messrs. Pryse & Redman, and Messrs. Calisher & Terry.

   John Deane the Younger also secured Br. Pat. 626/1862 for the rim-fire
adaptation to Harding's revolver that is shown in Plates 3 & 65, and this was
maintained until 1865, although weapons were made under it until 1870
(see also Chapter I).

   As part of their normal business, the firm also marked and retailed revolvers by other makers, and a selection of these arms are shown in Plate 51.

DEFTY, H. Engineer, from Middlesborough, Yorks, and patentee under Br.
Pat. 3766/1877. This protected a machine-gun of eccentric design, in which
the barrels were arranged radially about a central shaft. The inventor failed
to arouse interest in the development of his idea.

DELMAS, PERRIN &. See "PERRIN & DELMAS".

DICKSON, J., the YOUNGER. Gun manufacturer in Edinburgh, which he described as being in "North Britain". He secured Br. Pat. 873/1882 (with A. G. MURRAY; [q.v.]), in respect of self-cocking, drop-down small arms with one, two, or three barrels, and of the type noticed in Chapter V.

DIMANCEA, H. Occupation and nationality unknown. From 7 Staple Inn, London, he secured Br. Pat. 9973/1885 covering a breech-loading revolver; this had some external similarity to the "Kynoch" revolver (see Plate 33) patented in the following year by H. A. SCHLUND (q.v.).

In view of the length of time for which the patent was maintained, it can be assumed to have had a commercial value, but specimens are rare in British collections (see Plate 52).

Internally the weapon differed greatly from any Kynoch revolver, by being truly hammerless and in the method used for extracting the cartridge-cases. Kynoch revolvers had internal hammers, whilst the Dimancea used a separate firing-pin that was cocked and fired by the trigger; Kynoch revolvers broke open like any other hinged-frame revolver, to extract the cases, but Dimancea adopted another system of extraction. What appears as a hammer in Plate 52 was drawn down, and this permitted the barrel and cylinder to be twisted out of engagement with the standing breech. Once cleared, the two components could be pulled forward until a cartridge extractor in the rear of the cylinder pushed the cartridge-cases out of the chambers.

Sound American opinion has suggested that real interest in this curious revolver dated from 1916, with Austria's declaration of war upon Rumania. This act, it was suggested, cut off Rumania's supplies of her preferred sidearm, a Steyr-made, self-loading pistol, and forced adoption of the Dimancea.

To the present writer this dating seems unlikely, if it involved first manufacture at that late date. Since the revolver was patented in 1885, it seems more probable that any Dimanceas issued in 1916 were ex-store survivors from pistols made during and immediately after the Serbian–Bulgarian War of 1885.

Some slight evidence for this submission can be offered, for although Bock stated flatly that "Kynoch" were the makers, the only specimen so far traced does not support this statement. As can be seen from Plate 53, the revolver shown in Plate 52 was made by the "GATLING ARMS & AMMUNITION COMPANY LTD" (q.v.), then located at the old Holford works of the defunct National Arms & Ammunition Co., and not connected with the Kynoch group of companies. This barrel legend limits the date of manufacture between November, 1898, and September, 1890, although sale after the latter date was quite possible, since the Company Liquidator was not discharged until 1895.

DODGE, W. C. A former Examiner in the United States Patent Office, who retired from his duties of settling the exact subject matter of inventions sought to be patented, in order to concentrate upon designing improvements to firearms. He was then resident in Washington, D.C.

Two British patents related to revolvers and one of them (Br. Pat. 2050/1865) protected a most important extractor design, which was assigned to SMITH & WESSON (q.v.) in the Spring of 1868, along with its Austrian, Belgian, French and American equivalents.

Broadly, the patent protected plate or star-shaped extractors applicable to almost any revolver with a principle of frame construction that allowed the barrel to be swivelled or turned clear of the standing-breech on the action body, for *simultaneous* extraction of the cartridge-cases from its cylinders. (Multi-barrelled pistols with revolving strikers, of Remington-Elliot type, were also suitable.)

The extractors did not operate automatically on breaking open the weapon, but a spiral spring did snap them back into their housings after manual operation, and they could be used in revolver cylinders loading from the front as well as from the rear.

Examination of Fig. 20, and the notes upon SMITH & WESSON, will make clear that firm's reasons for securing Br. Pat. 2050/1865 from Dodge, along with the Continental and American counterparts for it, in 1868.

Their No. 3 Army revolver extracted all of its cartridge-cases automatically when broken open, and the firm's relevant British Patent (1510/1869, in the name of W. R. LAKE; [q.v.]) could almost certainly have been opposed successfully by Dodge as an infringement of his basic idea, if they had not come to terms with him.

In America, his position was probably even stronger for he held not only U.S. Pat. 45912 (issued January 17th, 1865: reissued as 4483 of July 25th, 1871) for his simultaneous extractors, but also U.S. Pat. 45983 (issued January 24th, 1865) covering the general construction of revolvers with a barrel/frame hinge at the bottom forward end of the action body.

SMITH & WESSON most sensibly came to terms with Dodge, and their Br. Pat. 1510, of May 17th, 1869 (in the name of W. R. Lake) is a mosaic of these novelties, with those of two other inventors whose patents they eventually controlled.

Dodge next appeared in our field with an application (communicated to W. P. THOMPSON; [q.v.]) for provisional protection only under Br. Pat. 772/1879. This covered a self-cocking, *smooth-bore*, revolver expressly designed to use buckshot or multi-ball cartridges.

The researches of John E. Parsons show that a U.S. Army equipment board met in December, 1878, to test such a weapon, then presented by Dodge, against a competing REMINGTON revolver, and that the board reported in August, 1879.

Unfortunately for Dodge, service interest became centred upon the development of multi-ball cartridges for use in the standard rifled Army revolver, and his weapon design was pushed aside. In the U.K., a few TRANTER smooth-bore revolvers are known to exist and presumably date from the expiry of the provisional protection secured here by Dodge (see Plate 54).

DOLNE, L. A Belgian "Armourer" (of 10 Rue Janfosse, Liège) and probably best known in Britain or America as the inventor and manufacturer of some rather unpleasant-looking pin-fire pocket weapons for what might be termed the "Apache market" (see Fig. 10).

These trivia enjoyed no traceable British patent protection, and the subject of Dolne's Br. Pat. 534/1875 was rather more sensible. He claimed a simplified method for the attaching of revolver-butts (or "handles", as he termed them) which obviated the need to inlet their edges. He also claimed pre-cast butt-cheeks as suitable for his invention.

DOOLITTLE, J. B. Joint inventor (with G. O. DOWNING, also of New Haven, Conn., U.S.A.) for communicated Br. Pat. 997/1866 for a revolver. The applicant was the British Patent Agent E. T. HUGHES (q.v.).

The revolver, in which a skeletal cylinder loaded with metallic cartridges had the chamber actually due for firing covered or completed by a sliding "yoke" at the moment of discharge, is assumed (by the writer) to be the subject of J. B. Doolittle's U.S. patents 35,996 of July 29th, 1862, or 54,065 of April 17th, 1866, and to be intended to circumvent the U.S. ROLLIN WHITE patent for a simple bored-through cylinder (see, further, remarks under the name of that inventor).

DOWNING, C. M. H. Lieut.-Col. Downing, Royal Artillery (of 36 Gloucester Terrace, Hyde Park, London), took the view that the needle-fire cartridge, with its ignition occurring at the front of the charge (next to the bullet) was more efficient than any cartridge fired at the rear. Accordingly he designed and patented special nipples with removable firing needles (Br. Pat. 2018/1868), which could be screwed into any conventional percussion cylinders and permit use of the favoured cartridge. Each needle could be removed from its nipple to convert the weapon back into a normal cap-lock revolver.

DOWNING, G. O. Joint applicant for Br. Pat. 997/1866; see DOOLITTLE, J. B.

DREVENSTEDT, F. Communicated, from Klein Ammensleben, Germany, to S. P. WILDING (q.v.), the invention for which provisional protection was achieved under Br. Pat. 1823/1882.

This was for a repeating *pin-fire* revolving firearm, in which the pivot-pin (bearing a radially bored "turret-type" charger) slid to and fro to effect a gas-seal of conical chamber-mouths in the end of a fixed barrel. The front end of the cartridge-case was also thrust into the gas-seal.

DREW, R. Communicated from Lowell, Mass., U.S.A., to J. G. ROLLINS (q.v.), the inventions for which provisional protection was achieved under Br. Pat. 1229/1867.

This was for ejection of cartridges from breech-loading revolvers by a spring-loaded rod or plunger, and for a loading-gate on such arms. The provisional description was broad enough to cover such refinements as they were used on a limited production run of the small, solid-framed, ·22 in., rim-fire revolvers made by the Lowell Arms Company of America. Reuben W. Drew was Superintendent in that Company and he secured U.S. Pat. 63450 of April 2nd, 1867, for these devices.

The Company was successor to the Rollin White Arms Company, of Lowell, which had earlier made similar, small, solid-framed revolvers (lacking the Drew improvements) as approved suppliers under the U.S. patent of ROLLIN WHITE (q.v.), to the firm of SMITH & WESSON (q.v.).

DRIVON, P. See BIRON, C. J.

ENVALL, G. Secured from "46 Lincoln's Inn Fields, W.C." the address suggests that Br. Pat. 5972/1885 (in this name) was either secured by a Patent Agent or filed from his offices. The drawings filed with the specification do not suggest to the writer any British revolver in commercial production at the time.

According to the invention, the hammer of the revolver was cocked by pulling the trigger and then held at full cock until aim had been taken, when pressure on a thumb-piece at the top of the *butt* caused the hammer to fall.

There was a thumb-piece of conventional appearance on the hammer, but this served only for letting down the hammer if it was not required to shoot after having cocked the weapon.

Since the patentee did not abandon his patent until the sixth year fees were due in 1891, some feature of the patent must have enjoyed commercial success somewhere but the nature of it has so far escaped the present writer.

EVANS, W. R. American inventor (of Lynn, Essex County, Mass.) of a lever-action magazine rifle which had some success in the U.S. The revolving feature of the weapon, and of Br. Pat. 2261/1873 which he personally secured for it, was in the cartridge magazine. This was in the the butt, and employed a large Archimedian screw conveyor to bring twenty-six cartridges forward for feeding into the breech (see Fig. 13).

In America, the Agents were Merwin, Hulbert & Co. (then at 83 Chambers St., New York) and manufacture by the "Evans Magazine Rifle Co." of Mechanics Falls, Me., U.S.A., was claimed. Whether, in fact, a larger company undertook the actual manufacture of this rifle remains to be established. The design did attract considerable attention and the ·44-in. rifle was noticed approvingly by Brig.-Gen. C. B. Norton in both the 1872 and 1880 editions of his book, suggesting a fairly long production span.

FABRE, E. Joint applicant with A. TRONCHE (q.v.) for Br. Pat. 15771/1888. The address given on the Complete Specification (47 Lincoln's Inn Fields, London) was presumably that of the Patent Agents advising the applicants.

The protected invention is more easily pictured than described, but the basic rotary principle was the manually-operated endless-chain magazine feed to a reciprocating barrel, an idea anticipated nine years earlier in Br. Pat. 197/1879 of P. GAY & F. GUENOT (q.v.) of Paris.

FAGNUS A. & CO. Belgian (Liège) applicants for communicated Br. Pat. 3353/1874. See, additionally, "ALTENDORF, O.".

The invention was a self-acting spring safety to rebound revolver hammers after firing and on releasing the trigger.

FARRINGTON, D. W. C. American firearms designer at Lowell, Mass., and patentee through W. R. LAKE (q.v.) and by Br. Pat. 1935/1878 of a four-barrelled machine-gun. Unlike the "Gatling" gun (see Chapter VI) only one barrel operated at a time, while the others cooled off.

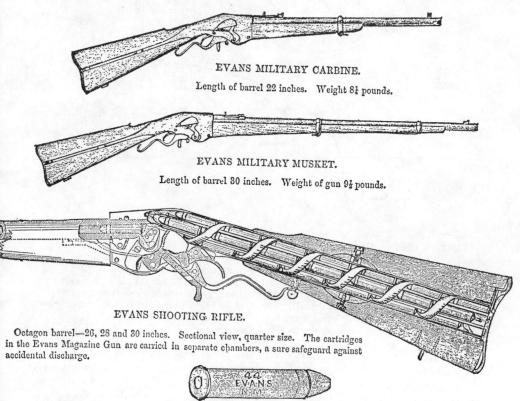

EVANS MILITARY CARBINE.

Length of barrel 22 inches. Weight 8¼ pounds.

EVANS MILITARY MUSKET.

Length of barrel 30 inches. Weight of gun 9¼ pounds.

EVANS SHOOTING RIFLE.

Octagon barrel—26, 28 and 30 inches. Sectional view, quarter size. The cartridges in the Evans Magazine Gun are carried in separate chambers, a sure safeguard against accidental discharge.

Exact size of cartridge for model of 1877, 26 rounds in magazine.

FIG. 13. *Evans's Magazine Rifle.*
(Br. Pat. 2261/1873.)

The revolving feature lay in two cartridge carrying-wheels which fed from an ammunition hopper into alignment with the breech of the firing barrel.

Subsequently (by the same Patent Agent) he secured Br. Pat. 3338/1879 of improvement to the above, one cartridge feed-wheel being eliminated from the design, and refinements made to the lock mechanism.

FELL & WILDING. See "WILDING, S. P.".

FLETCHER, W. Joint applicant (with H. A. SILVER [q.v.]) in Br. Pat. 16078/

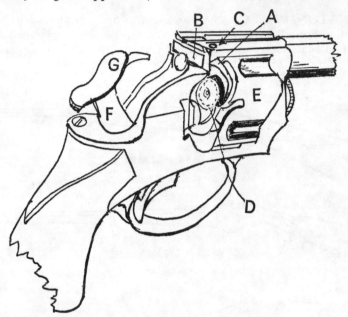

FIG. 14. *Silver & Fletcher's Extractor.*

On opening the loading-gate of a solid-framed revolver, the transverse lever "B" (which is vertically pivoted at "C") is freed to take hold of the cartridge rim "D" by its claw "A" as the cylinder revolves. When the hammer "F" falls, its forehead "G" strikes one end of "B" and this causes the claw "A" to eject rearwards the cartridge-case "D" upon which it is hooked. The cart-ridge-cases may thus be actually cleared whilst firing, or the operation may be delayed until all the rounds have been discharged, when the loading-gate may be opened and the pistol rapidly emptied by "snapping" the lock.

1884, which covered an automatic cartridge-case extractor, and a safety-hammer, both for solid-framed revolvers (see Fig. 14). The two devices were principally applied to Webley revolvers, the "R.I.C./83" being the one normally favoured (see Plate 55). On request, however, the hammer was fitted to other arms, and an adapted Colt pistol is shown in Plate 21.

The two applicants (filing from 166 Fleet Street, London), traded as "S. W. Silver & Co." at Cornhill, London, and secured a number of joint firearms patents and Registered Designs during the 1880's. None was of a very profound nature, and even the principle of their extractor had been anticipated by T. SEDERL (q.v.).

FRANCOTTE, A. Although the leading Liège-based revolver manufacturer of the period, the anonymity of his work has resulted in little notice of him in these pages. The Pryse-type revolver shown in Plate 56 was a typical example of his products and bore the name of a well-known British retailer. Only removal of the grips revealed the small "AF" stamp of its maker, although the lock mechanism was of a type not used by British manufacturers. This was based upon that used in the Swiss M/78 revolver discussed in Chapter IV (see also remarks under W. J. HILL and J. STANTON).

Through W. H. BECK (q.v.), Francotte secured communicated Br. Pat. 15891/1885, which covered a four-barrelled pistol design, of the kind noticed in Chapter V. British-made "Francotte" pistols are unknown today, but features from the patent were embodied into the "Martin Mitrailleuse" pistol described in that Chapter.

FRANKENAU, O. Secured (through F. WIRTH [q.v.]) communicated Br. Pat. 3375/1877, for a combination of purse and revolver that permitted firing the weapon at will. To avoid damaging the purse on discharge, the trigger

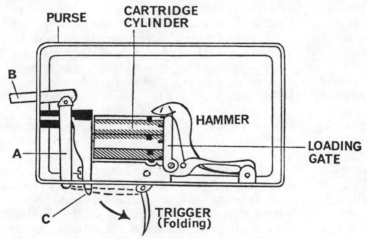

FIG. 15. *Frankenau's Purse Pistol.*
(Br. Pat. 3375/1877.)
(See also Plate 5.)

Originally conceived for a pepperbox (i.e. multi-barrelled) revolving firearm, the few specimens observed have been short-barrelled, conventional revolvers to ensure clearance of the muzzle-blast from the interior of the purse.

Actual embodiments vary in detail but, broadly, when the folding trigger is engaged in the retaining hook "C", its tip pushes up a spring-loaded rod "A" to close a hinged or sliding plate "B" over the muzzle of the pistol.

Other compartments in the purse or cigar-case serve a more normal purpose.

opened the purse when it was pulled. The weapon is shown in Plate 5, and Fig. 15, from which it should be clear that the revolvers chosen for use were standard small-calibre arms that displayed no unusual features.

GALAND, C. F. Belgian gun manufacturer at Liège, and joint-applicant (with A. SOMMERVILLE [q.v.]) for Br. Pat. 3039/1868. This protected the self-extracting features of three revolvers described in Chapter IV. The patent also claimed the improvement of attaching an auxiliary, self-extracting revolver to normal single-shot infantry rifles. This idea had been developed by P. A. MATHIEU & J. F. GÉVELOT (q.v.), and was not developed in this country.

Galand also secured Br. Pat. 2308/1872, from Rue D'Hauteville 13, Paris, in which he described himself simply as a "Manufacturer". This Patent is more important for what it shows to us now, than for what it claimed at filing.

The improvements described were for a revolver that could be dismounted without tools, and a series of thumbscrews or hooks and latches secured the various components of the lock and the frame. The interesting feature, to which little mention was given, lay in the lock mechanism shown as suitable for this construction. In essence, this is the lock of E. Nagant (see Plate 25) with an important modification. Galand showed a long combination trigger and pawl-spring mounted in the butt, and extending forward to operate these two components. De Mouncie accomplished the same thing (see Fig. 17) by extending the lower limb of the mainspring, and Warnant developed the idea further. The Swiss Schmidt M/78 revolver used a rather similar idea to Galand's, in using a separate lever or rebound which was operated by the lower limb of the mainspring. This lock is often referred to as the "Schmidt-Galand" lock, by collectors, but proof of the connection is wanting.

GATLING, R. J. American inventor (b. 1818; d. 1903) now best remembered as designer of the most famous revolving-barrel machine-gun. (see Chapter 6, and Plates 43 and 44).

Secured Br. Pat. 790/1865 in his own name, and then communicated Br. Pats. 3341/1869 and 2954/1871 to A. M. CLARK (q.v.), from Indianapolis, Maryland, U.S.A., and from Hartford, Conn., as to the last.

Formed the "GATLING GUN COMPANY" (q.v.) to develop and market his "Battery Gun", and actively promoted use of the weapon throughout the world, as manufactured by the "COLT'S PATENT FIRE ARMS MFG. CO." (q.v.).

In addition to the above-mentioned British Patents (and those held by the Gatling Gun Company), the following are also in point; 2463/1870 (G. O. KINNE), 2474/1870 (L. W. BROADWELL) 2865/1871 (J. TRAWNICZEK), 4211/1881 (R. H. BRANDON), 5436/1881 (J. G. ACCLES).

GATLING GUN COMPANY, THE. A company incorporated by Legislative Act of the State of Connecticut, U.S.A., to develop R. J. GATLING's machine-gun patents commercially, both in America and elsewhere. It was apparently based in Hartford, Conn., U.S.A. and later secured Br. Pat. 4211/1881 (through R. H. BRANDON [q.v.]) for an improved cartridge feed in the guns. This used vertical vibrating hoppers and a "fluted straightening roller", which brings the device into the field of this book.

It was presumably with this company (rather than with R. J. GATLING personally) that the British partnership trading as "Sir W. G. Armstrong & Co." reached agreement for making Gatling machine-guns in the United Kingdom (under Br. Pats. 790/1865 and 3342/1869) after the first British Army trials of 1871.

GATLING GUN LIMITED, THE. Later GATLING ARMS & AMMUNI-TION COMPANY LIMITED, THE. By 1888, the original patents of R. J. GATLING (q.v.), and the American-based Company mentioned above, had expired and only patents of detail survived.

Faced, presumably, with declining interest in American-made Gatling guns overseas, the Connecticut Company sold their rights in Europe and the Eastern Hemisphere to a new British-based limited liability company called THE GATLING GUN, LIMITED. The deal was apparently arranged through Frederick Courtland Penfield (former Vice-Consul General of the U.S.A. in London, and Attorney of the American Company), who became a director of this new off-shoot within a few days of its incorporation on April 4th, 1888.

The Company was a public one (with a nominal capital of £800,000) and there were many small shareholders, but it was starved of capital from the beginning and an application to the High Court in 1889 permitted operations to start with the capital reduced to only £371,270.

The Company's name was immediately changed from the official "THE GATLING GUN, LIMITED AND REDUCED" to the style of "THE GATLING ARMS & AMMUNITION COMPANY LIMITED", but investors must have scented failure, and a petition to wind up voluntarily was filed in the High Court on February 4th, 1890. The Order permitting this act was secured in the following September.

Although primarily formed to take over the extra-U.S. markets of the American Gatling Company, the British Company was empowered to manufacture and deal in all kinds of firearms and one product unrelated to machine-guns has already been noticed (see DIMANCEA, H.).

This is the only one of those products so far discovered by the present writer, but the Company (during its very short life) certainly held itself out as a supplier to the gun trade, and the manufacture of other revolving arms may have taken place. In the main field of its interest, the Company also purchased the following European patents from the American Company:

English Patents

Machine-Gun and Feeder	5436/1881
Cartridge Feeder for Machine-Guns	4211/1881
Cartridge Charges for M/G Feeders	6009/1886
Cartridge Feeding Devices for M/G.	7659/1886

French Patents

Machine-Gun and Feeder	147224
Upright Feed for Machine-Guns	175909

Italian Patents

Machine-Gun and Feeder	15682
Upright Feed for Machine-Guns	20049

Belgian Patents

Machine-Gun and Feeder	56986
Upright Feed for Machine-Guns	73398

Austrian Patent

Machine-Gun and Feeder	27250

The first two British Patents (those of R. H. BRANDON and J. G. ACCLES) have already been noticed, but those of 1886 (in the name of L. F. Bruce, of Springfield, Mass., U.S.A.), dated May 4th and June 8th respectively, cover cartridge feed-wheels to the true magazine and are NOT elsewhere mentioned.

As a base for manufacture, the old Holford Works of the National Arms & Ammunition Company Ltd. (which had failed in December, 1882) at Perry Bar, near Birmingham, were leased or agreed to be purchased. The measure of production actually achieved there is not clear.

The deal with the American Company included buying all its stock-in-trade in Europe and the Eastern Hemisphere (apart from *completed* Gatling guns) and the British Company may therefore have been able to assemble some guns, as opposed to actually making them, during its brief life.

Following this ill-fated venture the works at Holford were engaged in making weapons and fuses, in the hands of Messrs. Grenfell & Accles Ltd., 1891/1896. J. G. ACCLES (q.v.) was a shareholder and the Company manufactured machine-guns under his patents.

GAY, P. French Civil Engineer. Secured jointly with H. GUENOT, Br. Pat. 197/ 1879 for breech-loading magazine carbines, pistols, military and sporting guns, and "guns mounted on carriages so as to form field batteries of metrailleuses", an embodiment of which is shown as Fig. 16.

Similarities between this "endless chain" magazine pistol (with its reciprocating barrel or obturator to seal the breech on discharge) and the idea patented nine years later by E. FABRE & A. TRONCHE (q.v.) may be noted. The writer believes that the French "GUYCOT" series of rifles and pistols of this type are the product of the earlier applicants.

GEDGE, W. E. Well-known British Patent Agent (latterly at 11 Wellington Street, Strand, London) in the period 1860–80. Acted for M. KAUFMANN (q.v.), as applicant for communicated Br. Pat. 3313/1881, and the latter also filed for his Br. Pats. 4302/1880 and 3913/1881 from Gedge's address.

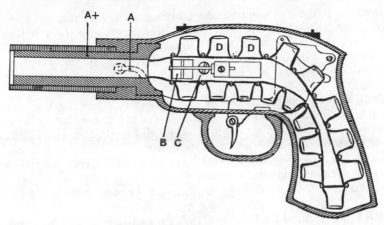

FIG. 16. *The Guycot pistol.*
(*Gay & Guenot's Patent.*)

The inner barrel "A+" is a sliding fit in its housing, and is linked to the trigger by the arm "A" on the far side of the trigger. When the latter is pulled, the barrel is drawn to the rear to mate upon the mouth of a cartridge "D" at the moment that the long firing-pin "C" is released.

The firing-pin "C" is linked to the trigger by a crank (not outlined) also on the far side of the action and passes through suitable passages in the rotating boss "B" on being released. The boss "B" is the means by which the chain of cartridges is wound through the weapon, and is successively turned on its pivot by a hooked arm linked to the crank which cocks the firing-pin.

The practice appears to have had a considerable Continental clientele and to have acted in other patents which (like Kaufmann's) were ultimately developed by the Webley firm (see Chapter IV). It may thus be noted that H. WEBLEY and J. CARTER filed application for Br. Pat. 4070/1885 from this address, and that it appears again on J. Carter's Br. Pat. 16638/1888.

GÉVELOT, J. F. Joint applicant (with P. A. MATHIEU [q.v]) for Br. Pat. 3452/1862 which survived into our period. W. CLARK (q.v.) acted in securing this communicated patent, under which it was proposed to attach a revolver to the stock of any single-shot rifle or gun for use in fighting at close quarters. This could be detached and used as a separate arm when required. C. F. GALAND (q.v.) also patented a later, self-extracting, variant.

Later (through A. M. CLARK [q.v.]) secured communicated Br. Pat. 118/1869, which did not cover any revolving arms but did include the "Gévelot" cartridge used in some Continental revolvers. In filing for this patent, he gave his address as 13 Boulevarte St. Martin, Paris, and his occupation as "Manufacturer".

GIFFARD, P. French Civil Engineer and specialist in the use and manufacture of liquefied gases. Patented a number of weapons employing compressed air or gas as the missile propellant (and the cartridges for them) and secured Br. Pat, 21/1872 specifically claiming lock mechanisms for revolvers and "mitrailleuses". In the application, his address was given as Rue de la Pépinière, No. 12, Paris, but the English headquarters of "The Giffard Gun & Ordnance Co. Ltd." was actually at Copthall House, London, E.C., whilst the factory was at Finsbury.

GIRARD, C. F. French associate of F. A. LEMAT (q.v.) in manufacturing and promoting the latter's famous, double-barrelled "grape-shot" revolver (see Chapter IV). Joint applicant with Col. LeMat in Br. Pat. 1081/1862, which survived into our period and protected features of construction and lock-work in the muzzle-loading percussion version of the revolver then in pro-duction. The association between the two men (at least in relation to revolvers or patents for them) appears to have ended in the mid-1860's.

GILBERT, T. Secured Br. Pat. 2215/1882 for small-arms sights to be used with both eyes open. A version for revolvers, or pistols, could be reversed if the weapon was switched from one hand to the other. Address given as 6 Upper Brook St., Grosvenor Sq., London. Stated occupation—"Gentleman".

GREEN, J. D. Secured Br. Pat. 2241/1875 for a rotating magazine feed, applicable to a bolt-action rifle (Br. Pat. 785/1874).

The application was filed as from the London address of the British Patent Agents "BRANDON & MORGAN-BROWN" (q.v.) and the applicant described in the Specification as "late Brevet Brig.-Gen., U.S. Army".

An officer of this name was active in the production of percussion rifles of his own design at Worcester, Mass., U.S.A., some twelve years earlier, and it is of interest to note that (in reversal of the usual trend) we have the backing of one American authority for believing that he used rifling equipment designed by Charles W. Lancaster of London.

GRÜNBAUM, J. Communicated Br. Pat. 610/1866 to D. L. COHN (q.v.), for provisional protection on the lock-work for firearms with grouped, drop-down barrels; the Lancaster and Martin pistols described in Chapter V were later developments of the same idea.

The Specification to the patent gave Grünbaum's domicile as in Vienna, and the Paris Universal Exhibition of 1867 was then imminent. One of the exhibits was a display of rim-fire, multi-barrelled pistols by "Biedermann, Grünbaum & Cie", in the Austrian section, and it can be assumed that the patent was secured against possible British commercial interest in the design.

The firm actually exhibited versions with four, five and six barrels, and the arms were not dissimilar in appearance to the pistols by "Tipping & Law-den", or C. SHARPS (q.v.) shown in Plate 41. However, the Grünbaum weap-ons had double-action locks instead of the single-action system adopted by the American, and their barrels tilted down for loading, and did not slide forward in the manner shown in the Plate.

In essence, these pistols were pocket arms in small calibres, but a few longer weapons with conventional trigger-guards were made for holster use.

GUENOT, H. French merchant; see, generally, GAY, P.

GUERRIERO, A. Communicated Br. Pat. 628/1863 to W. CLARK (q.v.), which survived into the period and covered eight improvements to the Lefaucheux pin-fire revolver. Protection was sought from 92 Bvte St. Martin, Paris, but this may have been the address of a Patent Agent. The improvements are discussed in Chapter II, and it is assumed that U.S. Pat. 39645 of August 25th, 1863, gave similar protection for so many of the ideas as the U.S. Examiner would accept as novel.

GUEURY, F. Secured communicated Br. Pat, 659/1865 with S. A. NOËL (q.v.) for "an improvement in revolving firearms". (See also CLARK, W.) This patent was presumably the same as their French patent 66493 of March 6th, 1865, for the "Rotovolver" as the inventors termed it.

This is another invention broadly more easy to illustrate than to describe. See Fig. 1 for a believed embodiment of the improvements claimed as applicable "to all kinds of firearms".

GUNTHER, P. J. X. Sought provisional protection under Br. Pat. 1119/1870 (with DE LATOUCHE, J. A. C.; [q.v.]) for improvements to revolvers in respect of (1) hinged or screwed covering plates for lock mechanisms; (2) ready access and safety-catch mechanisms; (3) quick dismount features for the components. Address given as 2 Rue Appoline, Paris.

HADDAN, H. J. A Solicitor of Patents, in the firm of "HERBERT & CO." at 67 Strand, London. Secured communicated Br. Pat. 87/1880 granting provisional protection to T. SEDERL for his automatic cartridge ejector for revolvers. Active into the late 1880's. Appears to have specialized in work from Germany and Austria.

HAMMOND, H. W. Engineer, of Manchester. See "DE DARTIEN, C. F. & J. E." for details of communicated Br. Pat. 778/1870.

HARDING, W. Although the important revolver patent (1159/1858) of William Harding barely survived into the period of concern to us, the reason for abandoning formal protection seems to have been in its success and not in failure. DEANE & SON (q.v.) had taken up the design and promoted the resultant "Deane-Harding" percussion revolver (see Plate 51) in both Army and Pocket sizes, with a fair measure of success. Actual manufacture had been entrusted to the Birmingham firms of "Tipping & Lawden", "Pryse & Redman" and "Calisher & Terry". Since a binding legal agreement must have existed between the inventor, the promoters, and the manufacturers, fixing their financial return in respect of the revolver mechanism, the need to pay the £100 renewal fee on the patent, in 1865, would be ended. No one else was likely to try to promote the design seriously, in competition with such established manufacture.

Information on the inventor remains obstinately sparse. He described himself as a "Gentleman", of Forest Hill, Surrey (in the Specifications to his various British patents) and although an interesting chain of *possible* identifications can be linked to this fact, it seems best not to drag it out for examination in these pages.

HARLOW. E. A Birmingham gunmaker at Sparkbrook, he secured Br. Pat. 2326/1866 for improvements in breech-loading and revolving firearms and cartridges for them. The revolving arm improvement is technically interesting, employing a chamber (or "cylinder", to misuse the term here) for the cartridges formed in a series of external flat planes (e.g. eight planes or flats for a six-chambered revolver) which served instead of the conventional ratchet for rotating the cylinder. From the stated address of the inventor, it seems more than possible that he was an employee or associate of the later partnership trading as "The Westley Richards Arms & Ammunition Company" in the early 1870's, or of the WESTLEY RICHARDS firm itself (q.v.).

HARRIS & MILLS. London Patent Agents (see MILLS, B. J. B.).

HASELTINE, LAKE & CO. London Patent Agents (see LAKE, W. R.).

HENARD, E. Communicated Br. Pats. 2500/1875 and 111/1876 to E. DE PASS (q.v.) for provisional protection. The inventions were in almost identical terms, and suggest that protracted negotiations were in progress for their development which required an extension of the patent term.

A reciprocating barrel/cylinder mechanism was claimed as applicable to "revolvers and other repeaters, pistols, carbines and other firearms of any calibre" to effect a gas-seal on firing. Automatic cartridge-case extraction occurred during the cycle.

The inventor's address was given as at 17 Boulevart St. Martin, Paris.

HERRICK, W. Secured communicated Br. Pat. 1007/1867, from New York City, U.S.A., through W. R. LAKE (q.v.).

Principally, the invention was a revolver cylinder made in two concentric parts, one sliding rearwards over the inner revolving case. Pulling forward the barrel separated the two parts of the cylinder, and bared loading-grooves for metallic cartridges on the inner core. The barrel and front portion of the cylinder were then slid back to embrace the cartridges.

The Complete Specification suggested the use of a modified Colt revolver using the main components of the Model 1860 percussion weapon, if the drawings are any guide. It is not clear if this modification had the backing of the "COLT'S PATENT FIRE ARMS MFG. CO.".

The device was, of course, one of the many attempts made to circumvent the U.S. master-patent of ROLLIN WHITE (q.v.) on the revolver cylinder with its chambers bored through from end to end.

HILL, W. J. Gun and pistol manufacturer in Birmingham and Wolverhampton. Secured provisional protection, by Br. Pat. 3645/1878, for a "lock mechanism of revolving firearms". The Provisional Specification had no drawings filed with it, but the brief written description suggested an improvement on DE MOUNCIE's Br. Pat. 3206/1876 (see Fig. 17).

Revolvers marked "Hill's Patent" are known, and embody De Mouncie's lock, with hinged side-plate, but their novel features of ejection owe nothing readily apparent to Br. Pat. 3645/1878. British revolvers of this type frequently bore the trade-mark "Stanley", along with an acknowledgement to the "Joint Patents" of STANTON (q.v.). Their source of manufacture is now obscure.

These designs were also developed by A. FRANCOTTE (q.v.) and F. A. BRAENDLIN (q.v.), who both used the same peculiar top-hinged cartridge extraction system, without the hinged side-plate.

Whether encountered in Braendlin, Francotte, or Hill versions, these revolvers broke open upwards, on a hinge at the top of the standing breech (see Plate 57). If this rearward tilting was continued, the barrel eventually pivoted on a second hinge at the forward end of the top strap (see Plate 57), and this caused the heavy "horns" to operate an extractor. This system may be read into the claims of DE MOUNCIE's Br. Pat. 2161/1878.

The revolver shown in Plates 56 and 57 is unmarked externally, except for Birmingham proof marks and a large figure "5". Internally, it is stamped with the mark of F. A. BRAENDLIN (q.v.).

HILLEBRANDT, H. Partner in the firm of "HILLEBRANDT & ALTENDORF", who secured provisional protection for the improvement in revolvers communicated to him by J. HILLEBRANDT (Br. Pat. 3943/1868).

The latter, a gun manufacturer at Liège, Belgium, claimed in his Provisional Specification the extraction of fired cases from metallic-cartridge revolvers by a "star-shaped plate" (recessed into the rear of the cylinder), which also carried the ratchet for revolving the cylinder.

HILLEBRANDT & ALTENDORF. Birmingham merchants. See HILLEBRANDT, H. for details of a patent in which this firm was interested. Another firm traded as "ALTENDORF & WRIGHT" at about this period, and may have been associated.

HOTCHKISS, A. Joint applicant (with fellow-Americans E. H. & A. P. PLANT) for communicated Br. Pat. 3987/1868 through W. E. NEWTON (q.v.), a London Patent Agent. All three applicants were apparently domiciled at Southington, Conn., U.S.A., at the date of application.

The patent related to a revolver loaded from the front of the cylinder; to a particular type of hollow-based, cup-primed, metallic cartridge for it;

and to various means for firing the cartridge and expelling the cartridge-cases.

It seems fairly certain that this Br. Pat. 3987/1868 embodied the satis-factory features of U.S. Pats. 24726 of July 12th, 1859; 39318 of July 21st, 1863, and reissue 1528 of August 25th, 1863, which had been originally secured in the U.S. by W. E. Ellis, and J. N. White of Springfield, Mass., U.S.A., and subsequently assigned to the three above-mentioned (and another man named H. Reynolds).

Hotchkiss and his associates probably therefore constituted the "Eagle Arms Co." of New York, which was promoting a revolver (commonly known as the "Plant Army Revolver") as made under the above U.S. patents, at the time of their application for British patent protection.

Why this shortlived British patent protection was so tardily sought remains a mystery, but specimens of such weapons (see Plate 15) are found in British collections with surprising frequency. It is possible, therefore, either that Merwin & Bray (the main U.S. distributors) received a United Kingdom order for them or (less probably) that U.K. manufacture occurred to meet a promising, but abortive, export inquiry.

HOTCHKISS, B. B. Noted American firearms designer (b. 1826; d. 1885) in the field of breech-loading magazine firearms, who also secured com-municated Br. Pat. 3017/1878 (through w. MORGAN-BROWN [q.v]) and 4454/1879 (in his own name) which have revolving features of concern here.

The two patents cover the basic features of the Hotchkiss "revolving cannons" (see Chapter VI) and certain refinements. The first was filed as from the Paris office of BRANDON & MORGAN-BROWN and the second from their London address. The weapon was, in fact, principally developed in France, although adopted for special purposes in a number of other countries.

HOWARD, R. Sought provisional protection under Br. Pat. 4038/1882 for a sword and revolver combined, the revolver being so mounted as to be usable by the hand holding the sword. Occupation unknown, but domicile stated as "of the town and county of the town of Southampton".

HOYT, J. K. Applicant (on behalf of B. F. JOSLYN [q.v.]) for the communi-cated Br. Pat. 2768/1863, which survived into the period of concern here. (This patent covered two revolvers using metallic cartridges; see, further, under the inventor's name.) Hoyt gave his own addresses as of New York, U.S.A., and 12 Southampton Buildings, London.

HUGHES, E. T. London Patent Agent at 123 Chancery Lane, who secured communicated Br. Pat. 997/1866 on behalf of J. B. DOOLITTLE and G. O. DOWNING (q.v.) for the revolver more particularly described under the first-named.

HULBERT, M. & HULBERT, W. A. American merchants, of Brooklyn,

King's County, New York State, and joint applicants with J. MERWIN (q.v.) for Br. Pat. 277/1878. This protected the method of extraction; the loading-gate, the barrel and frame assembly; and the barrel key-bolt features of the "Merwin & Hulbert" self-extracting revolvers described in Chapter IV, and shown in Plate 38. These were manufactured for them in the U.S. by the Hopkins and Allen factory of Norwich, Connecticut, and for European markets by others, including the "Charola Y Anitua" concern of Spain.

The partnership also distributed in America, the patented arms of W. R. EVANS (q.v.) during the early 1880's. It used the trading style "Merwin, Hulbert & Co." and survived until about 1891.

"INTERNATIONAL PATENT OFFICE, THE." Situated at 8 Southampton Buildings, off Chancery Lane, London, which was the address for the substantial patents practice of W. R. LAKE, in the 1860's and of HASELTINE, LAKE & CO. thereafter. Patentees frequently used it as the address which they were required to give on the various official documents in their application for protection, instead of their private addresses (see, for example, Br. Pat. 2241/1875).

The title had, of course, no more *official* standing than H. E. NEWTON's "Office of Patents" at 66 Chancery Lane, London (or FELL AND WILDING's "City Patent Office" in Fenchurch St.), so far as the true Patent Office provided by H.M. Treasury or the earlier office for the Commissioners of Patents was concerned. H. A. BONNEVILLE's "British and Foreign Patent Office" in the Rue du Mont, Thebor, of Paris, or in Porchester Terrace, London, should be regarded in the same light.

The point is not academic, for the establishing of the probable domicile of inventors at various dates is often a vital matter in tracing the places of manufacture for the weapons that have survived to us. The movements of really itinerant patentees like M. KAUFMANN (q.v.) or BARON DE MOUNCIE (q.v.) for example, may often be established for students of the Webley revolvers by reference to this sort of source, and from thence an inference drawn for the solution of other problems.

JACQUELIN, C. Obtained Br. Pat. 1936/1880 (and gave his address as 36 Rue des Écoles, Paris) for a walking stick embodying umbrella, revolver and sword. Such combination weapons are, like the poor, always with us but the principal improvement in this case was to conceal the revolver in the stick-handle to permit firing down a tube in the shaft. Moreover, all components retained distinct functions and could be detached for separate use at will.

JARRE, A. E. Secured communicated Br. Pat. 2002/1871, through J. H. JOHNSON (q.v.) for the curious "harmonica" arms mentioned in Chapter V. These have no proper place in a book upon revolving arms, except as examples of competing ideas.

JOHNSON, E. Sought (from Lee Villas, Addiscombe, Surrey) provisional protection under Br. Pat. 2004/1871 for a self-cocking revolving firearm with three chambers and a cartridge charge of twelve rounds "or more". The whole loading, firing and ejection cycle was accomplished by merely pulling the trigger. This protection was eventually NOT allowed.

Later, as Br. Pat. 1722/1875, secured provisional protection for a revolving magazine-feed for rifles and ordnance in terms suggesting that he had re-designed the system for which the earlier protection had been sought. This application was filed from St. Clement's House, St. Clement's Lane, London.

JOHNSON, J. H. Patent Agent at 47 Lincoln's Inn Fields, London, from the 1850's to the 1870's. Acted in communicated Br. Pats. 1251/1863 (POLLAK, A.); 182/1867 (ROPER, S. H.); 2002/1871 (JARRE, A. E.); and 922/1878 (MAUSER, P.); and for JAMES KERR (q.v.) in one American revolver patent of 1863, which are those of concern in these pages.

His principal claim to fame for our purposes lay in Br. Pat. 955/1854, which was allowed to lapse in 1861.

This communicated patent (for an unnamed principal) covered the Lefaucheux single-action pin-fire revolver, and probably accounted for the failure of ROLLIN WHITE (q.v.) to seek equivalent British protection for the American patent which gave him his stranglehold (from 1855 to 1869) on conventionally loaded metallic-cartridge revolvers in the U.S.A. Johnson's patent did not specifically claim the cartridge chamber bored through from end to end, but its existence would have destroyed this basic novelty in Rollin White's design.

JONES, O. Inventor and fairly prolific patentee, in the mid-1870's and 1880's for firearms improvements of every kind. Concerns us principally as designer and patentee of features embodied in the "Enfield" revolver; see Chapter IV. Communicated Br. Pats. 2777/1876 and 624/1878 (through W. R. LAKE [q.v]) appear to be those in point. The latter also secured pro-visional protection for Jones (under Br. Pat. 5266/1879) for "Revolvers with rifled chambers". In such weapons, the rifling in the chambers formed the commencement of the entire rifled portion of the arm. Lessened recoil was claimed as one benefit. All the above patents were communicated to W. R. LAKE (q.v.) as from Philadelphia, Pennsylvania, U.S.A.

JONES, T. A "Machinist" at Handsworth, Staffordshire, who secured Br. Pat. 1992/1869 for an improved method of uniting the barrel and frame of revolvers. This was broadly, along the same lines as that later used in the American revolvers of HULBERT, M. & W. A. and MERWIN, J. (q.v.) although a decade separated any activities under the two patents. The weapon shown on Jones's Specification was based on a frame similar to that in Plate 58, with the top strap and barrel rotating (on the cylinder axis) through 180° to free transverse bolting cuts from engagement with the standing breech and frame, so that the cylinder could be pulled forward for cartridge extraction. Loading was by gate, with barrel and frame united.

A star-shaped cartridge extractor fixed to the standing breech was shown, but not claimed. Presumably, Br. Pat. 2050/1865 by w. c. DODGE (q.v.) destroyed any novelty in this feature.

The slightly earlier patent 779/1869 of J. THOMAS (q.v.) must have embarrassed Jones, when it was duly published. Thomas chose to develop only one of the cartridge extraction systems covered by his patent, but it protected others which narrowed the field of promotion open to Jones.

JONGEN, J. Secured Br. Pat. 2383/1864, which survived into the years of concern here (see Table I), for improvements in the construction of percussion revolvers. Production was simplified by boring the chambers straight through in one machining pass, and closing their breeches with screwed blocks bearing the nipples. A "ram pin" was struck by the hammer, instead of direct contact between that member and the nipple. The applicant was presumably a member of the Liège gun-manufacturing firm of "Jongen Frères".

JOSLYN, B. F. Communicated Br. Pat. No. 2768/1863 to J. K. HOYT, which survived into the period of concern here (see Table I) protecting ten detailed features for two different metallic-cartridge revolvers, one with a side-hammer.

As to the conventional pistol, the patented features appear to be those of the American "Bacon Mfg. Co." rim-fire Navy revolvers, protected in that country by U.S. Patent 41117 of January 5th, 1864, in the names of H. A. Briggs and Samuel S. Hopkins of Norwich, Connecticut, and sold by the Bacon Mfg. Co. of the same town.

On both revolvers shown in the British Specification, the cylinder swung out sideways for loading and cartridge ejection, but this distinctive feature has not served to identify the origins of the side-hammer weapons.

Benjamin F. Joslyn was a manufacturer and inventor of breech-loading carbines and percussion revolvers at Stonington, Conn., U.S.A., and an associate of other American revolver manufacturers and designers during the Civil War. Under the press of need, 1,100 of his side-hammer Army percussion revolvers were purchased by the North, but he cannot be regarded as a major producer of revolving metallic-cartridge arms at any period known to the writer.

The reason, therefore, for this fairly elaborate British protection remains unclear. Particular attention is paid to these cases, in view of possible confusion or association with the protection secured by D. MOORE (q.v.) which also survived into our period.

KAUFMANN, M. Patentee of uncertain occupation and domicile, who secured six British revolver patents of importance; 5031/1878, 4302/1880,

3313/1881, 3913/1881, 189/1884, and 5308/1884. Apart from the first of these, the patents were developed by P. WEBLEY & SON (q.v.). and Kaufmann's own trade-mark ("MK" surrounded by a triangle) appeared upon the weapons embodying his ideas.

Br. Pat. 5031/1878 was secured jointly with J. WARNANT (q.v.), and a comparison between Fig. 8 and Plate 72 demonstrates that it protected the lock mechanism of the "Enfield" service revolver (see Chapter IV, and Plates 32, 49, 50). Kaufmann's address was given on the Specification as at Fenchurch Street, City of London (suggesting that the case was handled by S. P. WILDING [q.v]), and the lock was admitted to be an improvement upon Br. Pat. 3206/1876, which A. T. DE MOUNCIE (q.v.) had assigned to Kaufmann.

Br. Pat. 4302/1880 protected the lock mechanism used in the commercially developed Webley/Kaufmann and Webley "Improved Government Pattern" revolvers shown in Plate 35; these were produced in the early and mid-1880's, using a beautifully modified version of the lock-work in the "Enfield" revolver with only five components. This patent was secured by Kaufmann alone from 11 Wellington Street, Strand, which was the address of W. E. GEDGE (q.v.).

To the same Agent, Kaufmann communicated his next patent (No. 3313/1881), to protect the button-operated barrel latch used in the Webley/Kaufmann revolver shown at the top of Plate 35. In this Specification, Kaufmann described himself as of "Brussels, Belgium", and it is worth noting that J. WARNANT (q.v.), formally associated with him in one patent, gave domicile as of "Hognée, commune of Cheratte, Belgium", and "Liège, Belgium", in his two patents of 1881.

Kaufmann himself secured his next British Patent (No. 3913/1881), but again gave W. E. GEDGE's address. Primarily, this covered a loading-gate for use in revolvers embodying the lock-work of his own Br. Pat. 4302/1880, but a gate suitable for use in solid-framed revolvers was also claimed. This was used by P. WEBLEY & SON (q.v.) in revolvers of the type shown at the top of Plate 23; when opened, the gate freed the cylinder from the bolted position (for easier loading) and also disconnected the hammer from the lock-work.

Finally, Kaufmann secured Br. Pats. 189/1884 and 5308/1884; the former protected a cylinder-bolt, and the latter covered butt-cheeks and side-plates that could be removed without tools. Kaufmann's address on both patents was given as 8 Devonshire Road, Greenwich, and he described himself, simply, as a "Gentleman". He had been in occupation at this address in 1880, and it was presumably his home.

KERR, J. Factory Superintendent for the London Armoury Company Limited in the 1860's. James Kerr (b. 1825; d. 1888) carried on a firearms business of his own (which was the official armourer for the National Rifle Association) after the dissolution of that limited liability company. He used the trading style "James Kerr & Co. (successors to the London Armoury Co. Ltd.)" in this connection but revolvers bearing this name are clearly retailed and not manufactured by him (see Plate 58).

His Br. Pats. 242/1859 and 2896/1858, covering a well-known muzzle-loading percussion revolver, survived into the period of this book (see Table I) but he appears to have had no real interest in revolvers as a subject for further designs, and to have switched his very real talents as an engineer into other fields, quite unrelated. His firearms business flourished throughout the period of concern to us, but its backbone appears to have been the agencies which he held from the Winchester Repeating Arms Co. (from 1875) and other American companies, for the United Kingdom and its Colonies.

KINNE, G. O. Communicated Br. Pat. 2463/1870 to A. V. NEWTON (q.v.) for an improvement of "Gattling [*sic*] and other repeating field guns of like character", which gave an effective dispersal of fire. He gave his domicile as in Hartford, Conn., U.S.A., and was apparently associated with (or employed by) the Colt Company who were manufacturing Gatling guns at that time. That Company took the assignment jointly with Kinne, when Newton transferred the Br. Pat. to him (a necessary formality) in 1871.

KRAFFERT, J. J. Sought provisional protection, under Br. Pat. 1259/1867, for a "self-acting, lateral-fire needle, repeating magazine rifle and cartridge", which only concerns us because it included a rotary magazine feed for the weapon claimed. Kraffert (of Berlin, Prussia) presumably only took out the protection as a matter of normal commercial prudence, in case U.K. interest in his design arose from its appearance at the Paris Universal Exhibition of 1867.

KRNKA, K. One of a trio of very active Russian applicants for patents relating to bolt-action magazine small arms in the 1880's. Only Br. Pat. 14088/1888 concerns us here, and covered a manually operated bolt-action pistol (see Fig. 3) emobodying a *removable* rotary magazine.

The application was filed from 8 Quality Court, London, which was presumably the address of the Patent Agents handling the application.

KUFAHL, G. L. L. The exclusion of Br. Pat. 13994/1852 from Table I but mention of the applicant here is intentional.

Filed under the patent law operating before the Patent Law Amendment Act, 1852, became effective, the patent *could*, theoretically, have survived until 1866.

In the case of another patent in this class (see ADAMS, R.) ample evidence exists to show that steps were taken to maintain the patent. In Kufahl's case, this evidence has not been forthcoming.

However, the patent covered needle-fire weapons of various types, one of which was the so-called "Dreyse" needle-fire revolver.

These revolvers were apparently in production for a long time, despite their fragility, and the cartridges for them could still be purchased in the 1880's. However, no British specimen has been found whilst this book was in preparation, and it is therefore assumed that the protection was never invoked in the United Kingdom. Since Table I is based upon official records, it must exclude a patent for which no announcement of renewal or avoidance could be traced.

A Continental specimen of the revolver (made by F. Dreyse of Sommerda) is shown at the foot of Plate 2, and this was the version normally encountered.

LAKE, H. H. British Patent Agent at 45 Southampton Buildings, Chancery Lane, London, who acted for A. CHUCHU (q.v.) in Br. Patent 11201/1884. Equal in fame to his namesake W. R. LAKE (q.v.) but not involved in the filing of any revolving arms patents.

LAKE, W. R. Famous British Patent Agent, with an immense clientele in every field. Practised throughout our period and secured many well-known revolving arms patents.

Appears to have commenced as a Consulting Engineer (in Chancery Lane) in the mid-1860's and to have joined or set up the "International Patent Office" at 8 Southampton Buildings shortly afterwards. By 1869 this had become the equally famous (and still existing) firm of patent agents practising as "HASELTINE, LAKE & CO.".

Acted (by date order) for communicated Br. Pats.: 299/1866 (C. MASON); 1007/1867 (W. HERRICK); 3164/1868 (T. J. CRANMER & W. P. MOFFATT); 1510/1869 (SMITH & WESSON); 2865/1871 (J. TRAWNICZEK); 2579/1875 (E. REMINGTON & SONS); 445/1876 (E. P. BOARDMAN); 1703/1876 (F. L. BAILEY); 2777/1876 (O. JONES); 4831/1877 (D. B. WESSON); 624/1878 (O. JONES), with Disclaimer and Memorandum of Alteration of 1880 thereto; 1935/1878 (D. W. C. FARRINGTON); 4614/1878 (D. B. WESSON); 3338/1879 (D. W. C. FARRINGTON); 5266/1879 (O. JONES); 5569/1881 (J. H. WESSON).

"LANCASTER, CHARLES." See THORN, H. A. A.

LATOUCHE, DE, J. A. C. See, generally, GÜNTHER, P. J. X.

LE MAT, F. A. American physician, of French birth, and inventor of the muzzle-loading "grape-shot" revolver, for which his name is remembered.

This pistol was initially developed in the years prior to those of concern to us (the first U.S. patent being secured in 1856) under the flag of the Confederate States of America, but by overseas manufacture. Some, at least, of these revolvers are authoritatively regarded as made or finished by the Birmingham Small Arms Co., Ltd.

During the period of the Civil War, Col. (or Dr.) Le Mat was associated with C. F. GIRARD (q.v.) in French manufacture of the arm. For our purposes, it is sufficient to note here that their joint British Patent 1081/1862 survived until 1869 (see Table I), and that Br. Pat. 3181/1868 was secured by Col. Le Mat alone for the central-fire version of the weapon and its cartridges (see further, Chapter IV). Old records destroyed by the Patent Office in 1963 showed that interests in this patent were registered there by "Pielconi" during 1869 and by "Leprelre and Benjamin" during 1871 but the writer has not been able to establish either their nature or purpose.

However, Le Mat secured provisional protection (through British Patent Agent T. J. SMITH (q.v.) of ROBERTSON, BROOMAN & CO.) for loading-gate, hammer and lock improvements to the 1868 British Patent under communicated Br. Pat. 3218/1871, which does suggest that the pistol was being actively developed somewhere. He then gave his address as at 23 Bvte de Strasbourg, Paris, and used the same Agents to secure further provisionaf protection under Br. Pat. 3224/1871 for an idea relating to the rifling ol ordnance or small arms barrels by forcing a moulding mandrel through the metal when plasticized by heat.

In 1877 (from Bvde St. Denis, 1, Paris), Le Mat secured Br. Pat. 588/1877 for a hammer permitting "one-handed" fire-selection between cylinder or shot-barrel without altering the grasp on the pistol-butt, and this appears to have been his last attempt at improving the weapon peculiarly identified with his name. He died in the early 1880's, presumably prior to the seventh renewal date of Br. Pat. 588/1877, which lapsed by non-payment of fees in 1884 (see Plates 60 and 61 for his revolvers).

LILLIE, SIR J. S. Br. Pat. 1985/1863 survived into our period (see Table I) and covered "an improved revolving battery" based on earlier British patents of 1854 and 1855.

In this case, Sir John's fancy was for a revolving barrel cluster allied to revolving detachable chambers or cylinders for each individual barrel.

No drawings were filed with the Specification and I have never seen any specimens of the gun. It does seem possible, however, that an example was built, since the inventor mentioned a specific rate of fire for a six-barrelled cluster (with twenty chambers to a barrel) of 120 shots a minute.

LINBERG, C. J. American applicant (with W. J. PHILLIPS) from St. Louis, Missouri, U.S.A., for communicated Br. Pat. 3154/1870, which A. M. CLARK secured for them. The protection was for revolvers with side-swinging barrels and *two* cylinders in tandem on one axis to double the capacity of the arm.

After firing, the front cylinder was switched to the rear for the discharged chambers to be reloaded and capped, at leisure.

LINDNER, A. Secured Br. Pat. 17159/1888 (for an established bolt-action rifle design) from 52 Chancery Lane, London; the Specification included a spring-rotated magazine for the weapon.

LINDSAY, J. P. Provisional protection under Br. Pat. 2013/1864 just survived into our period.

The Lindsay double-hammer, single-trigger locks were not primarily intended for revolvers but were embodied in the American Walch percussion revolvers which had two charges in each chamber—"Roman candle" fashion.

Lindsay and Walch arms are rare and probably owed what small success they did achieve solely to the energy and enterprise of their promoters as salesmen (see also WALLIS, C. E.).

LOEWENTHAL, L. Secured provisional protection (with D. DE R. WIL-LOUGHBY (q.v.) under Br. Pat. 1489/1882 on variations of a sight for fire-arms, which included a white enamel or porcelain "night" foresight for revolvers. The address given for service was 1 Albemarle St., Piccadilly.

MANNLICHER, F. In only two cases (Br. Pats. 2915/1881 and 632/1888) was the rotating ammunition feed principle claimed by this famous Viennese de-signer to bring his name to our attention.

The first patent (communicated to C. D. ABEL [q.v]) included a revolving magazine for bolt-action rifles. This was mechanically rotated, and was to be embodied in the butt-stock of the weapon.

The second patent was secured by the inventor personally, and protected a spring-rotated magazine for the same kind of weapon. A detent controlled the accuracy of the rotation.

MARTIN, A. Secured Br. Pat. 1531/1880 from Store St., Bedford Square, London, and described himself as an "Engineer". Primarily, the protection related to pistols of the type mentioned in Chapter V.

The barrels of these arms were paired, and tipped down for loading. Un-like the comparable weapons of CHARLES LANCASTER (q.v.) each barrel had a separate striker, which was operated entirely by pulling the trigger.

Cartridges for these pistols were to be made up into charges, by riveting their heads between perforated plates of metal. This system was also offered as suitable for conventional revolvers.

By the late 1880's, Martin had become associated with H. A. SCHLUND (q.v.) in various other patents, not all of which related to firearms, The latter's Br. Pat. 11900/1886 is noticed in Chapter IV (in relation to the "Kynoch" revolvers), and should be noted as claimed for application to multi-barrelled pistols also.

MARTIN, F. Associated with R. C. ROMANEL and A. H. WILLIAMS (q.v.) in Br. Pats. 9998/1887 and 6994/1888, covering a "Martini-type" hinged breech block magazine rifle more particularly described under the former's name.

The appearance of the legend "F. Martin & Cie. Patent" on the revolver featured on Plates 47 and 48 is interesting, but both patent details and any tie-up between this inventor and that weapon have yet to be established.

MASON, C. Communicated Br. Pat. 299/1866 to W. R. LAKE (q.v.), for provisional protection, giving his address as of "Illiom [sic], New York, U.S.A.". The improvement claimed for revolvers is not easily grasped from the un-illustrated Provisional Specification but, apparently, the device hooked or clawed out one cartridge-case each time the pistol hammer was cocked. It may be similar to the conversion system of Joseph Rider, which was offered to COLT'S PATENT FIREARMS MANUFACTURING CO. (q.v.) in 1867, to adapt their Model 1860 muzzle-loading Army percussion revolver to use a flanged metallic cartridge.

MATHIEU, P. A. See, generally, GÉVELOT, J. F., in regard to Br. Pat. 3452/1862, which survived into our period.

MAUSER, P. This famous designer secured communicated Br. Pat. 922/1878 through J. H. JOHNSON (q.v.), covering revolvers in which the cylinder was rotated by a lock member engaging inclined and parallel grooves on the circumference, instead of using a conventional ratchet at the rear. Assembly and dismount features were also claimed, along with automatic cartridge extractors and lock mechanisms for such arms.

This was the only case in which he sought British patent protection under his own name, during the period of concern to us, and weapons thus described are illustrated in Plate 33.

MAYALL, T. J. Secured Br. Pat. 1046/1865 for a bolt-action, breech-loading rifle and its cartridge, which appear to have enjoyed some commercial success.

He also claimed, in the Specification, a revolver with the butt hinged to the lower rear action-body to permit changing the cylinder, and gave his address as of Roxbury, U.S.A., and Red Lion Court, Fleet Street, London.

The Complete Specification was fully detailed as to the revolver, and described an optional percussion or rim-fire weapon.

The claims related primarily to the hinged butt, the barrel/frame latch (which was locked by the hammer, in falling) and to the cylinder-bolt. The latch may have owed something to the earlier patent of T. J. VAIL (q.v.).

An ingenious compound rammer and cartridge ejector (operated by a rack and pinion) was also claimed, along with a detachable hammer nose which could be adapted for use with a cap and ball cylinder, or with rim-fire cartridges.

The purpose of the patent is not clear. It constituted an infringement of the basic ROLLIN WHITE protection on the bored-through cartridge cylinder, so far as any sale or manufacture in the U.S.A. was concerned, but is not seen to exist as a weapon in any collection known to the writer.

In 1867 an assignment was registered at the British Patent Office, in relation to this patent, under the names "Henderson, Nelson and Penkington". Destruction of the appropriate records has prohibited identification of these men, to date, and the destroyed Index gave no details as to whether the assignment stood for the whole, or only part, of the patent. However, Ordnance Committee trials for breech-loading rifles were in train at that time, and it is probable that interest would be concentrated on the rifle in

Mayall's patent, unless the assignment was that between Patent Agent and principals.

McLEAN, J. H. Secured communicated Br. Pat. 5613/1881, through B. J. B. MILLS, for a firearm "with a many chambered revolving cylinder or with barrels loaded from an automatic magazine by means of a plunger and having a shell extractor consisting of a hook working in a circumferential groove in the rear of the revolving cylinder or barrels and retracted by gearing connecting it with the loading plunger". Machine-guns, cartridges and a three-barrelled revolving small-arm, on which cocking the hammer rotated this barrel cluster for successive discharge from a 60-round magazine, were also claimed.

The applicant (a Doctor of Medicine, from St. Louis, Miss., U.S.A.) appears to have been operating amongst the lunatic fringe of firearms designers.

MERWIN, J. See, generally, HULBERT, M. & W. A., and Chapter IV. The legend that this particular member of the American merchant firm of Merwin, Hulbert & Co., was captured and burned at the stake by Indians has been disposed of authoritatively. The true account of the robbery and murder of this patentee, with other travellers at a trans-continental coaching station, make fascinating reading and it is to be hoped that the patient American who established the facts will republish his findings, one day, in a less ephemeral form.

MICHELONI, A. Secured provisional protection (through I. WILLIAMS (q.v.) under Br. Pat. 2513/1864, which barely survived into our period.

The protection was for yet another sabre/revolver combination, the hilt of the sword serving as a pistol-butt and the trigger being within the hand guard.

MILLS, B. J. B. Well-known British Patent Agent in the period 1870–1890 and member of the firm of HARRIS AND MILLS at 35 (later 23) Southampton Buildings, Chancery Lane, London.

Not noted for activity in relation to patents for firearms, but secured communicated Br. Pats. 1868/1871, 1549/1873 and 2811/1873 (J. P. TAYLOR); 1561/1878 (R. WHITE and A. W. WHEELER); 5613/1881 (J. H. MCLEAN) of concern to us here.

MOFFAT, W. P. See, also, "T. J. CRANMER", in relation to Br. Pat. 3164/1868.

The weapon protected was a "volley-gun" and not a revolving weapon, but is included briefly here as indicative of the ideas competing with that principle in America.

MONTIGNY, J. Belgian "Mechanician" and co-applicant for Br. Pat. 3553/

1867 on the "Montigny Mitrailleuse". See, generally, "CHRISTOPHE L." and Chapter VI.

His gun was probably the best-known of all those competing with the revolving feed principle in the battery or machine-gun field (see Plates 45 and 46).

MOORE, D. Secured Br. Pat. 2351/1862, which survived into our period (see Table I), for another rim-fire revolver in which the cylinder swung sideways for loading. The arc of travel was small, and not through 90° like a modern Colt or Smith & Wesson revolver. The barrel swung out with the cylinder, and Moore's patent also protected the rifling of the forward end of each cartridge chamber (an idea later adopted by O. JONES (q.v.); a type of rim-fire cartridge for his pistol; and the recoil plate for it.

Moore was a fairly substantial firearms manufacturer in Brooklyn, New York, who developed revolver and cartridge designs on his own account. In 1863, he fell foul of the U.S. master patent of ROLLIN WHITE (q.v.) for the bored-through cartridge chamber, and lost over 3,000 of his infringing revolvers to SMITH & WESSON (q.v.). The pistols were made to the same design as that protected by Br. Pat. 2351/1862.

Moore's answer was to produce a front-loading metallic cartridge (for which there was no traceable British patent protection) and these arms enjoyed a modest success until the expiry of ROLLIN WHITE's patent, in 1869. Moore crossed swords with Smith & Wesson again in 1875, when he sued them for a design infringement, and he was successful in securing an out-of-court settlement.

The side-swinging features of his Br. Pat. 2351/1862, were the subject of American patent protection, as U.S. Pat. 35419 of May 27th, 1862, which was secured by C. W. Hopkins, and assigned to himself, T. K. Bacon, and A. E. Cobb, of Norwich, Conn.

The side-swinging feature did not anticipate the protection secured under Br. Pat. 2768/1863 (by J. K. HOYT, for B. F. JOSLYN [q.v.]), since the later design swung out only the cylinder, and left the barrel *in situ*.

MORGAN-BROWN, W. English partner to the Anglo-French engineering and patent agency partnership of BRANDON & MORGAN-BROWN (q.v.).

MOUNCIE, DE, A. T. or BARON. Secured Br. Pat. 3206/1876 and provisional protection under 4163/1876, as "Baron T. de Mouncie of Paris, France, now of Queen Victoria St., City of London". Described himself simply as "A. T. de Mouncie of Hill Street, Rutland Gate, Middlesex, Gentleman", when filing for Br. Pat. 2161/1878, which he allowed to become void by failure to file a Final Specification after grant. Presumably he represented a Continental revolver maker.

Br. Pat. 3206/1876 was assigned to M. KAUFMANN (q.v.), and its principal claims can be readily grasped from Fig. 17, namely, the spring-loaded cover-plate; the rebounding lock-mechanism; and the notched cylinder-pin with

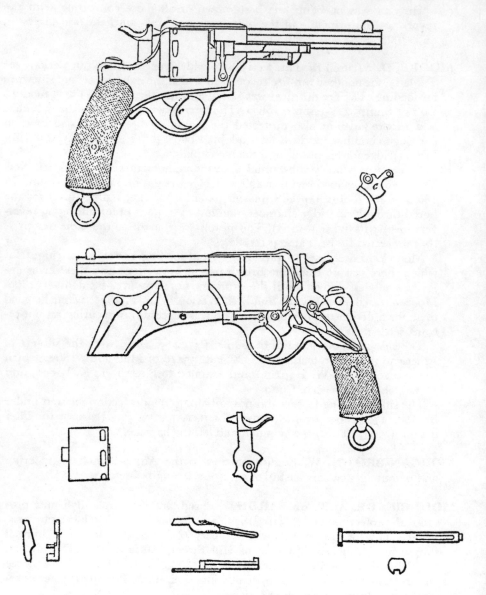

FIG. 17. *De Mouncie's Revolver.*

which the mainspring could be removed. A comparison of Fig. 8 with Fig. 17 will confirm the admitted parentage of KAUFMANN & WARNANT's revolver lock through this inventor, and the remarks upon w. j. HILL should also be studied.

The features claimed in the unillustrated Provisional Specification to de Mouncie's Br. Pat. 4163/1876 are temptingly broad and could cover the principal novelties in the externally unmarked, Birmingham-proved, Levaux revolver shown on Plates 49 and 50.

These pistols were not uncommon in the form shown, and it remains yet to be established whether their barrel latches can be demonstrated to spring from this patent. It is in point to record that the revolver illustrated is stamped internally with the mark of F. A. BRAENDLIN (q.v.) and "J. M. G. Levaux" and that identical specimens marked "D. Levaux" externally, but of Continental proof and manufacture, were equally well known. Quality varied in these Continental specimens, a variety of other names and trade-marks appeared upon them, and some refinements in the way of dimpled cylinders and manually operated safety-catches were met. However, the plate-type extractor seemed common to them all.

As to de Mouncie's abandoned Br. Pat. 2161/1878, this Specification was also unillustrated and strictly related to revolving arms only in part. For such arms it protected a manually operated cartridge extractor for hinged-frame pistols, and can be read as the basis for the cartridge extraction system used in the revolver shown on Plates 56 and 57, which is also discussed under w. j. HILL (q.v.).

MURRAY, A. G. An advocate, of Edinburgh, who secured Br. Pat. 873/1882 jointly with J. DICKSON (q.v.) for an improvement of "J. Dickson tertius'" Br. Pat. 294/1880. The earlier patent is not included in this work as it related to sporting weapons of the double- (or multiple-) barrelled variety.

The improvement is included as having possible use in the locks for multi-barrelled pistols of the types discussed as competitors of the revolver, in Chapter V.

NAGANT, E. Belgian firearms manufacturer. Secured (from 41 Quay de L'Ourthe, Liège) Br. Pat. 4310/1879 for improvements to revolver pistols and other small-arms. As in the the case of c. F. GALAND (q.v.), the patent illustrated a good deal more than it actually claimed.

Strictly, the protection was sought for methods of constructing a revolver so that it might be easily dismounted and assembled. The trigger-guard was hinged at the front of the frame, and when tipped down it released the tension on the three lock springs, and permitted easy stripping of the lock. Tipping it up "cocked" these springs again.

The patent also claimed a removable side-plate to the action body, and a rod-ejector lodged in a cavity in the cylinder axis-pin, which was suitably locked in position. The well-known "Nagant" sleeve round the barrel is shown, by which the rod was swung outwards into alignment with the chambers.

The revolver shown in the Complete Specification was the Belgian officers' M/78 pistol, which embodied all the features claimed in the patent, and used the lock mechanism shown (but not claimed) therein. The lock was also used in many other revolvers (see Plate 25) and must have been old when Nagant adopted it. C. F. GALAND (q.v.) illustrated it in his patent of 1872, and W. HARDING (q.v.) used a similar hammer-catch in 1858.

NEEDHAM, G. H. Gunmaker, of Wandsworth, Surrey, who secured Br. Pat. 4693/1883. Although claimed as applicable to revolvers, the patent really related to sporting guns or rifles for which barrel-bolts and grip safety mechanisms were described.

Theoretically, these features could have been applied to revolvers. The barrel-bolt used an interrupted screw thread engaging teeth cut in the rear of the barrel, and the grip-safety lever (which cocked the hammer as well) bore a resemblance to a device used in some rare revolvers. Such arms are known today as designed for "fingerless" men, and a Continental revolver embodying a similar type of bar-trigger is shown in Plate 62.

NEEDHAM, J. Gunmaker, of Hammersmith Terrace, Middlesex, and joint patentee (with J. J. ATKINSON [q.v]) for "repeating and revolving pistols and other small-arms, and cartridges" (Br. Pat. 716/1881). The Complete Specification included a firearm with a tubular magazine under the barrel. This fed a revolving twin-chambered breech-block, with a thimble-shaped centre-fire cartridge that loaded backwards and ejected forwards. The lock mechanisms described could be operated either by a ring-trigger or by a separate under-lever, and the ingenious cartridge embodied a separate metal collar within it to effect a true gas-seal between breech-block and barrel on discharge.

"The Needham Magazine Gun and Cartridge" of this patent does appear to have been developed and marketed by its inventors but the writer is uncertain as to the actual date when this took place.

The first edition of W. W. Greener's *The Gun and Its Development* appeared in the same year as this patent, but did not mention the weapon. The sixth edition (of 1896) dealt with it in some detail, as if it were a novelty, but the patent had, in fact, been allowed to lapse in 1886 and no other protection for the idea had been sought by the inventor in the meantime.

The puzzle must be solved by others, but it is worth noting that the Needham family as a whole appear to have had a genuine weakness for repeating firearm mechanisms. As early as April, 1851, Joseph Needham secured the Attorney General's 149th Certificate under the "Protection of Inventions Act, 1851" for a self-loading gun to be displayed at the Great Exhibition.

NEWTON, A. V. Probably the best known British Patent Agent of his day, Alfred Vincent Newton secured scores of English and British patents on behalf of their inventors (both for firearms and for numerous other devices) from the late 1840's until about 1870. He published a "London Journal" of patents news which appeared to have had at least semi-official blessing, and various pamphlets and books upon patented articles.

In our field, from the "Office of Patents" at 66 Chancery Lane, London, he secured communicated Br. Pats. 2263/1859 (PERRIN & DELMAS) and 902/1863 (J. C. CAMPBELL) which survived into our period, and 3258/1865 (S. CRISPIN); and 2463/1870 (G. O. KINNE) within it. He was succeeded by a namesake.

NEWTON, W. E. William Edward Newton matched the above-named in sheer bulk of patents secured but, whether by chance or by desire, the numerous patent applications in which he acted included only one within both our period and field of interest. From the "Office of Patents" above-mentioned, he secured Br. Pat. 3987/1868 (q.v.) for A. HOTCHKISS and E. H. & A. P. PLANT, giving as his occupation that of Civil Engineer. His exact relationship to A. V. NEWTON is unknown to the writer.

NEWTON, H. E. Another member of the famous family and also a Civil Engineer by profession. He acted (from the "Office of Patents") to secure provisional protection under Br. Pat. Nos. 4579/1881; 4602/1881; and 4689/1881 for THE COLT'S PATENT FIREARMS MFG. CO. (INC.), but for no other inventors of revolving arms known to the writer. The subject of this provisional protection is discussed further in Chapter IV.

NOËL, P. J. J. Secured communicated Br. Pat. No. 450/1868 through A. M. CLARK (q.v.) for improvements to battery guns, ordnance, projectiles and cartridges of only theoretical concern to us, which he abandoned at the earliest practicable date.

He was a dentist by profession, and gave his own address for service as at 29 Blvde St. Martin, Paris.

NOËL, S. A. See, specifically, F. GUEURY in regard to their jointly held Br. Pat. 659/1865 for a radially-chambered revolver pistol fired by a laterally falling hammer. The patent was communicated to W. CLARK (q.v.) from 29 Blvde St. Martin, Paris, which suggests either that this inventor was related to P. J. J. Noël above or that it was the address of a patent agent.

NORDENFELT, T. The manually-operated Nordenfelt machine-gun had a fame in its own field fully equal to that of the Gatling and other similar weapons discussed in Chapter VI, but lacked any rotary ammunition feed in the basic design to bring it to our attention.

This famous name appears here, therefore, only in relation to provisional protection under Br. Pat. 5324/1880 for a "breech-loading repeating bolt-gun" which embodied a rotating cartridge wheel-feed.

The applicant, a Civil Engineer, gave his address as 1 St. Swithin's Lane, City of London.

NORMAN, W. N. Joint-applicant, with J. RIGBY (q.v.) for Br. Pat. 899/1860 (see Table I) which they carefully maintained for its full life.

Specific claims in respect of revolvers with a hinged barrel moved by a lever, and connected with a rammer for loading the chambers, were included in the Specification, but the real value of the patent presumably lay in the cartridge and sporting gun designs which were its principal features.

OESTERREICHISCHE   WAFFENFABRIKS-GESELLSCHAFT. World-famous Austrian small-arms manufacturing firm based on the town of Steyr. Probably identical with (or the Parent Company of) the AUSTRIAN SMALL-ARMS MANUFACTURING CO. (q.v.) in relation to Br. Pat. 7989/1885, of concern to us.

First secured communicated Br. Pats. 1272/1878 and 1960/1878, in the Company name only, through A. M. CLARK (q.v.). The first related to the Company's original cylindrically-cased revolving cartridge magazine for bolt-action rifles, and the second to detachable magazines of this type.

Thereafter the British Patent applications by the Company, in our field, were communicated to the Patent Agents by J. WERNDL (the Managing Director) of O. SCHOENAUER (the Manager), under which names brief details of the other relevant Company patents appear: namely, 3878/1878; 2840/1879; 712/1882; 1982/1882; 229/1883 and 5793/1884.

The agents used were A. M. CLARK or G. E. VAUGHAN q.v.), and a specimen rifle appears in Plate 63.

O'MAHONEY, M. One of the few applicants in our field of stated Canadian domicile, at Toronto, Ontario.

Secured (through A. J. BOULT [q.v.]) communicated Br. Pat. 4146/1880 for a revolver combined with an ordinary walking stick. The protection was really sought in respect of the method of attachment by clamping plates grasping stick and revolver barrel.

OPPEN, VON, F. A. K. W. During the years of concern to us, the Colt Company had a sales depot at 14 Pall Mall, London, as the European base for this energetic salesman. He appears here as applicant for communicated Br. Pat. 3981/1868, on behalf of the COLT'S PATENT FIRE ARMS MFG. CO., of Hartford Conn., U.S.A.

This patent elaborated upon the claims of Alexander Thuer's U.S. Pat. 82258 of September 15th, 1868, or such features of it as the British Patent Office would accept for protection. It thus protected a system for the optional (and impermanent) conversion of muzzle-loading revolvers to use a special metallic cartridge. This was loaded from the front of the cylinder, and could be recharged in the pistol by using certain patented accessories. In this feature, the patent anticipated U.S. Pat. 98529 of January 4th, 1870, by which the reloading gear was later protected.

The cartridges were ejected from the front of the revolver cylinder by snapping the hammer against an ejector button, set in a movable ring at the breech. Pistols thus adapted were advertised as "Colt's New Patent Metallic Central Fire Cartridge Revolvers", and are rare today. Two weapons thus converted are shown in Plates 17 and 64.

Ingenious as the system was, appreciation of it is now clouded by wonderment as to why British patent protection was sought at all.

In America, the need for such a device rested on the Colt Company's failure to reach agreement with SMITH & WESSON (q.v.) for a licence to make conventional revolver cylinders under the master-patent of ROLLIN WHITE (q.v.).

In the United Kingdom, on the other hand, the White patent simply did not run, since it had been anticipated by J. H. JOHNSON (q.v.) in 1854. However, the researches of John E. Parsons have shown that conversion work on Model 1860 percussion revolvers was in hand, in London, in 1869, and he seems virtually committed to the view that American manufacture never occurred.

It may, of course, have been necessary to secure a British patent for technical reasons connected with the novelty requirements of American law, and Parsons has shown that the Colt Company had a fair investment in the Thuer mechanism. A U.S. patent of S. W. WOODS (q.v.) had been bought, which anticipated their basic idea for ejecting cartridge-cases by direct blows from the pistol hammer.

If the British patent suggests an intent to manufacture Thuer components in England for export to the U.S., it should be borne in mind that the U.S. import duty on gun parts was then 30% *ad val.*, and that no apparent attempt was made to pick up all possibly relevant British Patents. Thus, there is no trace of any appropriate assignment for T. POULTNEY's (q.v.) Br. Pat. 1625/1867, covering ejection of cartridge-cases from revolver cylinders by the blow of the hammer against the separate firing-pin provided for each chamber.

Parsons has demonstrated that the U.S. equivalent of this patent was there regarded as an infringement of the ROLLIN WHITE master patent, which accounts for the lack of Colt interest in America, but not for the United Kingdom where the Rollin White patent did not run.

A possible, if slender, clue to Colt's reasons for persisting with this patent may lie in the fact that the British services still held fairly large stocks of obsolete muzzle-loading revolvers (something over 12,000 serviceable weapons, in mid-1869) and the Company may have had hopes of securing an order for their conversion to the Thuer system.

Two weapons comprised these stocks; the old Colt "Navy", or Belt, Model of 1851, and the solid-framed British Beaumont-Adams' revolver (see Plate 1) of 1855.

As will be demonstrated below, the claims of von Oppen's patent placed considerable stress upon the conversion of solid-framed revolvers by use of the Thuer unit, as well as its use with the Colt system of construction by separate barrel and frame components.

Against this theory for Colt's interest in a British patent for the Thuer system is the inescapable fact that known service conversions of the

Beaumont-Adams' revolver (see Plates 19 and 20) were by using a conventionally bored-through cylinder, which seems to dispose finally of any idea that a bar existed to the use of such cylinders in the United Kindgom in 1869.

As to the actual claims of Br. Pat. 3981/1868, we have, firstly, the side-hammer, solid-framed "Roots Model", or Model 1857 Colt percussion revolver (see Plate 59) shown in the Specification as suitable for conversion, although actual specimens are almost unknown.

Secondly, the system was specifically claimed as applicable to revolvers of the "Remington-type", i.e. to revolvers having solid frames. This may suggest a possible link of interest between the two companies here, but seems more in point on the question of the use of the conversion system on solid-framed pistols.

Thirdly, a spring "snap" cartridge ejector ring *not* operated by a hammer blow was specifically claimed. The conventionally accepted picture of the Thuer conversion unit requires that the pistol hammer be used to eject the cases. and this refinement may bear further examination and inquiry by Colt enthusiasts.

Plate XVIII of U.S. Ordnance Memoranda No. 14, "Metallic Cartridges (Regulation and Experimental) as Manufactured and Tested at the Frankford Arsenal, Philadelphia, Pa.", submitted by Major T. J. Treadwell, U.S.A., in 1873 featured the curious cartridge shown as Fig. 18, under the heading "For the 1st Alteration, Colt's Pistol. Nov. 1868." This was not the conventional "Thuer" round.

Major Treadwell commented: "This cartridge was made as an experiment for use in the first alteration of Colt's army revolver. It was inserted into the chamber at front and held in place by the friction of the bullet and ignited at centre by a firing-pin; the friction of the bullet was not at all times sufficient to ensure ignition, necessarily resulting in misfires. A cartridge made with a thin cap and outside priming is said to have worked well."

It would be interesting to know if this cartridge and the second type of Thuer ejection ring should be associated.

OVERBECK, DE, BARON G. Secured (from 22 Ryder St., St. James's, London) Br. Pat. 3411/1883 for improvements to "breech-loading repeating and single-shooting small-arms" which included a claim for a rotary, screw-feed cartridge magazine in the butt and stock-wrist of an under-lever operated rifle.

PACE, G. Secured Br. Pat. 4378/1880 for improvement in "multitubular fire-arms", as he termed them. The weapon was a machine-gun of general "Gatling" appearance which (unlike that weapon) fired on minute intermittent pauses in rotation of the barrel cluster.

The applicant gave domicile in Valetta, Malta.

PALMER, W. Secured Br. Pat. 1592/1862 which survived into our period (see Table I) for a firearm in which the charges were successively supplied to the

EXPERIMENTAL CARTRIDGE

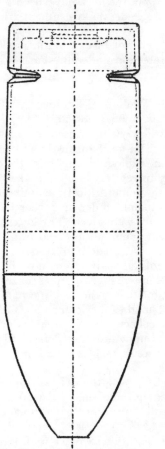

FOR THE 1st ALTERATION COLT'S PISTOL. NOV 1868

FIG. 18. *Major T. J. Treadwell, U.S.A. Ordnance Memorandum No. 14. 1873, Plate xviii, "Metallic Cartridges (Regulation and Experimental)," etc. (See F. A. K. von Oppen).*

barrel by means of movable chambers moved by a self-acting revolving carrier, which took them from a receptacle in the stock and deposited them in the breech of the barrel. After firing, each chamber "dropped away" from the barrel.

The name is too common to permit confidence, but the writer is inclined to the belief that this applicant may have been an American patent agent, based on New York, or a Federal Government arms purchasing agent.

PASS, DE., E. Patent Agent (of Fleet Chambers, 68 Fleet St., London) who secured provisional protection under Br. Pats. 2500/1875 and 111/1876 for E. HENARD OF Paris (q.v.).

PAULSON, R. Richard Paulson ("Engineer", of Boon Mills, Langwith, Notts.) secured Br. Pats. 10664/1885 and 14130/1886, of interest as containing about the earliest British-based concern with the operation of conventional revolver pistol mechanisms by utilizing either the recoil of discharge or the force of the exploding gases from the cartridge.

Br. Pat. 10664/1885 merely explored the idea generally. Revolvers were mentioned (along with Snider rifles!) as suitable for the application of systems protected in principle under an earlier Paulson patent, No. 14,015/1884, but no actual details were given. The latter patent has no place in our study, since the revolving ammunition feed principle was not applied in it.

The writer has never succeeded in tracing an actual embodiment of "Paulson's revolver", but the weapon shown in the drawing to one Complete Specification, as amended (see Fig. 19), does suggest that specimens may once have existed. The outline and basic lock-mechanism are those of a conventional, cheap, machine-made American single-action pocket revolver of the type known to modern collectors as a "Suicide Special".

Such weapons were abundant in the 1880's, and their cheapness and use of small-calibre, low-pressure cartridges would make them a most suitable test-bed for Paulson's ideas.

In May and November, 1888, the Official Journal of the Patent Office reveals that Paulson heavily amended the wording to his Specifications as originally filed, on the grounds that "I had no agent in the Country when I drew out and first sent in the Complete", and this does suggest to the writer that active experiment with his revolver may have continued over several years.

The relevant parts of the Complete Specification to Br. Pat. 14130/1886 are therefore included in this work (see Fig. 19) against the chance that specimens of experimental weapons have survived, and for the intrinsic interest of the design as a whole.

Lieut.-Col. R. K. Wilson has examined Paulson's ideas in his own writings, and students of semi-automatic or self-loading firearms employing non-rotary cartridge feed systems will (or certainly should be) familiar with them through this most able authority. For our purposes, pending identification of actual embodiments, Paulson unfortunately merits no further space in a

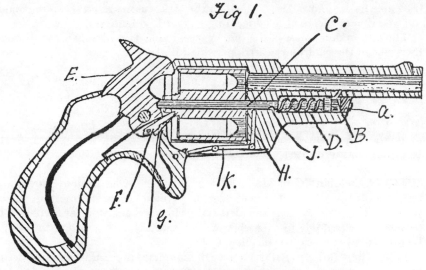

FIG. 19. *Paulson's Gas-operated Revolver.*

Fig. 1 shows the application of my invention to an ordinary revolver.

The piston "A", placed under the barrel, *being* operated by the gases generated by the explosion passing through the small perforation "B", in the barrel, forces the sliding-rod "C" against the resistance of the spring "D". And *thus* presses back the hammer "E", thereby cocking it, and turning the chamber by means of the pin "F" engaging in the teeth "G" in the ordinary way. The small lever "K" is controllable by the trigger and the *trigger*-spring. Thus the pin "H", may be made to enter the catch "J", which retains the sliding rod "C" back against the pressure of the spring "D", until the trigger is released from the pressure of the finger as the weapon is fired. When thus liberated the sliding rod "C" is forced back into its original position by the spring "D", and the weapon is thus again ready for firing. Without the aid of the said lever "K" and locking pin "H" to retain the rod "C" at each discharge as aforesaid, one pull or pressure on the trigger would cause the whole of the chambers to be discharged in rapid succession.

book of this size, since he abandoned his patents early in their potential lives (see Table II).

PERRIN & DELMAS. Secured communicated Br. Pat. 2263/1859 through W. E. NEWTON (q.v.), which survived into the period of concern to us and related both to revolving firearms and centre-fire cartridges. The firm was presumably French, and 200 "Perrin" revolvers are known to have been purchased by the Federal or Northern arms buyers under press of the Civil War.

Identification of a true and acknowledged specimen of a revolver made to the Specification of Br. Pat. 2263/1859 has always eluded the writer.

Revolving arms marked "Perrin & Cie. Brte" were not uncommon and many were designed for the Perrin cartridge, but they owed nothing readily traceable to the above design in which the lock was operated by an ingenious rod and detent mechanism connecting trigger and hammer.

The late maintenance of the patent (see Table I) probably arose through the value of the centre-fire cartridge which it also protected.

PHILLIPS, W. J. See, specifically, c. j. LINBERG and communicated Br. Pat. 3154/1870.

PIDDINGTON, J. Patent Agent at 53 Gracechurch Street, London. Acted for A. SPIRLET (q.v.) in communicated Br. Pat. 2107/1870, and c. f. TACKELS (q.v.) for communicated Br. Pat. 2662/1872.

PIEPER, H. Belgian "Gun Manufacturer" of Liège, who secured provisional protection under Br. Pat. 2043/1883 for "Rifled tubes for insertion in the barrels of firearms", which included claims for steel adaptors for revolvers, to be inserted separately in each chamber. A small cheap cartridge could thus be used in a heavy-calibre pistol.

Later (Br. Pat. 2167/1886) secured complete protection for his better known firearms design, in which a sliding barrel and over-long cartridge-case mated at the moment of firing to prevent gas-escape between chamber and barrel on revolving arms.

The so-called "Nagant" design (developed after the close of our period), in which the cylinder moved to and fro to effect the seal, was a rather better-known variant of this very old revolving arms principle.

Br. Pat. 2167/1886 was filed from 47 Lincoln's Inn Fields, W.C., which suggests that J. H. JOHNSON acted for the inventor.

PIRLOT & TRESART. Secured communicated Br. Pat. 10974/1887, through A. ARBENZ (q.v.) for a safety device for self-cocking revolvers with shrouded hammers. Normally, it was proposed to lock the hammer in the "down" position by an intercepting spring. Only deliberate depression of this spring (through the firer operating an external lever) would permit the weapon to be fired by pulling the trigger. The firm was Belgian-based and substantial; the associated firm of "Pirlot Frères" is also noticed in Chapter IV, and see Plate 24.

PLANT, A. P. & E. H. See, specifically, A. HOTCHKISS and communicated Br. Pat. 3987/1868.

POLAIN, P. Applicant (of Liège, Belgium) for Br. Pat. 2210/1865 protecting a pin-fire revolver with a sliding barrel and highly unconventional cylinder. Drawing forward the barrel withdrew sleeves in the cylinder and permitted loading of the cartridges *sideways* into the chambers then exposed to receive them.

Monsieur A. POLAIN was Director of the Liège Proof House at about this date, and may have been related to this inventor.

POLLAK, A. Secured communicated Br. Pat. 1251/1863 (through J. H. JOHN-SON [q.v.] which survived into our period. The writer has not encountered an embodiment of the inventions which were thus protected.

In relation to revolving arms a hammerless rifle employing a metallic cartridge longer than the cylinder was claimed, reciprocal movement being given to the latter by the lock mechanism.

POPE, A. A. Secured communicated Br. Pat. 1381/1876 as one of a string of successful spring-operated pneumatic weapon designs and patents. This was apparently the only patent which embodied a revolving pellet-feed for the breech-loading air pistol which it protected.

Pope was based on Boston, Mass., U.S.A.; A. C. CAREY (q.v.) was the communicant for the patent.

POULTNEY, T. Secured Br. Pat. 1625/1867 for "revolving small-arms for use with central fire metallic cartridges", under which prosaic title a most eccentric revolver pistol was duly protected. This was, in effect, a development of the weapon earlier patented by S. CRISPIN (q.v.).

The barrel and forward half of the cylinder tipped down on a frame-hinge for loading or unloading a centre-fire metallic cartridge flanged around its middle, instead of at the base of its case. On this annular flange or belt the round chambered in the rear half of the cartridge cylinder, before the two halves were united for firing.

Each chamber had a separate firing-pin and, when reloading, the hammer was used to eject the empty cases from the rear half of the cylinder rather in the fashion adopted by S. W. WOOD (q.v.), or that used in the well-known Colt "Thuer" conversions (see F. A. K. W. VON OPPEN) i.e. by cocking and snapping the pistol lock. Thus a blow from each firing-pin in turn ejected the cartridge-cases from Poultney's revolver.

Equivalent American patent protection ran for this particular attempt to avoid infringing the U.S. master patent of ROLLIN WHITE (q.v.) for the bored-through revolver cartridge-cylinder, but reasons for seeking a British patent on the system are not apparent. Apart from the fact that White's patent had no weight in England, no suitable British cartridge has yet been identified for the revolver. Even in America, the only suitable round seems to have been that later patented by L. A. Merriam under U.S. Pat. 86091 of January 19th, 1869.

Poultney gave his address for any service of papers under the British Patent as of Baltimore, Maryland, U.S.A., and the Langham Hotel, London (a noted haunt for American visitors), and his name turned up frequently in the field of Anglo-American firearms development. He took assignments of the U.S. rights to some quite well-known British revolver designs (including one of JOHN ADAMS's [q.v], and his exact status and position in the arms industry will one day have to be evaluated.

In the context of this particulat British Patent, his appearance here is probably almost accidental. Presumably some commercial manœuvre in the

M

U.S.A. prompted his interest in this extraordinary revolving weapon, and a British Patent was sought as a necessary part of its protection.

Parsons quoted the Colt Company's view that the device infringed Rollin White's U.S. master-patent, but suggested that the valuable feature of the patent lay in the possible priority of date that it gave to any holder, for the ejection of cartridge-cases by means of a blow from the revolver hammer.

Pending further research, this certainly seems a possible explanation for Poultney's interest in the design. Whether that interest was to be exercised for or against the ejection system of F. A. K. W. VON OPPEN (q.v.) also awaits explanation.

PRYSE, C., THE YOUNGER. Gunmaker (of Aston, near Birmingham) and patentee, under Br. Pat. 4421/1876, of a revolver lock modification for which modern writers claim more than was actually sought by its inventor.

An example of the classic Pryse pistol is shown at the foot of Plate 34, in the "Webley No. 4" version most commonly encountered, and it can be seen that the revolver was a pleasing hinged-frame design, with a "press-in" barrel latch, a turn-button cylinder release, and a double-action lock in which the sear tail protruded through the back of the trigger-guard. All these features are commonly regarded as identifying features of the arm, and the work of its inventor, Charles Pryse.

As a matter of cold fact, however, Br. Pat. 4421/1876 was entirely limited to claiming a cylinder-bolt jointed to the head of the trigger. This locked the cylinder after discharge (by the smaller locking notches to be seen in the Plate), as the trigger returned to rest. The bolt unlocked when the trigger was pulled, and the cylinder locked on firing by a lump on top of the trigger, which engaged in the large locking notches at the rear of the cylinder.

For the four features commonly claimed as Pryse's work, the Specification laid no claim, for it did not even illustrate the barrel latch or the cylinder release. It did show the rebounding hammer (commonly accomplished by resting the lower limb of the mainspring on a bent in the hammer tail, as claimed by J. STANTON [q.v]) but specifically disclaimed this lock-work as being "of the ordinary kind". This disclaimer presumably embraced the distinctive lower sear.

Distinct from this particular type of revolver, was a family that probably originated on the Continent, and a specimen made by A. FRANCOTTE (q.v.) is shown at the head of Plate 56. In these arms, a lock similar to that used in the Swiss M/78 revolver (see Chapter IV) was used, and the lower sear was not required. As can be seen from the revolver shown at the foot of Plate 35, the barrel latch was also used in cheaper revolvers that dispensed with Pryse's patented cylinder-bolt, and it is clear that further research will be needed to establish the true parentage of the type.

REMINGTON, E. & SONS. During the years of concern to us this was the trading name for an American corporation whose stock interest was largely or wholly held by members of the Remington family, until 1886, when it went into receivership.

In 1888 the company was reorganized by Hartley & Graham, of New York, and became the "Remington Arms Company" in which the Remington family ceased to have the controlling interest.

Although justifiably famous for quite a stable of fine revolving arms under the U.S. Patents of Beals, Rider, Elliott, Smoot and others, any searcher would have found surprisingly little to occupy his attention amongst the products of the Company so far as the United Kingdom was concerned.

Export drives were made just after the Civil War and in the mid-seventies but (apart from the Remington-Elliott revolving or "Zig-Zag" derringer pistol) the Company's revolving arms seem to have sold on the strength of quality rather than originality. The matchless Model 1875 Army revolver is shown in Plate 67, and specimens of their smaller-calibre pistols are also shown in Plate 10.

From the Company headquarters at Ilion, New York State, U.S.A., communicated British Patent protection was sought through w. r. lake (q.v.) for the spring-loaded rod-ejector used in Remington Army revolvers which has the return spring mounted on the cylinder-pin or arbour. This became Br. Pat. 2579/1875.

Apart from this case, British Patents traceably connected with the Company do not appear in the London Patent Office records, but remarks in relation to c. mason and f. a k. w. oppen may be noted. There is also the possibility (for more detailed researchers) that some of w. r. lake's more anonymous cases of U.S. background may repay attention in regard to its activities in Europe and the United Kingdom.

RICHARDS, T. Birmingham manufacturer (see specifically, c. h. carter).

RICHARDS, W. W. The appearance of this famous name on these pages may cause some surprise.

However, William Westley Richards's English Pat. 14027 of 1851 (a pre-Patent Law Amendment Act protection) would nominally have survived into our period. Two other relevant British patents had been abandoned.

The patent covered a variety of improvements other than those relating to revolvers, but the rather rare self-cocking revolving pistols protected by it form a definite field for study and its existence must be noted.

RICHARDS, W. Westley Richards (b. 1814; d. 1897) was the famous son of the above-mentioned, and carried a large measure of responsibility for the fame which his firm achieved in the years of concern here. Although a most prolific inventor and patentee, his interest was never apparently directed to revolving arms and his appearance here may cause the reader some surprise.

However, as one of the larger suppliers to the trade, he must be held to have concerned himself in such manufacture, and a persistent association links his name with revolvers of the type shown at the foot of Plate 35. For this reason he is included here, and it must also be remembered that the factory of the "National Arms & Ammunition Company" (which sprang from the old "Westley Richards Arms & Ammunition Company") was later the scene of manufacture for two weapons elsewhere noticed, namely, the Gatling machine-gun (Chapter VI) and the H. DIMANCEA revolver. It seems improbable that Westley Richards was not associated with this venture, in some way, or in the activities of H. SCHLUND (q.v.) later to be noticed.

RICHOUX, E. "Gentleman" of Paris, and joint applicant with E. BLED and J. WARNANT (q.v.) for Br. Pats. 5504/1881 and 5520/1888; see Fig. 6.

Since it seems likely that the latter, a Liège arms manufacturer, actually made the revolver locks thus protected, this interest was probably financial only.

RIGBY, J. Joint applicant for Br. Pat. 899/1860, which survived into the period. The relevant details are mentioned under W. N. NORMAN (q.v.), and Rigby merits notice here for activities earlier in the history of revolvers.

In the years preceding our own story, John Rigby had been active in the general promotion and development of ROBERT ADAMS's revolver, and in years later than those of concern to us another John Rigby served with distinction upon the Board of the Westley Richards Company amidst a variety of other duties connected with the British firearms industry.

Within our terms of reference, however, this brief note must serve.

RIGBY, T. Gun lock maker, of Bradmore (near Wolverhampton), who secured provisional protection under Br. Pat. 332/1867 for an improvement to "Gun and pistol locks" by which the cocks or hammers rebounded to half-cock after firing, through a modification of the standard form of mainspring and tumbler.

Application of the idea to revolvers was not claimed by the inventor, but he is included here as possibly associated with J. STANTON (q.v.).

ROBERTSON, BROOMAN & CO. Patent Agents at 166 Fleet St., and Southampton Buildings, London, from whose offices T. J. SMITH (q.v.) acted for communicated Br. Pats. 250/1871 and 380/1871 for L. W. BROADWELL and 3218/1871 and 3224/1871 for F. A. LE MAT.

Presumably T. J. SMITH was either a partner in the firm (or practised under that name) and it may also have acted for H. A. SILVER & W. FLETCHER (q.v.) in Br. Pat. 16078/1884, since the address for purposes of their application was given as 166 Fleet St.

ROLLINS, J. G. Secured provisional protection under communicated Br. Pat. 1299/1867 for R. DREW (q.v.). Address at Old Swan Lane, City of London, suggesting that he was a patent agent or otherwise only indirectly interested in the patent.

ROMANEL, R. C. Associated with F. MARTIN and A. H. WILLIAMS in two British Patents (Nos. 9998/1887 and 6994/1888) of minor concern to us.

The first protected a repeating magazine rifle of tilting breech-block or "Martini-type", in which a rotating cartridge magazine was embodied at the wrist of the butt. The second patent was for a refinement with added tubular magazine capacity within the butt proper.

The three men appear to have been definite joint applicants for the second patent, but the invention is mentioned under Romanel's name as he is believed to have been, initially, sole applicant for the first protection. The address for all three men for purposes of the application was 1 Dunning Terrace, Derby Road, Ponders End, N.

ROPER, S. H. Secured communicated Br. Patent 182/1867 (through J. H. JOHNSON; [q.v.]), giving his address at Roxbury, Mass., U.S.A. An U.S. patent (No. 53,881) had been secured on April 10th, 1866, and the inventor produced arms under it at Amherst, Mass., throughout the period. Four-shot shotguns were the standard Roper arm, having a revolving winged carrier to bear both loaded and discharged cartridges. An external, thumb-cocked hammer carried a linked plunger that chambered the cartridge into the barrel, fired it, and withdrew the case back into the revolving carrier. An alternative rifle barrel could be fitted to the shotguns, and a primitive muzzle-choke was also available to adjust the shot pattern. Originally, the guns were designed to use a reloadable steel charger, but later arms handled conventional centre-fire cartridges. ·

SALVATOR, E. A. Secured (from Washington, U.S.A.) Br. Pat. 12686/1886 for a water-cooled, manually operated magazine rifle, worked by an under-lever of Winchester type, which had two rotary features.

The magazine was not incorporated in the gun, but "strapped to the marksman" and contained a belt of cartridges wound upon a reel.

The breech mechanism of the actual weapon embodied a "feed-wheel" which carried live rounds to the breech (where they were fed to the firing chamber in the barrel) and fired cases away from it.

A certain similarity of principle may be noted with the weapon patented earlier in the year by L. & S. S. YOUNGHUSBAND (q.v.).

SCHLUND, H. or H. A. "H. Schlund" (from 28 Southampton Buildings, Chancery Lane, the address of patent agent C. D. ABEL [q.v.]) secured Br. Pat. 9084/1885 which protected most major features of the first Kynoch revolver (see Chapter IV).

"H. A. Schlund" (from 4 South Street, Finsbury, London) secured Br. Pat. 11900/1886 for certain improvements on 9084/1885, as to the bolting of the hinged barrel to the frame and for improvements to the lock that dispensed with the long lower trigger of the earlier design (see Plate 33).

Since the appropriate Abridgements of Patent Specifications, and the Journals, treated the two names as distinct, it is difficult to be certain now whether one man was involved, or two. Henry Schlund was an Engineer, and probably Birmingham-based at the time the patents were secured. Both versions of the Kynoch revolver were normally marked "Kynoch Gun Factory", and this was at Aston Cross.

However, patents for non-revolving firearms were secured under both initials during 1885 and 1886, and exhibited sufficient differences to suggest (if no more) that two men were involved.

The "H. SCHLUND" patents had the most distinctive appearance as being associated with the Kynoch works. They concerned Martini and Chassepot rifles which were produced intermittently at the Holford factory of the Kynoch group. Kynoch Ltd. did not take over this plant until 1901, but the works could still have been associated with George Kynoch himself. The previous owners, the National Arms & Ammunition Company, failed in 1882 and the enterprising George Kynoch was perfectly capable of operating one interest there, whilst maintaining another at the old Tranter pistol factory at Aston Cross. If this were so, it would have been reasonable for H. SCHLUND, as his associate, to be concerned with both enterprises.

The "H. A. SCHLUND" patents, on the other hand, related to recoil-operated semi-automatic rifles, a field of endeavour in which George Kynoch has not so far been traced. H. A. SCHLUND can also be found in association with A. MARTIN (q.v.) in patents entirely divorced from firearms, and his Br. Pat. 11900/1886 specifically mentioned multi-barrelled pistols as suitable for the application of its improvements. MARTIN's own Br. Pat. 1531/1880 for this type of pistol is described in Chapter V, with his association with the "BRAENDLIN ARMOURY CO. LTD" (q.v.).

The possibility of two related inventors need be pursued no further here. It is enough (in the present stage of the writer's knowledge) if the reader has grasped that a case can be made for two identities.

SCHOENHAUER, O. "Manager" of the OESTERREICHISCHE WAFFENFABRIKS-GESELLSCHAFT (q.v.) and applicant (through G. E. VAUGHAN [q.v.]) for communicated Br. Pat. 5793/1884. Presumably this protection (on a revolving cartridge magazine for bolt-action rifles) was sought on behalf of the Company. The reader's attention is also drawn to the notes upon THE AUSTRIAN SMALL ARMS MANUFACTURING CO.: F. MANNLICHER and J. WERNDL; and to Plate 63.

SCHULHOF, J. Probably best known for the Austrian repeating rifle that bears his name, and for his gallant attempts to produce magazine pistols operated entirely by trigger leverages, through their whole loading, firing and ejection cycle.

Secured Br. Pats. 9066/1886 (for a chain-wound rotary rifle-magazine); 10423/1887 (for an improvement thereto) and 10286/1888 (which included a spring-driven rotary magazine for bolt-action rifles).

The address of filing for the first of these patents was 8 Quality Court, London; for the second, 6 Paul's Churchyard; and for the third, 52 Chancery Lane, London. Presumably, they were all addresses of Patent Agents.

SCHNEE, G. H. Secured (from 39 Goethe Strasse, Munich, Bavaria) Br. Pat. 5607/1888, which included a rotary magazine (handling both the loaded and discharged rounds) for use in lever-operated rifles and pistols with sliding breech-blocks.

SEDERL, T. Secured provisional protection under Br. Pat. 87/1880 (through H. J. HADDAN) for a "Revolver with a device for automatically throwing out empty cartridge shells".

The idea broadly anticipated the relevant part of w. FLETCHER & H. A. SILVER's Br. Pat. 16078/1884 (q.v.) in that the falling pistol hammer struck a lever to eject rearwards the cartridge in the "one o'clock" chamber of a revolver cylinder at each discharge. The lever could be adjusted to spare a presumably loaded cartridge at the first shot.

Sederl communicated his patent from Vienna, Austria, and the idea received some attention on the Continent. The noted Swiss firearms designer Rudolph Schmidt actually embodied such an ejector ("du système Krauser") in one version of the Model 1882 (Officers) 7·5 mm. revolver which bore his name. This was rejected for service use and the writer believes that no such mechanism robust and simple enough for the field was ever evolved.

SHARPS, C. Noted American rifle and pistol designer (b. 1811; d. 1874), probably best known for his falling block rifles and for the ingenious, four-barrelled breech-loading pocket pistols mentioned in Chapter V; and see Plate 41.

Conventional revolving weapons apparently received some of his attention, and Br. Pats. 207/1859 and 1844/1863 (the latter communicated to G. DAVIES [q.v.]) survived into our period to protect improvements in such arms.

Curiously, in view of the care taken to maintain the earlier patent for half its potential life, signed Sharps's revolvers are almost unknown in both Britain and America, but since that patent also related to features of the above-mentioned pocket pistols, this contradiction may be more apparent than real. The inventor was never noted for a timid approach to production runs (American authority Robert E. Ernst estimated that over 148,000 of the pocket pistols were made), and interest in his revolvers may never have reached a level in either country to merit manufacture on a scale attractive to him.

However, a Continental literary reference of 1884 suggested that Sharps may have succeeded in a revolving arms venture towards the close of his life. The book mentioned that N.C.O.s of cavalry, artillery, etc., in the army of Saxony were still then armed with the "revolver Sharp, 1873".

No details of the arms were given, but the present writer would suggest that these weapons may have embodied features of U.S. Pat. 118752 of September 8th, 1871, for which no traceable British equivalent existed in Sharps's name.

Br. Pat. 1844/1863 protected two simple revolver cylinder designs quite suitable for use in small-calibre civilian revolvers. The Specification indicated the intention to use rim-fire cartridges, but nothing in the basic ideas (see Fig. 5) suggested that centre-fire cartridges would be unacceptable. The pistol sketched in Fig. 5 is a *suggested* embodiment only, but is based upon a known percussion weapon in an American collection which was signed "C. Sharps & Co., Phila., Pa.".

Basically, the two patented Sharps's cylinders were conventional, with the chambers bored through from end to end in defiance of the U.S. master-patent of ROLLIN WHITE (q.v.), but a backplate screwed on to, or into, them retained the cartridges and supported the heads against any tendency to bulge on discharge and jam the weapon.

In one version (see Fig. 5 for a suggested embodiment), the cylinder was removed entirely for loading or unloading, and the back-plate screwed on or off like the lid of a screw-capped jar, on threads cut on the rear periphery of the cylinder.

On the second version, the cylinder did not need to be removed for loading or unloading, since the back-plate had a loading-gate in it. On releasing a spring catch on the cylinder, the plate could be turned slightly on its seating to align chambers and loading-gate aperture for insertion or expulsion of the cartridges. Here the plate mounting-thread was cut in the rear wall of the hole (bored through the cylinder) in which the cylinder axis pin lay, and the plate was formed with a central threaded stem to mate with this hole.

The use of such devices in a service revolver is unlikely, and the above-mentioned "Saxon" revolver probably followed the principles of Sharps's U.S. Patent of 1871.

This patent protected a revolver with its barrel turning eccentrically upon a vertical axis to operate an automatic cartridge extractor. By using an eccentric pivot, the rear of the cylinder could be brought up hard against the standing breech without having to round off the edges.

Specimens of this revolver are rare, but a curiously similar pistol was developed in Switzerland, as the "Schmidt M/1874". This weapon used the pivoted barrel of Sharps's U.S. Pat., but the cartridge extractor was manually operated (by a button protruding beneath the barrel), and not of the automatic type.

The Swiss designer Rudolph Schmidt developed this weapon as a proposed replacement for the Chamelot, Delvigne & Schmidt service revolver, M/1872, of that country. It was not adopted, but a 9-mm. version was briefly considered for issue to unmounted officers.

SHEPHEARD, G. This applicant secured Br. Pat. 2214/1885, for a rotary-magazine firearm, with its metallic cartridges resting in a radially chambered drum behind the barrel. This embryonic "burp-gun" was powered by clock-work for rotation of the magazine, and operated automatically, after the first shot was fired, until the magazine was emptied.

The latter was controlled by an escapement mechanism, like a clock, to align it for loading the round into the actual firing-chamber. His address for filing was 35 Southampton Buildings, W.C., suggesting the employment of the Patent Agents HARRIS & MILLS (or B. J. B. MILLS [q.v]) as his advisers.

The writer has not seen an embodiment of the invention.

SILVER, H. A. Joint applicant for Br. Pat. 16078/1884. See, specifically, FLETCHER, W.

SKINNER, J. A. Co-applicant for provisional protection under Br. Pat. 2010/1872 (see, specifically, BROWN, J.).

SMITH, T. J. British patent agent (see, specifically, ROBERTSON, BROOMAN & CO.").

SMITH & WESSON. During the years of concern to us only one British Patent was secured in the joint names of these famous American revolver manufacturers. The partnership ended in 1874 (when Horace Smith sold his

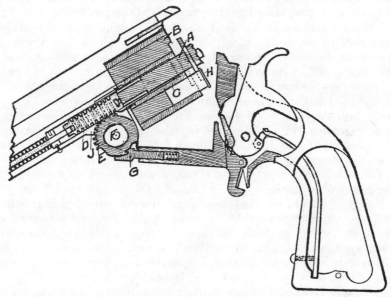

FIG. 20. *Smith & Wesson's Cartridge Extractor.*
(Br. Pat. 1510/1869.)

partnership to D. B. WESSON [q.v.]), and thereafter the title existed as a trading name only.

The partners communicated Br. Pat. 1510/1869 to the British Patent Agent W. R. LAKE (q.v.) as from their plant at Springfield, Mass., U.S.A. He duly assigned it to them, jointly, later in the year.

The patent protected the principle for extraction of all cartridges simultaneously from revolvers by "swinging the barrel forward away from the recoil block", and the automatic retraction of the cylinder rotation hand, or pawl, into the action body with the hammer at half-cock.

This cartridge extractor is justifiably famous, and warrants attention here despite repeated coverage in a number of most able works devoted exclusively to Smith & Wesson arms. It is shown in Fig. 20.

The extractor "A" has a recess for it in the rear of the cylinder "B", and thus forms part of the surface upon which the cartridge-rims rest.

The extractor has a long stem or shank to it (square in visible section, on the actual weapon) which passes through the hollow pin "C" upon which the cylinder revolves, and the forward end of this shank is coupled to a rack "D" in such a way that it can revolve without turning the rack.

A partially toothed wheel "E" in the joint "F" (which unites barrel and action body) engages rack "D".

To quote the Specification, "the peculiarity of this pinion (*i.e. wheel E*. Author) is that when the barrel is swinging forward the pinion first revolves about $\frac{1}{8}$ part of a turn, giving the cartridge shells room to clear the breech-block before they are started from the chambers of the revolving cylinder; the pinion is then caught and held by a pawl 'G' at the lower side, the rack 'D' being consequently forced back or left behind and with it the extractor 'A' which as the barrel is turned farther forward on the hinge 'F' pushes out the shells, the head of the extractor catching under their flanges, as shown at 'H'. A projection is formed on the stock in front of the pinion 'E' and when the barrel is swung far enough for this projection 'J' to strike against the head of the pawl 'G' and push it back, the pinion 'E' revolves freely, and the rack 'D' flies forward to its former position, carrying with it the extractor 'A', and also turning the pinion 'E' until it occupies its first place relative to the rack. In order thus to impel the rack 'D' forward when the pinion 'E' is released any suitably arranged spring may be used."

This extractor was used on the first of the really heavy calibred robust Smith & Wesson Army revolvers, namely the famous Model No. 3 Single Action American Model made briefly (but in some numbers) in 1869 or 1870, and shown in Plates 29 and 66. Specimens encountered are commonly chambered for the ·44-in. S. & W. Centre-Fire Cartridge, but variants exist chambered for the ·44-in. Henry Rim-Fire and ·46-in. Rim-Fire cartridges. The author once owned a cased, fully nickel-plated specimen of the former variant with serial number 12765 and Birmingham proof-marks.

A thousand of the centre-fire revolvers were delivered to the U.S. Army in 1871 and special cartridges (using Martin's pocket primer) were originally made up for them at Springfield Armoury.

The Br. Pat. 1510/1869 appears to cover the principle later protected as U.S. Pat. 94003 of August 24th, 1869 (which the Smith & Wesson partnership must already have secured from the inventor Charles A. King, of Springfield, Mass., U.S.A.) and although not maintained for its full life (see Table II) was a vital link in the chain of protection for the later, more numerous, refinements of the Model No. 3 design (see Plate 31).

Early weapons made on its principle additionally acknowledged, with others, the U.S. patent of w. c. DODGE (q.v.), No. 45912 of January 17th, 1865, which was assigned to Smith & Wesson by the inventor.

Other British patents to be associated with Smith & Wesson are noticed in relation to T. J. VAIL, D. B. WESSON and J. H. WESSON, A. W. WHEELER, and R. WHITE.

SOMMERVILLE, A. Partner in the firm of Birmingham gun manufacturers trading as "Braendlin, Sommerville & Co.",—see BRAENDLIN, F. A. & G. C.— and joint-applicant with C. F. GALAND (q.v.) for Br. Pat. 3039/1868, protecting the revolver known as "The Galand and Sommerville Patent Self-extractor Revolver" (see Chapter IV, and Plate 37).

The association with the Braendlin family had apparently ceased by March, 1871, when they formed "THE BRAENDLIN ARMOURY CO. LTD.," since neither Galand nor Sommerville figures in the records surviving for that Company as holders of any shares or assets.

However, the present writer remains convinced that the revolver was manufactured by this Company. The Complete Specification was signed by C. F. GALAND (q.v.) alone, and this does suggest that death had removed Sommerville from the scene. The trading name "A. Sommerville & Co." was one more familiar to those using percussion, rather than cartridge, weapons, and Sommerville must have been of some age. If death did intervene, it would be reasonable for manufacture of his revolver to remain with the Braendlin company, under patent royalty.

SPIRLET, A. Communicated Br. Pat. 2107/1870 to J. PIDDINGTON (q.v.) and described himself as "Armurier" of 5 Quai de la Boverie, Liège, Belgium.

The patent protected locks and lock actions; loading and cartridge extraction with one hand; and a cartridge extractor ideally requiring a special holster for satisfactory operation in a revolver.

This weapon was a top-hinged "break open" pistol with a star-shaped cartridge extractor and was rather similar in appearance to the revolvers described under W. J. HILL. The extractor, however, did not work automatically, but was operated by striking a knob under the barrel against the edge of a saddle-bow, holster or other suitably hard object. The design was a definite landmark in Continental revolving arms development, and a revolver using Spirlet's frame, but not his patented extractor, may be seen in Plates 47 and 48; this weapon is marked externally "F. Martin & Cie. Patent", but bears the internal stamps of "B. T. Rocour-Delsa & Cie.". Amusingly, there is no extractor, the cylinder being removed in order to punch out the cartridges separately against the cylinder axis pin.

STANTON, J. Gun lock manufacturer at 13 Clifton Street, Wolverhampton, noted for patents and refinements on sporting gun locks. His Br. Pat. 49/1867 (provisionally protecting the rebounding of cocks or hammers to half-cock after firing by a safety-spring bearing on the hammer breast); 367/1867 (similar rebound be modifying mainspring and lever of tumbler); 3774/1869 (rebound by lengthened tumbler engaging hook end of mainspring); and 928/1877 (primarily for a mainspring bearing for rebounding back-action safety-locks) are believed to be in point to our present study.

The last patent is included as apparently covering the principle of mounting hammers or tumblers on a separate centre screwed into the lock-plate, intsead of using the conventional trunnions or transverse screws.

Connection between Stanton and revolver manufacture in Britain can normally be demonstrated only by an internal examination of the pistol in question, but a few arms marked "Stanton & Co. With Self-Acting Safety" were made. Whether internally or externally marked, the protection recorded was that for the hammer rebound to prevent accidental discharge by a blow.

Two types of revolver were most commonly marked internally with a "C" prefixed serial number, and the legend "Joint Patents. Stanton & Co.", namely, the pistols of C. PRYSE THE YOUNGER (q.v.), and the lesser-known "Hill's Patent" weapons discussed under W. J. HILL.

STARR ARMS CO. This was a substantial American firm, based on New York City, but with factories elsewhere in New York State. It was active from 1858 until 1867, and made percussion revolvers, percussion or rim-fire carbines, and four-barrelled rim-fire pistols similar to those by C. SHARPS (q.v.) discussed in Chapter V.

Br. Pat. 880/1860 was communicated by the Company to W. CLARK (q.v.), and duly assigned to it after grant. This protected a double-action percussion revolver (see Plate 2), which was later protected as U.S. Pat. 30843/1861 by E. T. Starr. In fact, a single-action version was also made, and nearly 48,000 Starr revolvers were sold to the Union forces during the American Civil War; by embodying a frame hinge, the barrels could be tilted to allow removal of the cylinders (which turned on integral centres), and the double-action lock was cocked by the large trigger to be seen in Plate 2, and fired by the trigger bow touching a small sear at the rear of the trigger-guard.

The Company never bothered to secure British patent protection for the single-action pistol, but Starr revolvers were sold over here, usually after proof at Birmingham. One curious variant of the Starr pistols lay in a version converted to take metallic cartridges; many of these were proved in Germany, but the date and purpose of the conversion has not yet been established.

STRINGFELLOW, W. Secured Br. Pat. 5564/1881 (from Mistley, Essex) for "Pistols, guns or fowling-pieces, rifles, fieldpieces and other firearms, which can discharge shot, smooth or rifled balls, shells or other projectiles from the same set of horizontal revolving chambers".

The Specification described a radially-chambered "drum" or "turret" type revolving firearm which must have looked rather like a primitive Lewis machine-gun of the 1914–18 era. Discharge of the cartridge occurred in each chamber as its mouth mated with a cone in the end of the barrel, by a reciprocal or to and fro movement of the "drum".

The patent was maintained for a surprisingly long period (see Table II), but the writer has not seen an embodiment of the invention.

STURTEVANT, E. L. Secured Br. Pat. 798/1867 primarily concerned with breech-loading magazine rifles, but the Specification included a claim for a revolving magazine in the butt of such arms which requires that it be recorded here.

The applicant gave his address as of Boston, Mass., U.S.A.

SWINGLE, A. American "Machinist" of San Francisco, Calif., U.S.A., who secured Br. Pat. 2965/1879 for a breech-loading repeating small arm with a chambered magazine, which rotated behind a barrel upon a longitudinal pin or axis.

The Specification described a lever-operated rifle, with a "vertically moving" breech-block supporting the cartridge on discharge, after it had been fed from the revolving magazine into the barrel.

TACKELS, C. F. "Captain of Infantry" residing at Huy, Belgium, who communicated Br. Pat. 2662/1872 to British Patent Agent J. PIDDINGTON (q.v.) for improvements to revolvers. The writer is uncertain as to his relationship to the Continental small-arms authority Gerard Tackels, who published various papers on this subject (between 1866 and 1872) through the house of Ch. Tanera, of Paris.

Captain Tackels's original revolver was a "Break-open", hinged-frame weapon, with a star-shaped cartridge extractor in the cylinder operated by depressing the barrel in the same manner as for the SMITH & WESSON weapon protected under Br. Pat. 1510/1869 (q.v.). However, his extractor lacked the American refinement by which the plate snapped back into the cylinder after ejecting the cartridge-cases and the only way to return the plate was by closing barrel and frame to their normal position. This defect was eliminated in a later version.

The Specification to Tackels's British Patent described his extractor and barrel catch or bolt (which half-cocked the revolver when operated) but actually claimed protection as improvements only for the lock mechanism, the method of mounting and tensioning the two main lock springs, and the advantages of his lock as preventing fouling from entry to the action body of the pistol.

The lock-work was complicated and appeared delicate from the drawings. Its most noteworthy feature was the employment of rotation teeth (cut on the rear of the cylinder circumference) in engagement with "an oscillating rod, lever or plate receiving its motion from the trigger by means of a guide or intermediary lever", in place of the central ratchet-and-pawl combination used for cylinder rotation in the majority of revolvers.

The pistol was considered of sufficient merit to be tested in the Swiss revolver trials of 1871, but was eliminated in favour of the revolvers mentioned under SMITH & WESSON, GALAND, and Chamelot-Delvigne (see Chapter IV).

No British interest was aroused, whether as a service revolver or for commercial use.

TASSEL, Y. C. M. Communicated Br. Pat. 5420/1881 to W. H. BECK (q.v.) for provisional protection of a device by which spring-loaded, laterally closing safety-flaps boxed the triggers of firearms into their trigger-guards. Revolvers were specifically claimed as weapons suitable for this device.

TAYLOR, J. P. Communicated Br. Pat. 1686/1871 from Elizabethton, Carter County, Tenn., U.S.A., to B. J. B. MILLS (q.v.), for improvements to "Battery guns". Taylor's gun owed nothing to the famous design of R. J. GATLING (q.v.) and see Chapter VI, for it featured a multi-chambered breech-piece that revolved to align clusters of chambers with sets of barrels.

Later, Br. Pat. 1549/1873 was communicated to the same Agent for improvements to 1686/1871 and as to cartridges for use in it. Here, Taylor was acting as Trustee for the "Taylor Repeating Ordnance Association" of Knoxville, Tenn., U.S.A. Later in 1873, he communicated a further patent of improvement (Br. Pat. 2811/1873) to the same Agent, but in his own name. All three patents were void by 1876 (see Table II).

TAYLOR REPEATING ORDNANCE ASSOCIATION. See "TAYLOR, J. P.".

THOMAS, J. Birmingham gun and pistol manufacturer and patentee (under Br. Pat. 779/1869) of a cartridge extraction system for revolvers by which all the cases were extracted simultaneously on turning over the barrel and drawing it forward about 1 in. out of the frame. A stout knob rather similar to that on an old-fashioned door-bolt, and protruding from the bottom barrel-flat, was the normal means of the operation, but the patent actually sought to protect three methods of extraction.

The production weapon was unusual amongst early self-extracting designs in that the robust feature of a gate-loading, solid frame could be retained with the improvement. The barrel moved to and fro (dragging the cylinder with it in an unusually long frame aperture) and a star extractor fixed to the face of the standing breech held the cartridges by their rims until they could fall clear.

The principle of operation will be clear from Plate 37, but the feature not readily observable from any illustration is the quite powerful camming effect of the coarse barrel-bolting thread when engaged, but turning in its frame seating.

This camming effect can "unstick" fired cartridge-cases quite effectively, but if allowed to collect gummy oil or rust the thread freezes readily.

Although the inventor was unlucky in his timing for introducing the patent (more compact designs, like that of SMITH & WESSON, being evolved with it), he appears to have developed one version modestly, for about seven years, under licence or assignment to the firm of "Tipping and Lawden" (see P. WEBLEY & SON).

His revolvers are uncommon in that they often bear the true British Patent Number (i.e. "779") as well as a serial number presumably relating to this licensed arms production. Cast steel was the material favoured for the barrels and cyinders, but various modifications in detail, rifling and finish argue a fairly chequered production history.

W. W. Greener, in his "Modern Breech-Loaders", stated that the weapon was made in three sizes—450, 380 and 320 centre-fire, with five chambers—but the version most likely to be encountered is that in ·450 calibre. A fair market amongst provincial gunsmiths must have existed, since the patent was maintained for half its potential life (see Table II) but overall production cannot have been large. Pistols numbered between "2" and "621" have been personally owned by the writer, and serial numbers approaching "1100" reported to him.

The note upon JONES, T. should also be read in possible relation to this inventor.

THOMPSON, W. P. British Patent Agent, of the firm of w. p. thompson & co., who practised as Patent Agents and Consulting Engineers at 6 Lord St., Liverpool, and 323 High Holborn, London.

He acted for w. c. dodge (q.v.) in communicated Br. Pat. 772/1879, and continued active to the turn of the century.

THOMPSON, W. P. & CO. The identities of the men forming this firm (other than w. p. thompson) are unknown to the writer. However, it was from their London office that a. j. boult acted for m. o'mahoney (q.v.), and t. f. törnell (q.v.) filed for Br. Pat. 8331/1888 from their Liverpool address.

THORN, H. A. A., known as "CHARLES LANCASTER". In view of the attention paid in this book (see Chapter V) to the Lancaster pistols as competitor weapons to the conventional revolver (see Plate 42), it seems wise to set the record straight as to the identity of their inventor.

The original Charles Lancaster had been a barrel-maker with the great Joseph Manton and started his own business (at 151 New Bond Street) about 1826. He died in 1847, leaving two sons, Charles William and Alfred, who continued his business in partnership until 1859 when they split up.

Alfred opened his own business at South Audley St., switched later to Green Street, and died in 1890. His activities, so far as the writer is aware, have no bearing in our field.

Charles William remained at 151 New Bond St., until his death in 1878.

In 1870, he arranged for Henry A. A. Thorn (generally known as CHARLES LANCASTER) to be apprenticed to him for six years to learn the gunmaker's craft or trade and when he died arrangements were in train for a partnership between the two. Mr. Thorn, i.e. CHARLES LANCASTER, then bought the business at 151 New Bond St. (and the gun factory backing off it into Little Bruton St.) from the executors.

It was from this address that he secured three patents in point for us, under his true name, but trading as CHARLES LANCASTER.

Since the pistols discussed in Chapter V were *not* revolving arms, these patents must be dismissed rather summarily here, but under conditions of active service, they proved (along with more conventional double-barrelled weapons by Westley Richards and similar makers) to be a formidable competitor to the revolver.

Mr. Thorn's Br. Pat. 1242/1881 covered all his multi-barrelled, drop-down firearms (shotguns, rifles and pistols)as to their rotating-hammer lock-mechanism.

His Br. Pat. 213/1882 was a patent of improvement to its predecessor and followed the old WILLIAM TRANTER principle of a double trigger (one split to house the other) to share the duties of cocking and firing his weapons.

His Br. Pat. 3089/1882 was a comparatively shortlived protection (see Table II) for single- or twin-hammer locks with hinged hammer or tumbler noses to fire double- of four-barrelled arms respectively.

Mr. Thorn justly deserves his famous place in British gunmaking history, but so far as the writer is aware, true revolving arms never aroused his interest.

TÖRNELL, T. F. Br. Pat. 8331/1888 was secured from the Liverpool address of w. p. thompson (q.v.) in the name of this applicant.

The Complete Specification claimed a revolver lock mechanism, in which the trigger was used to bolt the cylinder in alignment with the barrel until it was rotated by the pawl. A lock of general "Nagant-type" was sketched in a solid-framed revolver, which clearly embodied the hinged trigger-guard of E. NAGANT (q.v.).

Since this applicant is so far unidentified, it is suggested that the design may have been under study in Scandinavia, where the leisurely revolver trials noticed in Chapter V were in progress at date of filing.

TRANTER, W. A portion of Chapter IV is devoted to the revolvers produced by this famous maker, who appeared to use every improvement that he patented. Little space is therefore devoted to his designs here.

As the bare list of his patents will show, he was obviously convinced as to the commercial value of such protection. Apart from his applications for refinements to conventional arms, thirteen British Patents related to revolvers and survived into our period, or were sought during its currency.

William Tranter died on January 7th, 1890, after nearly fifty years of activity in the Birmingham gun-trade, and it is important for the reader to grasp that revolvers never formed the base of his fortune, or business, during our period.

Prior to the years of concern to us, such arms may have absorbed a considerable part of his energies and the reader will probably be familiar with his famous double-trigger percussion revolvers. These were protected by Br. Pat. 212/1853 (see Table I) and marketed alongside their deservedly popular single-trigger stable-mates produced under the slightly later Br. Pat. 1913/1856 (see Plate 1).

However, the basic English Pat. 13527/1851 by which ROBERT ADAMS (q.v.) or his assignees virtually controlled manufacture of the solid-framed revolver in Great Britain forced Tranter, with others, into the position of mere licensee or lessee under it.

In 1864, however, an agreement between "Tranter & others" and "The

London Armoury Company & others", was registered at the British Patent Office which the writer believes related to the manufacture of revolvers under Adams's patent for the last year of its life. On Tranter's side, "the others" probably comprised (or included) the big Birmingham firm of I. Hollis & Son with whom he had been associated for many years and it is an indication of the strength of Adams's patent (if such it was) that formal action should have been thought necessary in the last year of its life. Unfortunately, 1963 saw the destruction of the surviving Patent Office records on the matter and it is doubtful if any papers now survive to settle the point.

What does seem clear, however, is that William Tranter (caught like so many others in the post-Civil War slump in the Birmingham gun-trade) still saw revolving arms as a useful part of his growing activities and moved into their manufacture on a much more substantial scale than he could comfortably handle from his original premises at 13 St. Mary's Square, Birmingham.

Accordingly, he built an additional and more roomy factory at Lichfield Road, Aston (near the Cross, there) which he then personally operated as the "Tranter Gun & Pistol Factory" until his retirement in 1885.

Exactly what was made at the factory is still not clear to the writer, but its products were apparently available to the Birmingham gun-trade as a whole and not sold exclusively by William Tranter (see Plate 68).

It will be observed that his revolver patents span the years 1865–79, and the writer therefore concludes that he moved into an almost pivotal position in the revolving pistol industry during that period to make and supply such weapons for all comers. His own patented mechanisms would have preference, but he would make special production runs under the patents of firms or individuals lacking manufacturing facilities of their own, as required, along with any other kind of small-arms for which he could secure orders.

Since he as a substantial property owner, a founder-shareholder in The Birmingham Small Arms Company Limited (ergo, a Director of it, in its earlier years), and a fairly prominent member of the Birmingham Small Arms Trade Association, the reader will appreciate that his interests were diverse and enabled him to keep his factory busy when more specialized firms were finding it hard to secure a continuous flow of orders.

His brother, David, was also a gunmaker (he died in 1884), and his son-in-law, Thomas William Watson (of Brixton, London), is believed by the writer to have been connected with the London gun-trade.

His own son, William Grosvenor Tranter, was apparently only slightly interested in the industry but his nephews, Alfred William Thompson and Thomas Musgrove Tranter, were raised in it, and the firm of "Tranter Brothers, Gunmakers," was still in business in Sand St., Birmingham during World War One.

In all, he can be seen as a man well-established in the industry of his choice, and well-cushioned against fluctuations in demand for particular types of weapon produced in it.

Pending further research upon his activities, he may safely be regarded as

N

having (between 1865 and 1879) either himself produced, or as having made for him, a considerable proportion of British revolving arms, but this must be accepted (in the writer's view) as indicating the modest size of the market and not the large scale of his operations.

Turning to his revolver patents, for the reason ealier stated a bare list of these numbers suffices here.

Br. Pats. 212/1853, 1913/1856, 2067/1862, and 1862/1863 survived into our period (see Table I).

During the period of this book, he secured: Br. Pats. 1899/1865, 2113/1866, 2228/1867, 285/1868, 3622/1868, 3557/1869, 2509/1871, 3171/1875, and 2855/1879 (see Table II). Not all of these patents related exclusively to revolving arms, but each contained claims applicable thereto.

Chapter IV discusses the arms produced under the above protection.

TRAWNICZEK, J. Secured communicated Br. Pat. 2865/1871 through w. r. lake (q.v.), describing himself as "Captain of Artillery", of Vienna, Austria. Only provisional protection was sought.

The improvement related to a cartridge-feed mechanism for revolving battery guns to replace the feed drum for the Gatling weapons, but was specifically claimed as adaptable to the "Albertine" and "Veltyl" guns.

TRESART. Joint applicant for communicated Br. Pat. 10974/1887 through a. ARBENZ (q.v.).

See, specifically, "PIRLOT & TRESART".

TRONCHE, A. Joint applicant with e. fabre (q.v.) for Br. Pat. 15771/1888, filed from 47 Lincoln's Inn Fields (once the address of j. h. johnson [q.v.]).

As to the claim for a pistol employing a "fore-and-aft" endless-chain cartridge feed to a reciprocating barrel, remarks under "GAY, P." should be noted. Manually operated chain-guns and pistols of this type never appear to have enjoyed popularity in the U.K. Presumably cleaning after use must always have presented a difficult problem with the types of ammunition then available.

TROTTER, J. F. Secured Br. Pat. 497/1879 for "Machine Guns", giving his address as 20 Southampton Buildings, Chancery Lane, London.

The patent is not stated to be for a "communicated" invention but is, in fact, for improvements on f. l. bailey's Br. Pat. 1703/1876 (q.v.) as to barrel mounts; automatic traversing of gun whilst firing; cartridge holders, etc.

TURBIAUX, J. E. Communicated Br. Pat. 2731/1882 from Paris, to e. g. brewer (q.v.), for protection of "A revolver which may be held in the hand with no part exposed except the barrel". This protected probably the best known of all "squeezer" pistols (i.e. pocket pistols of magazine type operated by clenching the entire fist) in the variety employing a rotary cartridge cylinder. This was marketed during our period by the "Minn. Fire

Arms Co.", of America as "The Protector" under U.S. Pat. 273644 of March 6th, 1883, and possibly made for them by the Ames Sword Co., of Chicopee, Mass., U.S.A., who manufactured an improved version for another company in the 1890's.

As can be seen from the patent dates visible in Plate 69, the specimen illustrated is this later model, embodying the grip-safety protected by P. H. Finnegan's U.S. Pat. 504154 of 1893. However, the Plate serves to show the weapon, and Plate 70 (of the mechanism) shows all too clearly the defect of such trochal arms in so often pointing a loader chamber at the firer.

VAIL, T. J. Communicated Br. Pat. 2250/1863 to British Patent Agent w. CLARK (q.v.), which survived into our period (see Table I). Vail was a curiously anonymous figure on this side of the Atlantic. The patent referred to him as of Hartford, Connecticut, U.S.A., and he duly took an assignment of it from Clark, after completion in 1864.

However, his name appeared in relation to other British patents (not necessarily connected with firearms) during this period and the writer suggests that he may have been a lawyer, patent agent or consulting engineer in Hartford.

Br. Pat. 2250/1863 related to hinged-frame "break-open" revolvers for metallic cartridges, and there were six claims in it. The first related to a flat-spring latch for uniting barrel and frame which also kept the cylinder on its axis pin; the second, to shaping the hammer-nose and latch to assist each other in locking barrel and frame together when the hammer was down; the third to use of the cylinder axis pin for punching out fired cases; the fourth to combining a detachable recoil plate and a spring to seal the lock frame against penetration of fouling; the fifth to a lock mechanism improvement; the sixth to a circular cap plate on the left of the action body combined with a securing screw permitting removal of the plate without stripping the lock parts.

The patent had an almost irresistibly Smith & Wesson "flavour", in association with their Br. Pat. 1510/1869 (q.v.). and the wide use later by that Company (and its licensees or imitators) of the Claim One method of anchoring cylinders, but the writer can produce no evidence to support the inference.

VAUGHAN, G. E. Prominent British Patent Agent at 67 (later 57) Chancery Lane, London. Active in various patents for firearms towards the close of our period, but of concern here only in relation to some of the communicated British Patents of J. WERNDL (q.v.) of the OESTERREICHISCHE WAFFENFABRIKS GESELLSCHAFT (q.v.) 712/1882, 1982/1882, 229/1883, O. SCHOENAUER (q.v.) 5793/1884, and the AUSTRIAN SMALL ARMS MANUFACTURING CO. (q.v.) 7989/ 1885.

VINE, J., the elder, and VINE, J., the younger. Joint applicants, with J. BROWN (q.v.) and J. A. SKINNER (q.v.) for provisional protection of a "Battery Gun" under Br. Pat. 2010/1872.

N*

WALKER, E. Secured Br. Pat. 3453/1867, for "Improvements in the construction of breech-loading ordnance", which protected a rotating ammunition feed. The device has no real place in these pages, but is included to show that the revolving principle was studied for this purpose.

WALLIS, C. E. This applicant produced few pistols under his patents, but he is still notable for the devotion with which he pursued three horribly dangerous ideas for improving the fire-power of revolvers. His two earlier systems were not new (see J. P. LINDSAY), but his insistence upon using a single hammer to fire superimposed charges was an act of faith in the accuracy of his machinists and the intelligence of his buyers.

Wallis's original idea (see Plate 71) had been provisionally protected as Br. Pat. 2248/1863, for a muzzle-loading revolver with two charges in each chamber. As can be seen from the Plate, the hammer *almost* struck the rear nipple, and the inventor hoped to fire the charges in the correct order by using a thicker (or larger) cap on the front nipple. When this had been crushed, the hammer could reach the thinner cap at the rear.

As a development of this idea, Wallis secured Br. Pat. 624/1864, which survived into the period. As envisaged, there was to be a movable striker on the hammer, which could be slid back to hit the rear nipple after firing the front charge. Given that the user remembered the setting required, there is no reason why this idea should not have been used in a weapon of the type shown at the top of Plate 33. However, the version adopted is shown at the foot of that Plate, where it can be seen that the rear nipples are now aligned with the bore and struck with an integral part of the hammer. The movable striker head is now missing, and it is not easy to see how it was to have served in regard to the front nipples, but it is safe to assume that it also served as a safety device to keep the hammer clear of both sets of nipples, when properly adjusted.

One of the curious features of Wallis's ideas was that he actually found someone to take an assignment of his patent, and records (now destroyed) at the British Patent Office revealed that someone called "Richardson" took such an interest at some time in 1865.

Two specimens examined by the writer were found in Ireland, but bore no maker's name. The suggestion is offered, without offence, that they were made by Richardson, of Limerick, since only an Irishman would be optimistic enough to want such a weapon.

Undeterred by the lack of commercial interest in these muzzle-loading arms, Mr. Wallis tried once again, in 1872, to interest the world in a revolver of conventional size, but abnormal fire-power. He was apparently unworried by the failure, commercially, of designs of J. P. Lindsay and J. Walch of America for doubly-loaded firearms.

Wallis's Br. Pat. 1605/1872 was secured from Albert Street, Peckham, Surrey, and provisionally protected a 12-shot revolver. The chambers were disposed in two layers, fired by separate hammers or strikers, but the single barrel could be aligned with either layer at the firer's election. Specimens are unknown, but one or two similar revolvers exist in which a movable switch-plate deflects the bullet into the barrel. These pistols are unmarked, but suggest themselves for association with this inventor.

WARNANT, J. Belgian firearms manufacturer, of Hognée, Commune of Cheratte, and Liège. Secured three British Patents for revolver locks, one of considerable importance and interest. Warnant was joint-applicant in each case, and all the designs embodied rebounds for the pistol hammers. None of the patents were maintained for their full lives (see Table II).

Br. Pat. 5031/1878 was secured jointly with M. KAUFMANN (q.v.), and was an admitted improvement of the 1876 patent of DE MOUNCIE (q.v.) shown in Fig. 17.

This Kaufmann/Warnant lock appears in Fig. 8, and should be compared with the lock of the "Enfield" service revolver shown in Plate 72.

The cartridge extraction system of that weapon was patented by O. JONES (q.v.), but a comparison of the two illustrations should establish the parentage of its lock mechanism.

Late in 1881, Warnant secured Br. Pat. 5504/1881 and 5520/1881 with E. BLED & E. RICHOUX (q.v.) of Paris, which protected the rebounding pistol locks shown in Fig. 6. The first patent also claimed the use of centres made integrally with the action-body upon which to mount the principal lock parts, but this idea may have been anticipated by the 1877 British Patent of J. STANTON (q.v.). Such centres permitted the use of hinged or removable side-plates to the locks of revolvers, but the idea was far from new.

Major Dowell paid an added tribute to the association of Warnant with the lock-mechanisms fitted to the beatifully made Webley-Kaufmann revolvers described in Chapter IV. Kaufmann patented the lock for these arms (and the so-called "Improved Government" Webley revolver) in his Br. Pat. 4302/1880, and the Bled-Richoux-Warnant patents of 1881 are a further refinement of his idea.

Since Warnant and Kaufmann were associated in the earlier patent of 1878, it seems reasonable to assume a connection also in the later lock of 1880. Postive proof is wanting.

WARRY, R. Armourer-Sergeant R. Warry (of St. Mary's Barracks, Gillingham, Kent) secured provisional protection under Br. Pat. 2066/1868 for improvements to "Central-fire, breech-loading, double-and single-barrelled military, sporting and magazine small-arms and revolvers".

The Provisional Specification failed to reveal how the magazine system described in it could be applied to revolvers, at least to this writer.

WEBLEY, T. W. & H. Thomas William Webley (b. 1839, d. 1904) and Henry Webley (b. 1846, d. 1920) were the surviving sons of Philip Webley (b. 1812, d. 1888) who founded the famous gun, rifle, revolver and implement manufacturing firm which bore his name.

The latter had been a revolver patentee in his own right during the years preceding those of concern to us, but all protection was void by 1865. His deceased brother, James Webley (b. 1807, d. 1856) had achieved some success with the single-action percussion revolver known to modern collectors as the "Long Spur" Webley, and this weapon would probably have been regarded (by 1865) only as an interesting but semi-obsolescent design.

Thomas William Webley's interest in revolving arms appears (from the other patents which he secured) to have been marginal to his concern with firearms mechanisms in general. However, he did secure provisional protection under Br. Pat. 2030/1865 which for its brief life covered the idea of adapting a pin-fire hammer to permit use of centre-fire cartridges in the same revolver. Unsigned, Birmingham-proved, weapons of this type are found in some collections but the cartridge was never really popular for British revolvers of quality, and they are rare.

Henry Webley was a remarkable revolver shot and appears to have been the driving force in what we might term the "Revolver Division" of the firm's many activities. In Br. Pat. 5143/1881, he was the joint applicant with his brother for "Improvements to drop-down guns and revolvers", which included devices for the retraction of cartridge extractors in revolvers, and means for mounting and dismounting their cylinders. It also protected a method for preventing fouling from clogging the cylinder axis.

In 1883, as Br. Pat. 542 of that year, Henry secured a patent of improvement (eliminating one spring) on M. KAUFMANN's Br. Pat. 3313/1881. This had protected the button latch shown on the Kaufmann revolver at the top of Plate 35, and Henry's improvement (shown below it) used a pivoted thumbpiece to work the latch.

Finally, he secured Br. Pat. 4070/1885, jointly with J. CARTER (q.v.). This covered the famous Webley "stirrup" or "bridle" latch, used to secure the barrels of all their heavy-calibre revolvers thereafter. The same patent claimed the lock mechanism used in what Major Dowell has termed the Model 1882 "W. G." Target and Army revolvers, of the type shown on Plate 35. Whilst not anxious to cross swords with this formidable authority, the present writer cannot accept his dating for this weapon on the grounds that P. WEBLEY & SON could not have been rash enough to release it on to the market if they seriously considered patenting major features of it. As may be seen from Plate 35, this writer prefers to designate this weapon as the "Model 1885".

The patent was probably secured under the guidance of W. E. GEDGE (q.v.), and its two principal features can be studied in Plate 73. The "W.G." mechanism illustrated was actually made a few years after the close of the period, but the barrel latch and long trigger lever (powered by the lower limb of the mainspring) are identical to those claimed in the patent.

WEBLEY, P. & SON(S). During the years of concern here, the firm did not apparently trade as a limited liability company, and references in trade literature (and on their own revolvers) were made indifferently to "Son" or "Sons" in the suffix to their trading style. Without labouring the point, we thus have the "wedge-frame" Webley revolver in Plate 2 labelled "Webley & Sons" whilst the "Army" revolver at the top of Plate 10 was engraved "P. Webley & Son". This sort of variation makes it extremely difficult to guess at even the family constituents of what presumably a partnership, but may have been something larger.

As a further example, we have the title "P. Webley & Sons. Proprietors" appearing on their Registered Design No. 4634 of 1864, which survived into our period to protect briefly an ungainly but effective lever-rod cartridge ejector for solid-framed revolvers.

The point is not academic for our purposes. Trading names bury many identities of interest to our student.

It is a matter of record that "P. Webley & Son" [sic] took transfer of the Business trading as "Tipping & Lawden" on May 8th, 1877, but the basis of the transfer is not clear. If this was simply a purchase of books, goodwill, and an old and well-known trading name, then the purchaser's already widely based activities would have altered little. If, on the other hand, the purchase carried with it premises, machinery, patents, patent licences, etc., in respect of some specialized types of weapon, then the transaction probably heralded an appropriate change in policy for a range of products thereafter offered by the purchaser.

"Tipping & Lawden" (which the writer believes to have been the trading style for the family partnership of Caleb and Thomas Tipping Lawden of Birmingham and Liverpool) are one of the firms whose contribution to the history of British revolving arms must one day be assessed.

As original licencees or lessees of the Harding revolver patents controlled by DEANE & SON (q.v.) the partnership had been of sufficient weight and standing to hold sixty founder shares in the Birmingham Small Arms Company Ltd., and if it had survived the 1873 reorganization of that Company with shareholding status, and those shares were included in any assets transferred to P. Webley & Son, then the acquisition of the partnership may have opened an important door to fresh business for the Webley concern.

"Tipping & Lawden" are well known too as the British developers of the "Sharps's Patent" four-barrelled pistol, which could have constituted a serious competitor to cheap pocket revolvers even as late as 1877 (see Plate 41).

The relevant British Patents of CHRISTIAN SHARPS (q.v.) had certainly been void for ten years by 1877, but their indefatigable inventor was still turning out an improved version in the U.S. (the ·32 rim-fire "Bull Dog" pistol) when he died in 1874, and "Tipping & Lawden" may have been considering British production of such an arm based on their manufacturing experience of a decade before.

Certainly, as Major Dowell showed in his book, P. Webley & Son were no strangers to the original Sharps weapon and catalogued it for a while (in three calibres) as one of their standard "lines".

However, the unknown identity of a participant named Wade in the original Sharps/Lawden patent link-up of 1860 makes Webley's position over these weapons very difficult to date or assess, and the 1877 takeover of the Lawden business could as well have been aimed at the sensible suppression of a competing weapon as at its development and further marketing.

Again, it was until recently a matter of official record that Tipping & Lawden held an interest in British Patent 779/1869 for the self-extracting revolver of J. THOMAS (q.v.) and it does seem significant that this patent was allowed to lapse in the year preceding formal takeover by the Webley concern (see Table II).

Not only were P. Webley & Son firmly wedded to the solid-framed, rod-ejecting revolver as a principal line for many years (as late as 1883, they produced improved models; see Chapter IV), but the year after they took over "Tipping & Lawden" saw the grants of the early protection sought by DE MOUNCIE, M. KAUFMANN and J. WARNANT (q.v.) from which evolved the splendid series of Webley's own self-extracting revolvers in the 1880's.

The reason for listing P. Webley & Son here (when no patent in the firm name exists) should now be clear.

"Webley's Patent" (or the latter, more familiar, "Webley Patents") was a legend engraved upon almost all the revolvers that they produced, but (see Table II) patents secured in the firm name are non-existent and number only four in the names of the family. Yet the boast was not idle and the firm clearly had the right to operate under the patent protection of numerous inventors, of whom C. PRYSE, THE YOUNGER (Br. Pat. 4421/1876) seems another case in point.

Details of the absorption of houses other than "Tipping & Lawden" within our period may one day be revealed. Until then, the writer hopes that his note is enough to suggest that so far unrecorded events important in the history of British revolving arms may have occurred during that period to set the stage for the Webley triumph that closed it.

WERNDL, J. Managing Director of the OESTERREISCHISCHE WAFFENFABRIKS GESELLSCHAFT (q.v.) and communicant as such for their patents in our field after Br. Pat. 1272/1878 (see also O. SCHOENAUER and the AUSTRIAN SMALL ARMS MANUFACTURING COMPANY).

He secured communicated Br. Pats. 3878/1878 and 2840/1879 through A. M. CLARK (q.v.). The former was for repeating or magazine attachments to breech-loading "bolt-guns", and included a claim for the rotary feed principle; the latter protected magazine repeating small-arms and included revolving tubular magazines in the fore-end of bolt-action rifles.

Subsequently, he communicated Br. Pat. 712/1882 (an improvement on 3878/1878, for a detachable magazine with a semi-rotary feature) to G. E. VAUGHAN (q.v.) and used the same agent later in the year for Br. Pat. 1982/1882 which improved the Provisional Specification to 712/1882 by refinements for easier insertion of cartridges, and the prevention of spillage.

The same agent secured Br. Pat. 229/1883 for him, which protected further magazine improvements (including rotary features) on his Br. Pats. 3878/

1878 and 1982/1882. The Steyr/Spitalsky rifle shown in Plate 63 may have embodied the subject of this patent, and is dated 1883.

WESSON, D. B. Daniel Baird Wesson (b. 1825, d. 1906) was the younger brother of Edwin Wesson, whose firearms might have been of academic interest only, by 1865. In 1851, Edwin had been involved in a lengthy legal brawl between the Massachussetts Arms Company and the famous Colonel Colt. The point at issue was the latter's claim to exclusive use of mechanically revolved pistol cylinders under his U.S. patents, and this claim was up-held.

D. B. Wesson appears to have learned well from his brother's bitter experience. A decade before our period opened, he and Horace Smith had secured the right to use the U.S. master-patent of ROLLIN WHITE (q.v.), which included a fortunate claim for revolver cylinders with chambers bored clear through from end to end. This patent eventually cornered the market for conventional metallic cartridge revolvers in the hands of the partners (and the patentee) from 1855 until 1869.

The matter of this monopoly has been too ably covered by others for re-capitulation here, but it must be made clear that Rollin White secured no equivalent patent in Britain. As a result of the voiding of the pin-fire revolver patent of J. H. JOHNSON (q.v.) in 1861, any student would have been faced by a wide variety of conventional metallic cartridge revolvers from the outset of our period.

Important as he therefore was in America, D. B. Wesson concerns us here only as having bought out his partner in 1874, and as having communicated two interesting revolver patents to the British Patent Agent W. R. LAKE (q.v.).

This note gives no indication of his activity as a patentee in America on behalf of his business, where his pistol and revolver patents alone totalled nineteen.

British Patent 4831/1877 protected "Small-arms in which the hammer is caused to rebound after having struck the firing-pin or shell to explode a cartridge", for which improvement the stirrup or link connecting mainspring and hammer was modified. In Wesson's rebound (see Fig. 7) the hammer could only reach the cartridge under impetus from the mainspring. When "at rest", the link-belly fouled the heel of the hammer and trapped it with the nose clear of the chambers; the pocket revolver shown in Plate 31 has this rebound.

Br. Pat. 4614/1878 protected "Revolver magazine small-arms". Although never commercially developed here or in the U.S., it warrants attention, and was specifically noticed in a roughly contemporary American book (published in 1884) by W. Bartlett who wrote that "a revolving magazine gun of Mr. D. B. Wesson's invention has a series of magazines under the barrel, which feed the cartridges back into the cylinder".

The weapon envisaged was a rifle with tubular magazines beneath the barrel from which *rimless* metallic cartridges were fed backwards into a revolving and reciprocating carrier, which also initially retained discharged cases, after firing, for transport to an ejection position.

Loaded cartridges were pushed forward in the carrier's chambers to mate with the breech-end of the barrel in a gas-seal, by a linked hammer/piston which fired them there. Re-cocking the hammer caused the empty case to be drawn back into the carrier chamber by an extractor on the end of the piston. Empty cases were ultimately ejected *forwards* from the carrier by a rod linked to the hammer which cleared the "3 o'clock" chamber each time the latter fell.

A general impression of the arm appears as Fig. 21, and some evidence exists to suggest that the design did not remain merely upon paper.

Thus, what appears to have been an intended patent model for an improved version was formerly in the collection of the American authority, G. Charter Harrison, Jun., although the design was represented to him as the work of William Wurflein, of Philadelphia, and not that of D. B. Wesson.

This model (if Mr. Charter Harrison correctly interpreted the principals of operation) was for a semi-automatic development of Wesson's basic idea. In it, the firing recoil of the cartridge-case powered the loading, cocking and rotation cycle of the mechanism, and the weapon thus anticipated the basic ideas of R. PAULSON (q.v.) by a number of years, if made at the time that Wesson secured his protection for the manually operated principle.

WESSON, J. H. Josph H. Wesson was the youngest son of D. B. WESSON (q.v.), and communicated Br. Pat. 5569/1881 to W. R. LAKE (q.v.). The protection can be assumed to have been made for the firm of SMITH & WESSON (q.v.) in which Joseph then worked. Six years later, he became a partner with his father.

A Complete Specification was filed with the application for the patent, and suggests that the design was completely satisfactory at the date of the patent. It related to the cylinder-stop/sear assembly of Smith & Wesson's double-action, self-extracting revolvers of the type shown in Plate 34, and described in Chapter IV.

WHEELER, A. W. Joint applicant (with ROLLIN WHITE [q.v]) for Br. Pat. 1561/1878, through the British Patent Agent B. J. B. MILLS (q.v.).

The application was communicated from Lowell, Mass., U.S.A., and was for a "Magazine, suited for revolving small-arms (adapted to be secured to the body of a horseman) capable of holding a large number of charges of ammunition and having contrivances by means of which all the chambers of a revolver may be charged instantly and in any weather".

In view of the obvious association of the device with Smith & Wesson revolvers (see Figs. 22 and 23), the loader is more fully discussed under the name of ROLLIN WHITE (q.v.) as the probable driving force in the venture.

WHITE, R. Rollin White (b. 1817, d. 1892) was an American inventor with a

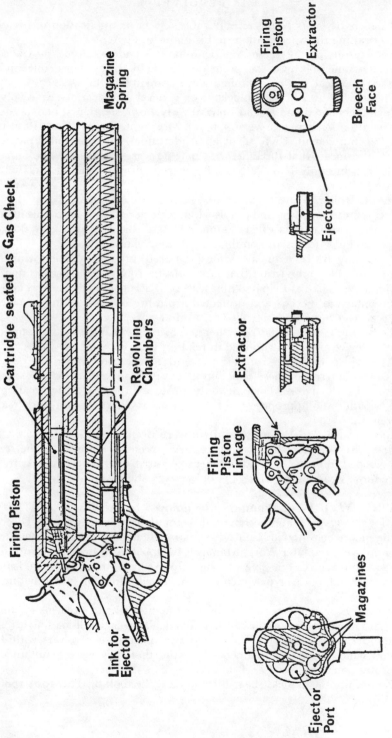

Magazine Spring

Cartridge seated as Gas Check

Revolving Chambers

Firing Piston

Link for Ejector

Firing Piston

Extractor

Breech Face

Ejector

Extractor

Firing Piston Linkage

Magazines

Ejector Port

FIG. 21. *D. B. Wesson's revolving magazine rifle, to Br. Pat. 4614/1878.*

real penchant for covering *every* possible aspect or application of his ideas when drafting the Specifications to his numerous patents.

As a result, one of these American-patented ideas turned into a commercial winner because the protection covered a basic principle and so blocked practical, but more limited, development by others.

The story of his successful blockade on general American use, in revolvers, of "cylinders bored end to end" has already been mentioned and needs no further attention here (see WESSON, D. B.). Most writers date it flatly from 1856 to 1869, but remain coyly silent as to identifying the particular patent in point. It appears that three firearms patents were issued to White on April 3rd, 1855, but only U.S. Pat. 12648 covered this vital matter, under "Repeating Firearms".

In all, Rollin White took out about a dozen American patents for improvements to revolvers and pistols within our period, but unless his identity is buried in so far unlabelled "communicated" British patents, he does not appear to have been active on this side of the Atlantic.

As to any British equivalent for his bored-through cylinder winner, it seems probable to the writer that J. H. JOHNSON (q.v.) acting for an unnamed communicant, had anticipated him with Br. Pat. 955/1854. This was allowed to become void in 1861 and protected a pin-fire breech-loading revolver of the type known to modern collectors as that of Lefaucheux.

Accordingly, for our purposes here, White figures only as joint applicant for the device already mentioned in relation to A. W. WHEELER (q.v.).

As will be plainly seen from Figs. 22 and 23, the contrivance can be fairly regarded (in terms of sheer bulk and ingenuity) as the revolver quick-loader to end all such engines. The patent also protected the charger for loading the quick-loader and appropriate holsters for carrying the pistol and loading therefrom.

In typical Rollin White style, there were twenty-seven claims to Br. Pat. 1561/1878! Comment here is unnecessary, except to ensure that the reader has grasped from Fig. 22 that revolvers of SMITH & WESSON (q.v.) Army size were those weapons for which the device was obviously intended.

WHITING, W. J. W. J. Whiting was employed by the firm of P. WEBLEY & SON for many years, and became a director (later joint Managing Director) of the succeeding limited liability Company after the period of concern to us. As employee, and later Works Manager, he apparently gave special attention to the manufacture of revolvers for his employers and to many design features in the weapons of this type which they marketed or manufactured within our period.

Although probably better known to students of hand firearms for his inventions after the turn of the century (particularly as to self-loading arms) or in the decade preceding it, he secured two patents for revolvers within the period which were so fundamentally sound that they were maintained for their full potential lives (see Table II).

From Sutton Coldfield (near Birmingham) he took Br. Pat. 1923/1886 for

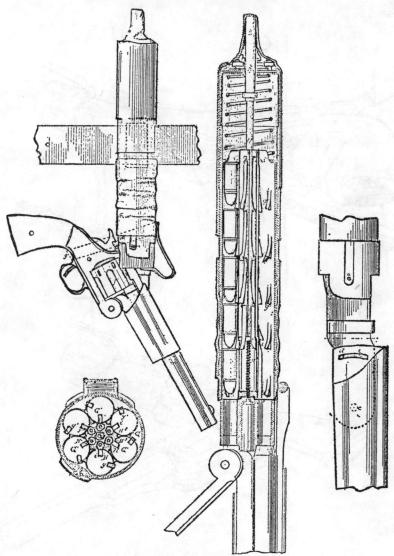

FIG. 22. *Sections and details of Wheeler & White's revolver charger.*
(Br. Pat. 1561/1878).
The cartridges were released into the chambers of the pistol as appropriate
charges for the capacity of the cylinder.

the well-known Webley anti-fouling sleeve which protected the front end of
cylinder spindle (see Fig. 24).

From 6 Livery St., Birmingham, he took Br. Pat. 5778/1888, jointly with
J. CARTER (q.v.) and left something of a puzzle for students in later years.

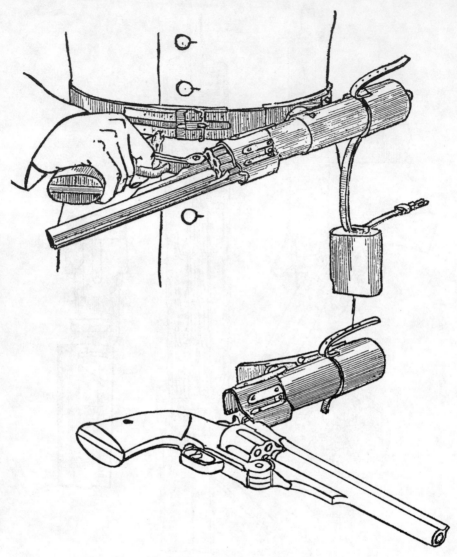

FIG. 23. *Loading a Smith & Wesson Army revolver, using Wheeler & White's magazine.*
(Br. Pat. 1561/1878.)

At first glance, the patent appears to merit small attention since it relates to a revolver lock mechanism in which a shrouded or "hammerless" firing member is rebounded to full cock after each shot in a frame configuration or outline unknown to British collectors generally.

However, examination of Table II shows that the patent was maintained

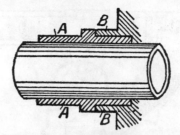

FIG. 24. *W. J. Whiting's Anti-Fouling Sleeve.*
(Br. Pat. 1923/1886.)

In revolvers, in order to protect the forepart of the cylinder spindle from being fouled by the flash on discharge, the lump and the cylinder are recessed for a short distance to receive a sleeve "A", within which the spindle turns freely. The cylinder has a projecting ferrule "B", which fits over the sleeve, to increase the distance between the flash and the spindle.

for its full life, suggesting that it protected a feature of real commercial value either to Whiting and Carter or their employers.

After consideration, the writer can only suggest that the feature of importance turned out to be the twin-cylinder bolts on top of the trigger.

Although not identical with the form actually embodied in the famous Webley Mark I service revolver (see Chapter IV), the principle claimed in the patent and the bolts used in the weapon seem to the writer to marry. Taken with the long patent life (it expired in 1902) it is suggested that our puzzle may be thus resolved.

WHYTE, C. C. B. Secured Br. Pat. 10651/1888 for a revolver-carrying device for belt or saddle which also prevented accidental pulling of the trigger.

Since a Complete Specification was filed with the application, and clearly showed (see Fig. 25) a solid-framed RIC type revolver mounted in the device, it seems probable that the idea went beyond the mere design stage but the writer has never seen an embodiment.

The address for filing the patent suggests that C. D. ABEL (q.v.) acted as adviser on the invention.

WILDING, S. P. Patent Agent (of the firm of FELL AND WILDING, "City Patent Office", 23 Rood Lane, Fenchurch St., City of London) active only occasionally in patents relating to firearms.

Secured provisional protection under Br. Pat. 1823/1882 for F. DREVEN-STEDT (q.v.) in regard to the latter's curious "turret-type" small arms.

WILLATS, W. H. Secured provisional protection as Br. Pat. 2495/1882 for an "Apparatus for sounding alarms, applicable as a bird scarer, as a fog signal and for other purposes". This had a clockwork-driven rotating platform operating a rebounding hammer to fire caps upon it at timed intervals. The

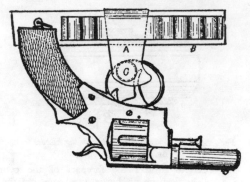

FIG. 25. *C. C. B. Whyte's Carrier.*
(Br. Pat. 10651/1888.)

Relates to a holder for revolvers, carbines, and other firearms, for attachment
to a belt or other garment or to a saddle. The holder "A" consists of a bent steel
spring, which may be suspended from the belt "B". The spring has two limbs,
and one of them carries a boss "C" which projects across the space between the
limbs. The pistol or other arm is suspended by its trigger-guard, which is
pushed up between one limb and the boss "C" on the other. The boss "C"
prevents accidental discharge by blocking all movement of the trigger.

applicant filed from Denton Court, Canterbury, and described himself as
"Esquire".

The device can hardly be regarded as a firearm, but would have a marginal
interest for any student in its rotary cap-feed.

WILLIAMS, A. H. See, specifically, R. C. ROMANEL and Br. Pats. 9998/1887
and 6994/1888.

WILLIAMS, I. Secured provisional protection for A. MICHELONI (q.v.) under
Br. Pat. 2513/1864 which barely survived into our period.

Isaiah Williams's name appeared only upon this one occasion in the
appropriate Abridgement of Specifications for Patents, suggesting either that
he was not a patent agent or else that, if he were so, firearms were not regarded as his forte.

WILLOUGHBY, D. DE R. Secured joint provisional protection with L. LOE-
WENTHAL (q.v.) for the "sight for firearms" covered by Br. Pat. 1489/1882.
Willoughby's address was given as 25 Duke Street, St. James's, London.

WILSON, G. H. Secured provisional protection as Br. Pat. 129/1872 for
"Self-acting safety appliances for firearms" which included a handgrip
safety specifically claimed as applicable to revolvers. This device locked the
tumbler or striker and/or the main spring. The address given by the applicant was 2 Ebenezer Cottages, Warner Road, Camberwell, Surrey, but no
occupation was stated.

WIRTH, F. Secured communicated Br. Pat. 3375/1877 for O. FRANKENAU (q.v.) on the latter's "Revolver purse" (see Plate 5).

Herr Wirth was a member of the firm of Patent Solicitors, "Wirth & Co." at Frankfort-am-Maine, Germany.

WOOD, S. W. Stephen Wells Wood secured Br. Pat. 309/1865 for a metallic cartridge revolver loading from the front of the chambers, and for the specially primed cartridges to be used with it.

The point of the hammer struck the cartridge from above, through an aperture in the side of each chamber in the revolving cylinder, and thus fired it by means of a fulminate primer coating sandwiched between the cartridge charge and the inner wall of its case.

Wood (of Cornwall, New York State, U.S.A.) secured some half-dozen American pistol and revolver patents through the early years of our period, but this (which is presumably the British equivalent of one of his attempts to avoid the ROLLIN WHITE (q.v.) master-patent) is the only British protection that the writer has been able to trace for revolving arms.

The "Connecticut Arms Co." of Norwich, Conn., U.S.A., appear to have used his patent as at least the basis for a front-loading metallic cartridge pocket revolver, but the writer has never seen an English embodiment.

WOOD, T. P. This inventor (of 35 Nicholas Street, Bristol) secured Br. Pat. 4427/1883 for "Igniting and discharging by electricity, cartridges containing gunpowder or other explosive compounds for .`. . revolvers . . . and cartridges and safety-triggers for same".

Since he allowed the patent to become void by failing to file a Final Specification it only remains to comment here that this method of cartridge ignition remains a hardy annual for exploration by inventors to this day. Revolving arms, however, are not usually regarded as suitable for this improvement.

WOODWARD, T. and WOODWARD, T. the younger. Secured provisional protection as Br. Pat. 2505/1880 for "Lock mechanisms of guns, rifles, pistols, revolvers and other firearms which are raised to full-cock automatically and rendered safe while in that position . . ."

Since both applicants were gunmakers (of 10 Steelhouse Lane, Birmingham) the writer assumes that the improvement had a strong practical element to it. Briefly, a tensioning change-lever was applied to the locks of firearms, which could alter the setting of the mainspring so that its effect upon the hammer altered, i.e. to force the latter back off the cartridge instead of downwards towards it.

The Woodward name being well known in Birmingham over a quite considerable period, the writer is frankly uncertain as to whether or not one of the above-named should be identified with the rare, but well known, double-barrelled turnover pistols for rim- and centre-fire cartridges (which

P. WEBLEY & SON and other houses catalogued during the 1860's and 70's) or if the honour should lie elsewhere.

The design is commonly called "Woodward's Patent" but the parentage still remains as vague as the identity of the Registered Design or Patent alleged to protect these weapons.

WYLEY, A. Secured Br. Pat. 1785/1864 which survived in to our period protecting a general application to small arms and ordnance of yet another "quick-thread" breech closure.

Although application to revolvers is specifically claimed, the writer suspects that this type of weapon was included by the agent drafting the specification as a technical matter in his craft rather than that of the inventor's.

YOUNGHUSBAND, L. and YOUNGHUSBAND, S. S. Joint applicants for Br. Pat. 3047/1886 protecting a belt-fed, shoulder small-arm employing a feed-wheel between barrel-chamber and a cartridge drum strapped to the firer.

As in the weapon of E. A. SALVATOR (q.v.) the mechanism was manually operated by an under-lever of Winchester rifle type.

The address for application was 53 Chancery Lane, W.C., suggesting the services in the matter, of Patent Agent A. M. CLARK (q.v.) or his successor.

ANNOTATED BIBLIOGRAPHY

Apart from Chapter III, titles are arranged as they appear in the text of the book.

Foreword
    Trevelyan, G. M. *History of England*, 3rd edn. (Longmans, Green & Co. Ltd., 1945).
    Allen, G. C. *The Industrial Development of Birmingham*, etc. (London, 1929).

Chapter 1
    Norton, C. B., Brig.-Gen. *American Breech-Loading Small Arms* (New York, 1872:1880).
    Parsons, John E. *The Peacemaker and its Rivals* (New York, 1959).
    Brackenbury, C. B., Capt. *European Armaments in 1867* (London, 1867)
    Majendie, V. D., Capt. *Reports on the Paris Universal Exhibition, 1867*. Vol. IV included *Portable Arms* (London, 1868).

Chapter 2
    Skaar, F. C. & Nielsen, O. *Haerens Handvapen. Pistoler og revolvere 1814–1940* (Oslo, 1954).
    Majendie, V. D., Capt. op. cit.
    Brackenbury, C. B., Capt. op. cit.
    Cuttat, J. N. *Armes à Feu Portatives* (Paris, 1877).
    Dowell, W. C., Major. *The Webley Story* (The Skyrac Press, 1962).
    Greener W. W. *Modern Breech-Loaders; Sporting and Military* (Cassell & Co., 1871).
    Le Commandant Bornecque. *Les Armes à Feu Portatives*, etc. (Paris, 1905).

Chapter 3
    Parsons, John E., *Smith & Wesson Revolvers. The Pioneer Single Action Models* (New York, 1957).
    McHenry, R. C. and Roper, W. F. *Smith & Wesson Hand Guns* (Huntingdon, 1945).
    Norton, C. B. op. cit.
    Dowell, W. C. op. cit.
    Gould, A. C. *The Modern American Pistol and Revolver* (Boston, 1888).
    Tryon, Edward K., Company. *The History of a Business Established One Hundred Years Ago. 1811–1911.*
    Webster, D. B. *Suicide Specials* (Pennsylvania, 1958).
    Serven, J. *Colt Cartridge Pistols* (California, 1952).
    Karr, L. K., Jun. & Karr, C. R. *Remington Handguns* (Pennsylvania, 1956).

Chapter 4, Section 1, Part 1
    The material for the Adams revolver was based upon observed specimens, and matter compiled from papers relating to the limited liability Company. These documents are preserved at the Public Record Office, London (Ref.

BT 31/996. Coy. No. 1529c). See also Major Sir V. D. Majendie's *The Arms and Ammunition of the British Service* (Cassell 1875).

The Colt revolver notes are based upon the contemporary catalogues of that Company, with notations upon W. W. Greener (op. cit.); C. B. Norton (op. cit.); John E. Parsons (op. cit.); W. C. Dowell (op. cit.).

Parsons, John E. (1959). op. cit.

Gould, A. A. op. cit.

Greener, W. W. op. cit.

Norton, C. B. op. cit.

Karr, L. K. op. cit.

Walsh, J. H. *The Modern Sportsman's Gun & Rifle* Vol. II (London, 1884).

Tranter material based on the Complete Specifications to his cited patents.

Schmidt, R. *Les Nouvelles Armes à Feu Portatives* (Paris, 1889).

Chapter 4, Section 1, Part 2

Colard, R., Capt. *Les Armes Portative en Autriche-Hongrie* (Paris, 1874).

Le Commandant Bornecque. op. cit.

Serven, J. op. cit.

Figuier, L. *Armes de Guerre* (Paris, 1870).

Parsons, John E. (1959). op. cit.

Chapter 4, Section 2, Part 1

Parsons, John E. (1957). op. cit.

Gould, A. C. op. cit.

Bond, H. *Treatise on Military Small Arms*, etc. (London, 1884).

Dowell, W. C. op. cit.

Bartlett, W. A. *Some Weapons of War*, etc. (Washington, 1884).

Norton, C. B. *op. cit.*

Engineering, January 1886.

Walsh, J. H. op. cit.

"*Artifex*" and "*Opifex*". *The Causes of Decay in a British Industry* (London, 1907).

Greener, W. W. *The Gun and its Development* (Cassell & Co., London, 1881; 1896).

George, J. N. *English Pistols & Revolvers* (T. G. Samworth, 1938).

Chapter 4, Section 2, Part 2

Karr, L. K., Jun., & Karr, C. R. op. cit.

Serven, J. op. cit.

Gluckman, A., *United States Martial Pistols and Revolvers* (New York, 1939).

Schmidt, R. (1889). op. cit.

Greener, W. W. (1871; 1881). op. cit.

von Sauer, K. T. *Grundriss der Waffenlehr* (Munich, 1876).

Parsons, John E., (1957; 1959). op. cit.

Norton, C. B. (1880). op. cit.

Stelle, J. P. & Harrison, W. B. *The Gunsmith's Manual, etc.* (New York, 1883).

Harrison, G. Charter. op. cit.

Chapter 5

Schmidt, R. op. cit.

Anon. *Les Armes à Feu Portatives des Armée Actuelles et Leurs Munitions, par Un Officier Superieur* (Paris, 1894).

Hentsch, F. *Die Entwickelungsgeschicte und Construction Sämmllicher Hinterlader-gewehr der Nordichen Staaten (Schweden, Norwegen, Dänemark).* (Leipzig, 1879).

von Sauer, K. T. op. cit.

Majendie, V. D., Capt. op. cit.

Witte, W. *Gemeinfassliche Waffenlehr* (Berlin, 1887).

Leveson, H. A. *England Rendered Impregnable* (London, 1871).
Lancaster, C. *Illustrated Treatise on the Art of Shooting* (McCorquodale & Co. Ltd. 1894).
Greener, W. W. (1881; 1896; op. cit.)

Chapter 6
Chinn, G. M. *The Machine Gun*, Vol. I (Washington, 1951).
Norton, C. B., Brig.-Gen. op. cit.
Bartlett, W. A. op. cit.
Longstaff, F. V. & Atteridge, A. H., *The Book of the Machine Gun* (London, 1917).
Greener, W. W. (1871). op. cit.
Leveson, H. A. op cit.

Appendix 1
Lund, H. *A Treatise on the substantive law relating to Letters Patent for Inventions* (London, 1851).
Carpmael, W. *The Law of Patents for Inventions*, etc. (London, 1860).
Higgins, C. *A Concise Treatise on the Law and Practice of Patents for Inventions* (London, 1884).
Dowell, W. C., Major. *The Webley Story* (The Skyrac Press, 1962).
The London Gazette (1865–1878).
The Commissioners of Patents' Journal (London, 1865–1883).
The Official Journal of the Patent Office (London, 1884–1888).

Appendix 2
Abridgements of the Specifications relating to Fire-Arms and Other Weapons, Ammunition, and Accoutrements (Eyre & Spottiswoode, 1859).
Abridgements, etc. Part II—A.D. 1858–1866 (Eyre & Spottiswoode, 1870).
Patents for Inventions. Abridgements of Specifications. Class *119*, Small-Arms. Periods—A.D. 1867–1876. A.D. 1877–1883 (H.M.S.O. 1904). A.D. 1884–1888 (H.M.S.O. 1896).
Marks, E. C. R. *The Evolution of Modern Small Arms and Ammunition* (Manchester, 1898).
Bock, G. *Moderne Faustfeuerwaffen und ihr Gebrauch* (Neudam, 1911).
The Commissioners of Patents' Journal, op. cit.
The Official Journal of the Patent Office, op. cit.
Carey, A. M. *English, Irish and Scottish Firearms Makers* (New York, 1954) and *American Firearms Makers* (New York, 1953).
Brandeis, F. *Die moderne Gewehrfabrikation* (Weimar, 1881).
Satterlee, L. D. & Gluckman, A., Major. *American Gun Makers* (New York, 1940).
Smith, W. H. B. *The N.R.A. Book of Small Arms. Vol. I. Pistols and Revolvers* (Washington, 1948).
Winant, L. *Firearms Curiosa* (New York, 1955).
Chapel, E. C. *The Gun Collectors Handbook of Values* (New York, 1951).
Gluckman, A. op. cit.
Chinn, G. M. op. cit.
Harrison, G., Charter, Jun., & Smith, S. E. *The Gun Collector Magazine* (Wisconsin 1946–1949), *The Gun Collector* (Wisconsin. Issues 27–47).
It would be a considerable undertaking to list every detail of assistance from this invaluable collection of articles. The writer hopes that no contributor will doubt the warmth of his appreciation for the information imparted or suggested by this source.
Parsons, John E. (1957). op. cit.
o

Norton, C. B., Brig.-Gen. *American Inventions and Improvements in Breech-Loading Small Arms* (Springfield & London, 1880).
Greener, W. W. op. cit. (1881 ; 1896).
Parsons, John E. (1959). op. cit.
Dowell, W. C., Major. op. cit.
Karr, L. K., Jun. & Karr, C. R. op. cit.
Commerce, Nov. 11th, 1896.
Bartlett, W. A. op. cit.
Wilson, R. K., Lieut.-Col. *Textbook of Automatic Pistols* (Plantersville, S.C. 1943).

INDEX

Page numbers in **heavy type** refer to pages with Plates or Figures.